Systèmes de gestion de bases de données orientés objet

COLLECTION SYNTHÈSES INFORMATIQUES DU CNAM
sous la direction de Nicolas Manson

déja parus :

L'approche objet, Christophe PASQUIER, Philippe ROUCOULET et Marie-Line LANASPÈZE

ATM, Bernard WEISS

Calcul coopérant par passage de messages, Philippe VETTER

La compression des images numériques, Hervé GUITTER

Stockage des données distribuées, les disques RAID, Renaud HILLERET

Répartition d'objets dans les bases de données, Lionel MALLORDY

Temps réel, Jean-André BIANCOLIN

Architecture de Windows NT, Bruno DARDONVILLE

Techniques du Multithread – du parrallélisme dans les processus, Bernard ZIGNIN

L'informatique, mémoire de l'entreprise, Florent BASTIANELLO

Logiciels serveurs et outils d'administration pour le Web, Laurent SCHNEIDER

CONSERVATOIRE NATIONAL DES ARTS ET MÉTIERS
Centre Régional Associé de Lille

Systèmes de gestion de bases de données orientés objet

Ricardo Ruiz

HERMES

Editions Hermès
14, rue Lantiez
75017 Paris

ISBN 2-86601-596-7
ISSN 1272-078X

Catalogage Electre-Bibliographie
Ruiz Ricardo
Systèmes de gestion de bases de données orientés objet.– Paris : Hermès, 1997. – (CNAM. Synthèses informatiques)
ISBN 2-86601-596-7
RAMEAU : bases de données orientées objets
conception orientée objets (informatique)
ODMG-93 (norme)
DEWEY : 005.6 : Programmation. Programmes. Logiciels.
Fichiers et systèmes de gestion de bases de données

Présentation de la collection

Pour bien comprendre la genèse de cette collection, il faut d'abord rappeler l'originalité de la formation de l'ingénieur CNAM, en informatique en particulier. En effet, elle s'adresse à des personnes qui sont entrées dans une vie professionnelle et qui occupent déjà des fonctions informatiques.

C'est pourquoi un complément de formation est d'abord proposé, le plus généralement en cours du soir ou le samedi. Ces enseignements, qui tiennent déjà compte de l'expérience professionnelle, doivent permettre de faire le point sur les connaissances de base et les savoirs en informatique. Puis lorsque les bases ont été revisitées, on passe à la partie la plus féconde et la plus originale de la formation car elle s'appuie sur l'expérience et la personnalité acquises dans la vie professionnelle. Un travail probatoire sert à déterminer si le candidat montre les aptitudes minimales pour réaliser, dans son entreprise ou dans un laboratoire, le projet qui le mènera au diplôme d'ingénieur. On notera que le document probatoire est le fruit d'un travail confié au candidat pendant une durée de six semaines; il représente l'état de l'art à un moment donné; on ne saurait garantir la pérennité de son contenu ni sa complétude, qui est liée au temps imparti pour étudier le sujet.

Cela étant, le projet défini en commun accord par le CNAM et l'équipe professionnelle d'accueil doit aboutir à une réalisation qui sera validée par ses utilisateurs. Le candidat doit, in fine, rédiger un mémoire et exposer son travail lors d'une soutenance orale devant un jury mixte comprenant des représentants du CNAM et la profession.

Comme on le voit, les capacités de synthèse, d'analyse, de présentation, de communication technique, écrite et orale, sont fondamentales. En 1994, à l'occasion du bicentenaire de sa création, le CNAM a mené une réflexion en profondeur avec les partenaires socio-économiques sur les formations d'ingénieur; cette profondeur avec les relaxions a rappelé avec force l'importance de la communication, sous ses aspects socio-économiques, relationnels et techniques.

L'examen probatoire rentre tout à fait dans cet aspect, en donnant toutefois la priorité à la communication technique. Le sujet du travail probatoire se situe dans le domaine de l'information mais est choisi hors du champ d'activité habituel du candidat. Il s'agit d'apporter la preuve que le candidat pourra faire un bon ingénieur en informatique.

L'informatique est le science du traitement automatique de l'information. Son développement résulte des progrès technologiques extraordinaires obtenus en électronique dans les domaines de la miniaturisation et de la fiabilité des composants. L'une des constantes de l'évolution de l'informatique est la rapidité du changement technologique. Les gammes de matériel se renouvellent tous les trois ans, les réseaux deviennent omniprésents. Les logiciels se succèdent à un rythme effréné dans des domaines nouveaux comme les bases de connaissances, les systèmes experts, le génie logiciel, les messageries électroniques, la conception assistée par ordinateur, la conduite de trafic, le contrôle de procédés industriels. L'autre constante de l'évolution est son extension rapide. Technique diffusant, l'informatique pénètre peu à peu tous les secteurs d'application et cette diffusion commence souvent avec des prototypes qui intègrent logiciels spécifiques et logiciels généraux.

Il résulte de cette évolution que l'on attend d'un ingénieur à la fois une solide base scientifique, technique et technologique et une bonne aptitude à l'analyse et à la modélisation, mais aussi qu'il soit capable de s'adapter aux divers contextes d'application ainsi qu'à une mise à jour technologique permanente.

L'ingénieur CNAM en informatique doit concevoir et réaliser des travaux reposant sur les résultats de la science et des techniques. Il lui faut donc une culture scientifique et technique solide qui, face au totalitarisme de la technologie informatique, l'aide à faire preuve d'esprit critique, à avoir un irrespect réfléchi face aux solutions imposées et matraquées par les grands groupes qui installent leurs rapports de puissance sous le masque des « standards de fait ». Il doit se rappeler que « si ce n'est pas le capitaine sur la passerelle du navire qui dirige la manoeuvre, ce sont les rats » (René Char), et encore et toujours le leçon de Louis Pasteur: «Il faut avoir le culte de l'esprit critique».

L'ingénieur CNAM doit montrer un savoir-faire indéniable, mais pour cela il doit appuyer sa pratique sur la réflexion, contrôler son action par la pensée et de plus en plus expliquer pour rendre naturelle son autorité. Expliquer pour justifier ses choix, expliquer pour convaincre, expliquer pour rendre naturelle son autorité. Ne jamais oublier que celui «qui, dans la controverse, s'appuie sur l'autorité ne travaille pas avec l'esprit, mais avec la mémoire» (Léonard de Vinci).

Nous attendons des candidats ingénieurs qu'ils nous montrent toutes ces aptitudes. L'oral probatoire nous sert à vérifier les acquis et à apprécier les capacités à aborder un domaine nouveau. Dans ce dernier aspect il faut conduire une recherche bibliographique, réaliser un travail de synthèse et en faire une présentation écrite et orale. Lors de cet oral le candidat doit prouver qu'il est capable de tirer l'essentiel de textes le plus souvent composites, de comprendre les points importants, les apports et les limites du sujet abordé. Il doit se comporter en informateur pertinent, capable de s'appuyer sur ses lectures, sur son expérience personnelle, sur son environnement professionnel pour apporter un avis personnel et pour convaincre son jury, ou sa hiérarchie professionnelle. Nous demandons au candidat de gérer son temps en respectant rigoureusement le délai imparti (en général 20 minutes), d'utiliser au mieux les supports de communication, d'organiser sa présentation orale différemment de sa présentation écrite et surtout de s'exprimer dans une langue pure, purgée autant du «franglais» que des tics et sigles à la mode, c'est-à-dire de faire, autant que possible, un exposé sobre et élégant.

Le CNAM fonctionne en réseau et l'idée de la présente collection est née lors d'une réunion de responsables de l'enseignement de l'informatique dans différents centres du réseau.

Cette collection regroupe une série de travaux probatoires qui ont abouti à des synthèses jugées, en leur temps et lieu, pertinentes pour la profession informatique ou pour la formation des ingénieurs CNAM en informatique. Je pense que les conditions dans lesquelles ces synthèses ont été faites, le souci permanent de la mise en œuvre des savoirs ainsi explorés, le soin de dégager l'utilité des recherches et développements dans notre discipline, donneront une forte unité à cette collection. Je la recommande donc vivement aux candidats ingénieurs, tout comme à ceux qui veulent maintenir leur culture informatique et plus généralement à tous ceux pour qui «penser, c'est avant tout vouloir créer un monde» (Albert Camus).

C. KAISER
Professeur titulaire de la chaire d'informatique programmation
Président du département d'informatique du CNAM

Table des matières

Chapitre 1. Introduction 13
1.1. L'origine 13
1.2. Historique 15

Chapitre 2. Les nouvelles approches 17
2.1. Apports et limites du relationnel 17
2.2. Le modèle relationnel étendu 18
2.2.1. Les modèles NF2 18
2.2.2. Modèles à objets complexes 20
2.3. Les modèles avec identité d'objet 21
2.4. Les modèles sémantiques 24
2.5. Systèmes de types 26
2.6. SGBD et langage de programmation 28

Chapitre 3. L'approche objet 31
3.1. Les langages 31
3.2. Concepts orientés objet applicables aux bases de données 32
3.2.1. Objets 33
3.2.2. Encapsulation 33
3.2.3. Messages 34
3.2.4. Classes 34
3.2.5. Héritage 35
3.2.6. Surcharge sémantique et résolution tardive 35
3.2.7. Uniformité 36
3.3. Concepts propres aux bases de données orientées objet 36
3.3.1. Objets complexes 36
3.3.2. Identité d'objet 37
3.3.3. Persistance 38

Chapitre 4. Définition 39
4.1. Systèmes de gestion de bases de données 39
4.1.1. Persistance des données 39
4.1.2. Modélisation des données 39
4.1.3. Gestion du disque 40
4.1.4. Partage des données 40
4.1.5. Fiabilité des données 40
4.1.6. Sécurité des données 40
4.1.7. Interrogation adéquate de la base de données 41
4.1.8. Indépendance des données 41
4.2. Systèmes de gestion de bases de données orientés objet 41
4.2.1. Les règles obligatoires 42
4.2.2. Les règles optionnelles 43
4.2.3. Les règles ouvertes 44

Chapitre 5. Méthodologie 45
5.1. Cycle de conception 45
5.2. Modélisation 47
5.2.1. Représentation d'une classe 47
5.2.2. Attributs 47
5.2.3. Les contraintes 48
5.2.4. Les relations 48
5.2.5. Les méthodes et les messages 49
5.2.6. Héritage 49
5.2.7. Classes abstraites 50

Chapitre 6. Technologie et technique 51
6.1. Architecture 51
6.2. Gestionnaire d'objets 52
6.2.1. Limites fonctionnelles du gestionnaire d'objets 54
6.2.2. Mécanismes d'adressage 54
6.2.3. Représentation de l'identité d'objet 55
6.3. Représentation d'une structure de données 56
6.3.1. Implémentation d'un n-uplet 56
6.3.2. Implémentation d'un ensemble 57
6.3.3. Représentation normalisée 57
6.4. Représentation physique en mémoire secondaire 58
6.4.1. Taille des objets 59
6.5. Représentation de l'héritage 61
6.5.1. Organisation en vrac 62
6.5.2. Répartition horizontale 62
6.5.3. Répartition verticale 63

6.5.4. Attribut Objet Valeur (AOV) 63
6.6. Techniques d'optimisation de stockage 64
6.6.1. Indexation 64
6.6.2. Le regroupement 64
6.6.3. Gestion des transactions 65
6.6.4. Gestion des versions 66
6.7. Langages 67
6.7.1. Langage de définition des données 67
6.7.2. Langages de manipulation des données 67

Chapitre 7. Normalisation 69
7.1. Standard ODMG-93 69
7.1.1. Propriétés d'un SGBD orienté objet respectant le standard ODMG-93 69
7.1.2. Caractéristiques du modèle objet ODMG-93 70
7.1.3. Le langage de requêtes Object Query Langage (OQL) 71
7.1.4. Les langages de programmation intégrés 72

Chapitre 8. Aspects socio-économiques 73
8.1. SGBD orientés objet et mythes 73
8.2. Le marché 75
8.2.1. Applications dans les télécommunications 75
8.2.2. Applications dans l'industrie 76
8.2.3. Application à la gestion de documents multimédias 76
8.2.4. Applications dans la finance 76
8.2.5. L'état du marché 76
8.2.6. Les offres 77

Chapitre 9. Conclusion 79
9.1. Le modèle objet 79
9.2. Le passé 80
9.3. Le présent 81
9.4. Le futur 81

Glossaire 83

Bibliographie 85

Contacts 87

Index 91

Chapitre 1

Introduction

1.1. L'origine

Années 1960 : Les systèmes de gestion de fichiers

L'informatisation de la gestion des entreprises nécessitait le stockage de volumes de données importants. Il n'était pas possible de stocker de tels volumes de données en mémoire centrale, ce qui a conduit à l'introduction des mémoires secondaires.

Ces années ont connu le développement des systèmes de gestion de fichiers qui permettent de faciliter l'utilisation des mémoires secondaires.

Les données, en quasi totalité de type numérique ou alphanumérique, étaient stockées dans des fichiers et étaient manipulées au travers de langages de programmation tels que *Fortran*, PL1, *Pascal* ou *Cobol*. A cette époque, des efforts considérables ont été faits pour améliorer les supports physiques et les techniques d'accès aux fichiers et aux enregistrements

Mémoire secondaire

Mémoire non directement adressable par les instructions du processeur central, mais par des instructions d'entrée-sortie spécialisées et dont les temps d'accès sont très supérieurs à ceux de la mémoire centrale **[GARDARIN89]**.

La naissance des bases de données

Les données de gestion des entreprises sont devenues de plus en plus complexes et interdépendantes. Les applications associées à ces données étaient développées de manière isolée. Elles définissaient spécifiquement les données qu'elles utilisaient et stockaient, sans souci de partage. Cette démarche a donc révélé les inconvénients suivants :

- redondance des données stockées,
- difficulté d'accès aux données,
- problème de partage des données,
- risques d'incohérence,
- problèmes de sécurité et de confidentialité,
- non-portabilité des applications,
- problèmes de maintenance.

La multiplicité des systèmes de gestion de fichiers dans la même entreprise induit la réplication des mêmes informations dans différents systèmes.

Du fait de la spécificité de la définition des données par chaque programme d'application, les accès et l'interprétation des données sont spécifiques et rendus difficiles aux autres programmes d'applications.

La duplication des informations génère des incohérences si les mises à jour de données ne sont pas faites avec de grandes précautions. Les mises à jour doivent être propagées sur toutes les copies existantes pour assurer la cohérence des informations stockées.

Les informations de niveau d'abstraction logique sont trop étroitement liées à des informations d'ordre physique.

Toutes ces contraintes accroissent inutilement la complexité des programmes d'application. La modification de la définition des données entraîne la réécriture partielle ou totale des programmes d'application.

Les utilisateurs de ces systèmes ont donc ressenti le besoin d'intégrer les fichiers et les applications, qui jusque là étaient utilisés isolément. Ils ont également voulu représenter des liens plus complexes entre les différents enregistrements.

Les concepts de fichier et de système de gestion de fichiers ont donc progressivement été remplacés par ceux de base de données et de système de gestion de bases de données.

1.2. Historique

Années 1965 : Systèmes de Gestion de Bases de Données (SGBD) hiérarchiques et réseau

Le milieu des années 60 a vu la naissance de la première génération de systèmes de gestion de bases de données. Celle-ci a été marquée par la séparation de la description des données des programmes d'application et l'avènement de langages d'accès navigationnels, c'est-à-dire permettant de se déplacer dans des structures de type graphe et d'obtenir, un par un, des groupes de données appelés *articles*.

Le modèle hiérarchique

Dans le modèle hiérarchique, les données sont organisées selon une arborescence. Chaque nœud de l'arbre correspond à une classe d'entités du monde réel et les chemins entre les nœuds représentent les liens existants entre les objets. Le système IMS d'IBM se fonde sur ce modèle. De nombreuses situations peuvent être représentées, mais la nature arborescente du graphe devient limitative lorsque l'on veut modéliser le partage de certaines données.

Le modèle réseau

Le modèle réseau est une extension du modèle hiérarchique dans laquelle le graphe d'objets n'est pas limité. Il permet de représenter le partage d'objets, ainsi que les liens cycliques entre les objets. Ce modèle répond aux recommandations des systèmes CODASYL. Un schéma conceptuel dans le modèle réseau est composé de définitions d'enregistrements décrivant des entités et des liens unissant ces entités, et d'ensembles exprimant des liens multivalués entre les enregistrements.

Années 1970 : Le modèle relationnel

Le modèle relationnel a été inventé par CODD à IBM-San Jose en 1970 [CODD70]. Il est basé sur des concepts très simples qui sont définis rigoureusement sur le plan mathématique. Le concept central du modèle est la relation. Une théorie lui est associée : la théorie de la normalisation.

Années 1980 : Systèmes de gestion de bases de données relationnels

Les premiers systèmes ont été commercialisés au début des années 80. Le modèle a connu une très grande popularité grâce à la définition rigoureuse, sur le plan mathématique, de ses concepts, ainsi qu'à leur grande simplicité.

Les facilités d'interrogation de la base de données, à l'aide de langages déclaratifs de manipulation de données, ont également contribué à la popularité des systèmes relationnels.

Langage de programmation déclaratif

Un langage déclaratif est un langage avec lequel l'utilisateur décrit le résultat et non pas le moyen d'obtenir le résultat par opposition aux langages impératifs.

Années 1985 : Le modèle orienté objet pour les bases de données

La notion de systèmes de gestion de bases de données orientés objet commence à émerger avec l'élaboration du prototype *Gemstone* dès 1983. L'approche suivie par ce système consistait à étendre le langage de programmation orienté objet *Smalltalk* aux fonctionnalités des systèmes de gestion de bases de données.

Années 1990 : Commercialisation des premiers Systèmes de Gestion de Bases de Données Orientés Objet (SGBDOO)

1988 : commercialisation du système *Gemstone*.
1991 : commercialisation des systèmes *ObjectStore*, O_2, *Versant*.

Chapitre 2

Les nouvelles approches

2.1. Apports et limites du relationnel

Depuis leur apparition sur le marché, au début des années 80, les performances des systèmes relationnels n'ont jamais cessé de croître comparativement aux systèmes de la première génération. Ces systèmes se sont considérablement diffusés, au point d'occuper actuellement la première place sur le marché des bases de données. Parallèlement à leur développement rapide et important sont apparues certaines limitations. De nombreuses solutions pour remédier à ces problèmes ont été proposées.

Les apports par rapports aux SGBD précédents sont les suivants :

- le modèle est d'une grande simplicité,
- le modèle apporte un fondement théorique aux bases de données,
- les langages de manipulation de données relationnels sont déclaratifs,
- l'intégrité et la confidentialité des données sont améliorées dans les SGBD relationnels,
- les SGBD relationnels offrent des techniques d'optimisation des accès aux données très avancées.

Les limites des SGBD relationnels sont les suivantes :

- la pauvreté du modèle ne permet pas de modéliser les besoins des nouvelles applications telles que la Conception Assistée par Ordinateur (CAO) qui manipule des données complexes,

– les langages de manipulation de données associés, bien que de haut niveau d'abstraction n'apportent pas la puissance des langages de programmation. On est amené, pour résoudre les problèmes, à immerger le langage de manipulation dans un langage de programmation hôte qui ne manipule pas les mêmes structures de données. Ces inconvénients ont été évoqués sous le terme de *dysfonctionnements* par Delobel, Lécluse et Richard **[DELER191]**.

Les solutions aux insuffisances des systèmes relationnels

Les inconvénients des systèmes relationnels ont conduit au développement de nouveaux systèmes de gestion de données. Ces systèmes offrent les fonctionnalités traditionnelles des SGBD et intègrent un modèle de données plus riche avec un langage de programmation évitant le problème du dysfonctionnement.

La pauvreté sémantique du modèle et l'insuffisance du langage de manipulation sont les principaux points faibles du système relationnel. Les recherches entreprises pour améliorer le traitement des applications actuelles et pour prendre en compte les nouvelles applications se sont principalement orientées vers ces deux aspects.

Trois grandes approches se sont dégagées :

– les modèles relationnels étendus,

– les modèles sémantiques,

– les modèles orientés objet.

2.2. Le modèle relationnel étendu

Le modèle relationnel offre des possibilités restreintes de modélisation à cause de l'atomicité des types des attributs des relations. L'approche relationnelle étendue consiste à élargir les possibilités du modèle relationnel.

2.2.1. *Les modèles NF2*

Makinouchi **[MAKINOUCH117]** propose une première extension du modèle relationnel permettant de représenter des structures plus complexes en décrivant un modèle « Non sous première forme normale », communément appelé modèle NF2 *(Non First Normal Form)*.

Dans ce modèle, les contraintes de relations sous première forme normale sont abandonnées. Les n-uplets peuvent prendre comme valeur sur un attribut, soit des valeurs atomiques, soit des ensembles de n-uplets. Ceci permet de manipuler des relations dont les attributs sont eux-mêmes des relations.

Relation

Une relation est le produit cartésien d'une liste de domaines. Une relation peut être vue comme un tableau à deux dimensions appelé *table* **[GARDARIN89]**.

Première forme normale

Une relation est en première forme normale si tout attribut de la relation contient une valeur atomique **[GARDARIN89]**.

n-uplet

La structure d'un n-uplet est celle d'une relation. Un n-uplet correspond à une ligne de la relation. Nous employons le terme « n-uplet » d'une manière générale, dans tous les modèles, alors que nous utilisons le terme « relation » dans le contexte relationnel.

Attribut

Un attribut correspond à la colonne d'une relation caractérisée par un nom **[GARDARIN89]**.

Ce modèle a continué à évoluer jusqu'à offrir des relations constituées de n-uplets acceptant comme valeurs d'attributs, des valeurs atomiques, des ensembles de valeurs atomiques, et des relations NF2.

La figure ci-dessous donne l'exemple d'une relation NF2 qui décrit, pour chaque interprète, le ou les rôles qu'il a tenus et sa discographie, décrite par le titre des disques qu'il a enregistrés, leur date de parution et la marque du disque.

Interprète	Rôles	Discographie		
		Titre	Date	Marque
Berganza	Chérubin Rosine	Les noces Les noces Le barbier	58 65 80	Decca Philips D.G
Callas	Rosine Traviata Norma	Le barbier La traviata Norma	56 58 52	Decca Decca D.G
Caballe	Norma Traviata	Norma Traviata	72 76	Philips Decca

[BENDOU93]

2.2.2. *Modèles à objets complexes*

La poursuite des recherches sur les modèles NF2 a conduit aux modèles à objets complexes **[ZIANIOLO85] [BANKHO86] [ABIGRU88]**. Ce modèle propose deux constructeurs principaux : le produit cartésien et l'ensemble, qui peuvent s'appliquer l'un à l'autre. Le concept principal est l'objet, obtenu en appliquant récursivement ces constructeurs.

Les objets complexes sont constitués d'objets atomiques (entiers, réels : booléens, chaînes de caractères, etc.) et des constructeurs n-uplet et ensemble.

On peut donner une définition formelle du modèle à objets complexes.
Soit les symboles [ ] *et* { } *pour désigner respectivement les constructeurs n-uplet et ensemble.*
[ ] *désigne le n-uplet vide.* { } *ou* ∅ *désignent l'ensemble vide.*
Supposons l'existence d'un ensemble d'attributs $\{A_1, A_2, \ldots\}$ *et un ensemble de domaines* $D = \{d_1, d_2, \ldots\}$ *dont les éléments sont des valeurs atomiques.*
Les objets complexes se définissent par les règles suivantes :
– Soit A un attribut et D un domaine. Pour tout élément $a \in D$, *A : a est un objet atomique.*
– Si $v_1, v_2, \ldots, v_n$ *sont des valeurs et* $A_1, A_2, \ldots, A_n$ *sont des attributs distincts alors* $A : [A_1 : v_1, A_2 : v_2, \ldots, A_n : v_n]$ *est un objet n-uplet.*
– Si $v_1, v_2, \ldots, v_n$ *sont des valeurs distinctes,* $A : \{v_1, v_2, \ldots, v_n\}$ *est un objet ensemble.*

[DELERI91][BENDOU93]

Dans ce modèle, un objet complexe peut être représenté sous forme d'un arbre fini dont les nœuds, selon leur nature, sont étiquetés différemment : les feuilles correspondent aux éléments de *D*, le symbole ⊗ représente les nœuds n-uplets, le symbole ⊕ représente les nœuds ensemble, les arcs des n-uplets sont étiquetés avec les noms des attributs.

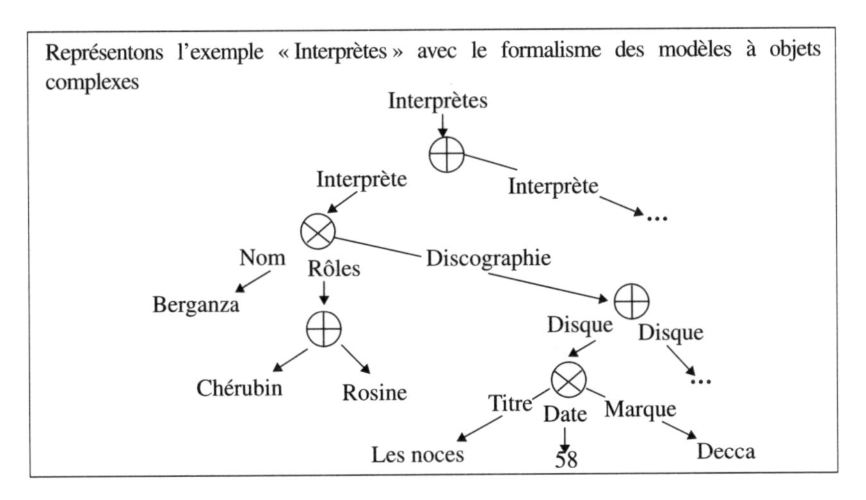

[BENDOU93]

Conclusion

Le modèle relationnel étendu est une généralisation du modèle relationnel. Il élargit les possibilités de modélisation en permettant aux attributs de prendre des valeurs complexes.

Les langages de manipulation pour objets complexes sont plus puissants que les langages pour le modèle relationnel, essentiellement parce qu'ils permettent d'utiliser des variables de type ensemble dans le calcul, ce qui autorise les requêtes récursives et les opérations telles que la fermeture transitive.

2.3. Les modèles avec identité d'objet

Tel que défini dans les modèles précédents, un objet complexe ne peut être partagé.

Considérons l'exemple suivant : l'objet Personne est composé d'un nom, d'un âge, et d'un ensemble d'enfants, qui sont eux-mêmes des personnes.
Dans la famille Bach, Jean-Sébastien et Anna-Magdalena ont un enfant de 10 ans, prénommé Jean-Chrétien. Ces faits se représentent par les objets suivants :

[Nom : *Jean-Sébastien,* **Age :** *35,*
Enfants : { [Nom : *Jean-Chrétien,* **Age :** *10,*
Enfants : { }] }]

[Nom : *Anna-Magdalena,* **Age :** *33,*
Enfants : { [Nom : *Jean-Chrétien,* **Age :** *10,*
Enfants : { }] }]

[BENDOU93]

La situation décrite dans l'exemple ci-dessus est ambiguë : en effet nous ne pouvons pas distinguer si l'enfant de Jean-Sébastien est le même que celui de Anna-Magdalena ou s'il s'agit de deux enfants ayant le même âge et le même prénom.

Ceci pose également le problème des mises à jour ; s'il s'agit du même enfant, la mise à jour de l'enfant de Jean-Sébastien implique automatiquement la mise à jour de l'enfant d'Anna-Magdalena ; or dans le modèle à objets complexes décrit précédemment, les mises à jour de ces deux objets sont faites séparément.

La représentation d'objets cycliques met en évidence une autre limite des modèles précédents.

Imaginons que l'on ajoute le champ conjoint dans la description d'une personne. Ce champ est du même type que l'objet *Personne*. Pour exprimer le fait que Jean-Sébastien est le conjoint de Anna-Magdalena, il faut disposer de l'objet décrivant Anna-Magdalena. Mais pour décrire cet objet, il faut la description de Jean-Sébastien. Chacun de ces objets a besoin de l'autre pour pouvoir être défini. Il n'est donc pas possible de décrire ce cycle.

Une des solutions à ce problème consiste à introduire le concept d'*identité d'objet*. Cette solution consiste à affecter un identificateur unique à chaque objet, permettant ainsi de les distinguer quelles que soient leurs valeurs.

L'objet n'est plus référencé par sa valeur, mais par son identificateur qui permet l'accès à sa valeur.

> Redéfinissons les objets présentés dans les exemples suivants, en y ajoutant des identificateurs.
>
> (i_1, [**Nom :** *Jean-Sébastien,* **Age :** *35,* **Enfants :** {i_3}])
>
> (i_2, [**Nom :** *Anna-Magdalena,* **Age :** *33,* **Enfants :** {i_3}])
>
> (i_3, [**Nom :** *Jean-Chrétien,* **Age :** *10,* **Enfants :** { }])

[BENDOU 93]

L'objet Jean-Sébastien devient (i_1, **[Nom :** Jean-Sébastien, **Age :** 35, **Enfants :** {i_3})]. Il est identifié par i_1 et sa valeur est **[Nom :** Jean-Sébastien, **Age :** 35, **Enfants :** {i_3}]). i_3 est l'identificateur de l'objet représentant l'enfant de Jean-Sébastien.

Les modèles avec identité d'objet permettent de distinguer sans ambiguïté les objets et de résoudre les problèmes de modélisation précédemment décrits.

Imaginons la situation où Jean-Sébastien et Anna-Magdalena ont chacun un enfant de même âge et même prénom.

(i_1, [**Nom :** *Jean-Sébastien,* **Age :** *35,* **Enfants :** {i_3}])
(i_2, [**Nom :** *Anna-Magdalena,* **Age :** *33,* **Enfants :** {i_4}])
(i_3, [**Nom :** *Jean-Chrétien,* **Age :** *10, Enfants :* { }])
(i_4, [**Nom :** *Jean-Chrétien,* **Age :** *10, Enfants :* { }])

[BENDOU93]

Les modèles avec identité d'objet permettent la représentation d'objets cycliques.

Ajoutons le champ conjoint dans la description d'une personne.
(i_1, [**Nom :** *Jean-Sébastien,* **Conjoint :** i_2 , **Age :** *35,* **Enfants :** {i_3}])
(i_2, [**Nom :** *Anna-Magdalena,* **Conjoint :** i_1 , **Age :** *33,* **Enfants :** {i_4}])
(i_3, [**Nom :** *Jean-Chrétien,* **Conjoint :** ∅, **Age :** *10,* **Enfants :** { }])

[BENDOU93]

Conclusion

La mise à jour des objets avec les modèles à identité d'objets est plus cohérente. Les objets étant référencés par des identificateurs, une modification de la valeur d'un objet est aussitôt répercutée sur les objets dont il est un des composants.

Le concept d'identité d'objet dans les bases de données n'est pas nouveau ; il existe sous forme de clef interne. Dans le modèle relationnel, les identificateurs sont les attributs-clefs, créés par le programmeur, et qui sont identifiés par une clef interne dans le système. Mais la gestion de ces identificateurs et surtout de leur unicité est laissée au programmeur.

L'apport essentiel des modèles avec identité d'objet est d'offrir une gestion automatique de l'intégrité référentielle.

2.4. Les modèles sémantiques

Une autre approche, totalement déconnectée du relationnel, a consisté à introduire de nouveaux concepts plus riches en sémantique et plus puissants que le relationnel. Cette approche s'est développée dans le milieu des années 70 et a généré les *modèles sémantiques*.

La plupart des modèles sémantiques n'ont pas donné lieu à une implémentation et sont restés des propositions « papier ».

Les concepts de base des modèles sémantiques sont des *entités* reliées par des *liens*. Les entités modélisent les données, et les liens, leurs associations.

Les entités ont un nom et sont composées d'attributs. Elles possèdent une identité au sens de l'identité d'objet définie précédemment. Le pouvoir de modélisation de ces modèles est comparable à celui des modèles à objets complexes. La diversité des liens et la sémantique associée à ce modèle lui donnent un grand pouvoir de modélisation.

Les entités de même structure sont regroupées dans des classes, ce qui permet de modéliser des ensembles d'éléments possédant les mêmes caractéristiques. Les classes ont un nom désignant l'*extension* de la classe, c'est-à-dire l'ensemble des entités de cette classe à un moment donné.

Les modèles sémantiques offrent des primitives de modélisation plus riches que le relationnel. Ces primitives permettent de modéliser plus finement et plus fidèlement la réalité.

Ces mécanismes d'abstraction s'expriment par les différents liens qu'offrent ces modèles.

Mécanismes d'abstraction

Classification

La classification permet de rattacher une entité désignée par un nom, à une classe. La classification correspond au constructeur ensemble, utilisé dans les modèles à objets complexes.

Instanciation

L'instanciation est le mécanisme inverse de la classification. Il permet de considérer une instance particulière d'une classe.

Association

L'association permet de relier plusieurs entités par une relation sémantique.

Il est possible de préciser le nombre d'instances d'entités impliquées par les associations. par des contraintes de cardinalité. On peut avoir les associations : 1:1, 1:N, N:1 et N:P.

Une association est caractérisée par son nom et sa cardinalité.

Agrégation

L'agrégation consiste à regrouper différentes entités élémentaires en une entité de niveau supérieur.

L'agrégation correspond au produit cartésien des entités dont elle est composée. C'est le mécanisme qui correspond au constructeur n-uplet.

Généralisation et spécialisation

La généralisation consiste à définir une classe d'entités comme l'union de plusieurs autres classes de plus bas niveau.

Ce mécanisme ignore les différences entre les sous-classes et ne retient que leurs points communs dans la super-classe.

La classe de plus haut niveau ne contient pas d'instances propres. Ses instances sont celles de ses sous-classes.

La spécialisation est l'opération inverse de la généralisation. Elle consiste à définir une ou plusieurs sous-classes en lui ajoutant des caractéristiques propres.

La spécialisation peut être *explicite*. Ceci signifie que l'appartenance d'une entité à une des sous-classes est spécifiée par l'utilisateur.

La spécialisation peut être *dérivée* : La sous-classe dérivée est définie à l'aide d'un prédicat spécifiant un sous-ensemble de la classe de départ.

Le graphe de spécialisation-généralisation forme une hiérarchie classiquement appelée hiérarchie « ISA » ou encore « hiérarchie d'héritage ».

Les entités des sous-classes sont aussi entités de la super-classe. Toutes les propriétés de la super-classe s'appliquent aux entités de la sous-classe. On dit que la sous-classe hérite des propriétés de sa super-classe.

Les abstractions de spécialisation et de généralisation permettent de décrire les schémas de manière compacte et structurée.

Groupement

Le groupement permet de regrouper certains éléments d'une classe ayant des caractéristiques communes, sous une nouvelle entité.

Plusieurs abstractions aboutissent à la création d'une nouvelle entité en fonction de celles déjà décrites. Les différences résident dans la façon de créer cette entité et dans le niveau d'abstraction de cette nouvelle entité.

Conclusion

Certaines abstractions se recouvrent partiellement, et il est possible de représenter les mêmes informations de manière différente. Une des richesses des modèles sémantiques est d'offrir de nombreux concepts qui permettent de modéliser les informations avec précision.

Comme pour le relationnel, il existe plusieurs types de langages de manipulation de données associés aux modèles sémantiques : impératif, logique et fonctionnel.

Malgré l'intérêt qu'ils suscitent, les modèles sémantiques n'ont pas donné lieu à une implémentation et sont restés des propositions « papier ». Ces modèles sont surtout utilisés comme modèles intermédiaires et supports d'une méthodologie de conception. C'est le cas, par exemple, d'un des premiers modèles sémantiques, le modèle Entité/Relation [CHEN76] qui est utilisé comme intermédiaire dans les étapes de conception avant d'être traduit en relationnel ou réseau.

Parmi les principaux modèles sémantiques, on peut citer :

– le modèle Entité/Relation,

– le modèle FDM,

– le modèle SDM,

– le modèle SAM,

– le modèle IFO.

2.5. Systèmes de types

Il est important de pouvoir contrôler les types des objets, qui permettent de regrouper les objets de structure identique, ou de même type. Les types permettent d'assurer la correction des programmes et la conformité des opérations. Ils sont essentiellement utilisés, à la compilation, pour vérifier les programmes.

Considérons une application, décomposée en divers sous-problèmes, et supposons que l'un de ces sous-problèmes soit la gestion d'une pile de mots. Le problème peut être spécifié dans les termes suivants :

problème *Pile_de_mots*
opérations *créer une nouvelle pile*
ajouter un mot dans la pile
retirer le dernier mot empilé
tester si une pile est vide
contraintes *On ne peut dépiler que si la pile n'est pas vide*

On résout ce problème, en employant le langage Ada, de la manière suivante :

```
/*Spécification*/
package PILES is
type pile is private ;
type mot is private ;
function créer ( ) return pile ;
function insérer (p:pile, m:mot) return pile ;
function retirer (p:pile) return pile ;
function vide (p:pile) return boolean ;
private
type mot is string ;
type pile is
record
taille : integer ;
donnée : array (1..1024) of word ;
end record
end
```

La spécification se compose d'un module (package) contenant l'ensemble des types et des opérations contribuant à la définition d'une pile. Les types pile et mot sont privés. Cela signifie que seul leur nom sera connu des utilisateurs du module. Cette spécification définit le type abstrait PILES.

[DELERI91]

Un type caractérise les valeurs qui sont manipulées dynamiquement lors de l'exécution d'un programme. On peut souvent associer un type à un ensemble de valeurs.

Le système de types permet de gérer une collection de types, ainsi que les liens entre eux. Il comprend :

- l'ensemble des types de base du système : entier, flottant, types énumérés, images, etc ;
- l'ensemble des constructeurs de types : n-uplet, ensemble, tableau, liste, etc.

L'évolution des systèmes de types a amené à la création de types abstraits. Un type abstrait peut définir une structure de données et un ensemble d'opérations associées à cette structure.

La méthode consiste à spécifier informellement les sous-ensembles du problème, en ne décrivant que ce que les autres composants ont à en connaître pour les utiliser. La description de l'implémentation des données et des opérations n'est pas rendue accessible aux autres modules du programme.

La motivation des types abstraits de données est née du besoin d'aborder les problèmes complexes par sous-ensembles de niveau de complexité maîtrisable et d'abstraire ainsi les problèmes de manière modulaire.

Dans la plupart des modèles, les propriétés d'un type abstrait ne sont que des attributs. Le comportement des instances n'est pas décrit dans le type lui-même. La modélisation du comportement est un des apports des modèles orientés objet.

2.6. SGBD et langage de programmation

L'enrichissement des modèles de données n'est pas le seul axe de recherche pour résoudre les problèmes des bases de données. Il faut également résoudre les problèmes de *dysfonctionnements* des langages de manipulation de données.

La communauté des bases de données s'est donc tournée vers le domaine des langages de programmation. Dans le sens inverse, le besoin d'ajouter la persistance et d'intégrer des modèles de données puissants aux langages de programmation se fait sentir.

Les deux approches ont été suivies :

- interfacer un SGBD et un langage de programmation,
- ajouter la persistance aux langages de programmation. Cette approche est encore appelée « intégrer un langage de programmation et un SGBD ».

Le rapprochement de ces deux domaines a donné naissance aux langages de programmation de bases de données.

Première approche

La première approche a révélé les difficultés suivantes :

- les SGBD et les langages de programmation utilisent des systèmes de types différents. Des problèmes de cohabitation entre systèmes de typage existent ;
- la persistance des données est limitée à des types de données spécifiés.

En revanche, les essais réalisés ont démontré l'intérêt de l'intégration de bases de données et de langages de programmation. Cette dernière permet de conjuguer la puissance de manipulation offerte par le langage de programmation avec la persistance des données offerte par les SGBD.

Deuxième approche

La deuxième approche présente les avantages suivants, par rapport à la précédente :

- il n'y a qu'un seul système de types. Il n'existe donc pas de problèmes de cohabitation entre systèmes de typage différents ;
- la persistance s'applique à tous les types de données.

En revanche elle présente quelques inconvénients :

- la seule fonctionnalité des bases de données, véritablement remplie, est la persistance. Les autres fonctionnalités sont absentes.
- ces langages ne fournissent, généralement pas, de moyens simples pour interroger les données.

Conclusion

Ces recherches montrent :

- la nécessité d'un modèle de données puissant,
- la difficulté à faire cohabiter deux systèmes de types différents,
- la nécessité de posséder toutes les fonctionnalités des SGBD.

L'approche des langages de programmation persistants offre une meilleure solution de base, puisqu'elle n'est pas confrontée aux problèmes de cohabitation de systèmes de types. Cependant, pour qu'elle soit intéressante, elle doit s'appuyer sur un modèle de données puissant et offrir toutes les fonctionnalités d'un SGBD.

Chapitre 3

L'approche objet

Le choix du langage de programmation est important. Parmi les différents modèles présentés dans le chapitre précédent, les modèles sémantiques sont incontestablement les plus puissants, en particulier grâce à leurs mécanismes d'abstraction qui permettent une modélisation précise des informations complexes. Les modèles orientés objet correspondent bien aux concepts des modèles sémantiques.

La puissance et la modularité offertes par les langages orientés objet répondent bien aux problèmes de génie logiciel. Ils connaissent donc une grande popularité depuis le début des années 80.

Ajouter la persistance aux langages de programmation orientés objet est non seulement devenu une nécessité mais offre une bonne approche du problème posé.

Ce chapitre décrit les concepts des Systèmes de Gestion de Bases de Données Orientés Objet (SGBDOO).

Il présente, dans un deuxième temps, une technique de modélisation.

Il conclut par une définition des SGBDOO.

3.1. Les langages

Les principes de la programmation orientée objet sont issus de deux courants de pensée amorcés dans les années 1960.

- Le premier courant a abouti à la notion de programmation structurée. La complexité et le volume des programmes ne cessant de croître, ceux ci sont devenus difficiles à exploiter et à réutiliser. La programmation structurée a apporté une solution à ce problème. Elle consiste à décomposer les programmes importants en un ensemble de modules indépendants.

– Le deuxième courant s'est concrétisé par la programmation dirigée par les données. La complexité et le volume des données se sont également accrus. La nécessité de structurer et de regrouper les données en fonction de caractéristiques communes s'est imposée.

Les premiers langages de programmation orientés objet sont apparus en 1966 avec le langage *Simula* qui était utilisé pour simuler des comportements de systèmes. *Simula* a généré le langage *Smalltalk*.

Ensuite, ce sont des évolutions de langages existants qui vont produire des langages de programmation objet.

La figure ci-dessous présente une vue non exhaustive de l'évolution des langages de programmation orientés objet.

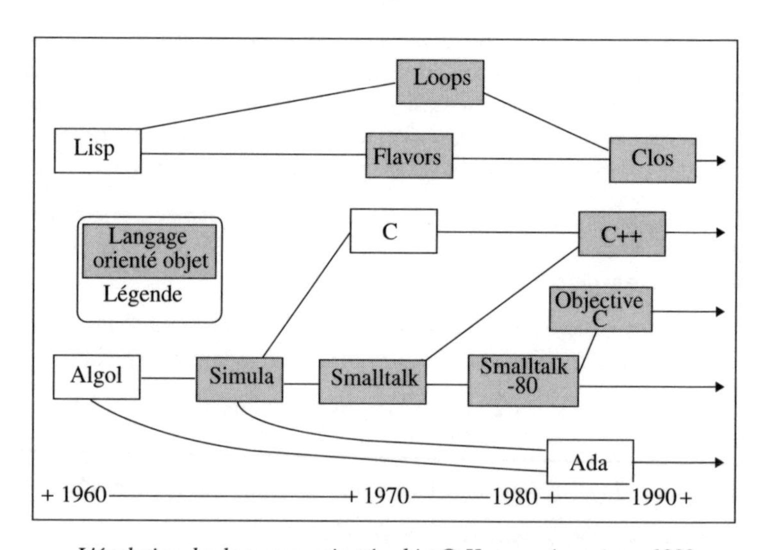

L'évolution des langages orientés objet © Harmon Associates 1992

3.2. Concepts orientés objet applicables aux bases de données

Les concepts des langages de programmation objet sont nombreux et variés, seuls certains d'entre eux ont un intérêt pour les bases de données.

3.2.1. *Objets*

Le concept principal des langages orientés objet est *l'objet*. Les données et les opérations sont regroupées sous la notion unique d'objet. La structure d'un objet est composée :

- de données : il s'agit de la partie statique de l'objet, représentée par les attributs qui décrivent l'état de l'objet ;
- d'opérations : il s'agit de la partie dynamique de l'objet. Les opérations que l'on peut appliquer à l'objet sont appelées « méthodes ». L'ensemble des méthodes décrit le comportement de l'objet.

3.2.2. *Encapsulation*

Un objet comporte :

- une partie visible, son interface,
- une partie cachée, son implémentation.

L'interface spécifie les opérations applicables à l'objet et constitue la seule partie visible de l'objet.

- Les méthodes ont une *spécification* ou *signature* et une implémentation. La signature est composée du nom de la méthode, des paramètres avec leur type, du type du résultat.
- La spécification des opérations fait partie de l'interface.

Dans les langages de programmation, seule la spécification des opérations fait partie de l'interface. Dans les bases de données, il est souvent intéressant de connaître la structure des données. La limite entre partie visible et partie cachée ne se trouve pas au même endroit :

- La structure peut faire partie intégrante de l'interface.
- Le système peut fournir automatiquement des méthodes de lecture et d'écriture pour chaque élément de la structure.

L'encapsulation, comme les types abstraits, contribue fortement à la programmation modulaire. Ces règles imposent une discipline de programmation qui favorise la lisibilité et la réutilisation du code. En revanche, l'encapsulation peut s'avérer pénalisante lorsque l'on veut extraire des informations, à l'aide du langage de requêtes. La plupart des systèmes permettent de briser l'encapsulation dans ces situations.

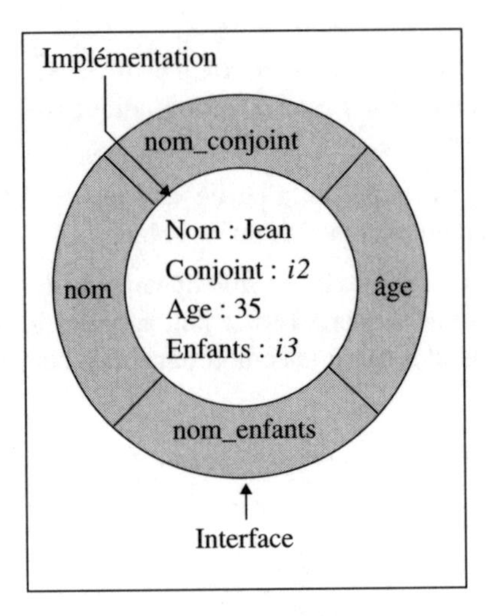

Principe d'encapsulation

3.2.3. *Messages*

Les objets communiquent entre eux par des messages. L'envoi d'un message correspond à l'invocation d'une méthode d'un objet. L'objet qui reçoit le message est appelé « receveur ».

Chaque message précise l'objet receveur, la méthode à appliquer et éventuellement des paramètres. Un objet peut également appeler une de ses propres méthodes.

3.2.4. *Classes*

Une classe représente un modèle de construction d'un objet. Il s'agit d'une description abstraite en termes de données et de comportements d'une famille d'objets. Les objets appartenant à une classe sont appelés les *instances* de la classe. L'ensemble des instances d'une classe forme son extension.

La notion de classe est très proche de celle de types abstraits. Le standard ODMG-93 [**ODMG93**] utilise les types objets, que l'on peut comparer aux types abstraits, pour regrouper les objets en familles. Il considère qu'une classe est l'association d'un type et d'une implémentation.

3.2.5. *Héritage*

Les classes sont organisées en hiérarchie et forment un graphe d'héritage. L'héritage est un mécanisme destiné à exprimer les similitudes entre classes. Il met en œuvre deux mécanismes : la généralisation et la spécialisation.

- La généralisation consiste à factoriser les parties communes de plusieurs classes en les regroupant dans une classe de plus haut niveau appelée super classe.
- La spécialisation consiste à créer, à partir d'une classe, des sous-classes héritant des caractéristiques de la classe de départ, mais se distinguant par des caractéristiques propres.

Il faut distinguer différents types d'héritage :

- Héritage simple : une classe fille n'a qu'une seule classe mère et elle hérite des attributs et méthodes de celle-ci, en ayant ses caractéristiques propres.
- Héritage multiple : une classe fille hérite de plusieurs classes mères. Elle hérite des attributs et méthodes de ses classes mères, en plus de ses caractéristiques propres.

Il peut y avoir conflit entre attributs et spécifications de méthodes de même nom, lors de l'héritage multiple. La solution à ce problème est de préciser la source de l'attribut ou de la méthode, ou de les redéfinir au niveau de la sous-classe.

L'héritage permet la réutilisation de code, en autorisant la personnalisation des classes. La structure hiérarchique des classes facilite la recherche lors de la réutilisation.

3.2.6. *Surcharge sémantique et résolution tardive*

La surcharge sémantique permet de définir un même nom de méthode pour plusieurs méthodes appartenant à des classes distinctes, qui correspondent à autant d'implémentations différentes.

L'intérêt majeur de la surcharge est de simplifier l'écriture et la maintenance des programmes.

Il n'est pas possible de savoir, à la compilation d'un envoi de message, le code qu'il faudra exécuter. Le corps de la méthode à exécuter dépend de la classe à laquelle il s'applique et ne peut être connu qu'à l'exécution.

Considérons la classe *Musicien* qui se spécialise en deux sous-classes : *Interprète* et *Compositeur.* Imaginons les méthodes *Prestations* qui portent le même nom, mais renvoient un résultat de type ensemble de n-uplets [œuvre, instrument, date-interprétation] dans le cas de l'interprète et de type ensemble de n-uplets [œuvre, date-création] dans le cas du compositeur.
Le programme peut demander les prestations des objets de la classe *Musicien,* il lui est impossible, à la compilation, de déterminer le corps de la méthode à exécuter, entre ceux des classes *interprète* et *compositeur.*

La correspondance entre le nom d'une méthode et le corps à exécuter ne peut donc se faire qu'à l'exécution. Ce processus de sélection de la méthode à l'exécution s'appelle « résolution tardive » ou « liaison dynamique ».

La résolution tardive offre un grand dynamisme au système puisqu'elle autorise le polymorphisme. En revanche, elle nuit aux performances du système, puisqu'elle reporte à l'exécution, des opérations traditionnellement effectuées à la compilation.

3.2.7. *Uniformité*

Certains langages orientés objet considèrent toutes les entités qu'ils manipulent comme des objets, c'est le cas de *Smalltalk* et de la plupart des *Lisp* orientés objet. On dit qu'il y a *uniformité totale*.

D'autres langages, comme *Eiffel* ou *C++*, ne considèrent pas les classes et les méthodes comme des objets, et ne sont donc pas uniformes.

3.3. Concepts propres aux bases de données orientées objet

Des concepts spécifiques s'appliquent aux bases de données orientées objet.

3.3.1. *Objets complexes*

Les modèles orientés objet modélisent les objets complexes d'une manière similaire aux modèles à objets complexes. Leur pouvoir de modélisation est équivalent.

Les objets complexes sont construits à partir d'objets atomiques : caractère, entier, réel, booléen, chaîne de caractères, etc., et de constructeurs qui s'appliquent indépendamment du type des objets : liste, n-uplet, ensemble, tableau, etc.

La possibilité de construction d'objets complexes structurés donne au modèle un grand pouvoir de modélisation qui le rend capable de prendre en compte les données des nouvelles applications.

3.3.2. *Identité d'objet*

Dans les bases de données objet, ce principe est fondamental, il permet d'identifier les objets, de modéliser les cycles entre objets, de partager les objets et de résoudre certains problèmes de mise à jour.

Pour assurer une bonne cohérence sémantique, l'identité d'objet doit être gérée par le système, de manière transparente pour le programmeur. Ceci permet un contrôle exhaustif des mises à jour.

Des opérations spécifiques permettent de traiter ce concept. Comme l'identité qui consiste à comparer les identificateurs, à distinguer de l'égalité qui consiste à comparer les valeurs.

Il existe deux types de comparaisons :

- l'égalité superficielle : les valeurs des objets sont égales ;
- l'égalité profonde : les valeurs des objets, après développement en remplaçant les identificateurs par les valeurs des objets qu'ils représentent, sont égales. L'égalité superficielle implique l'égalité profonde.

Considérons les deux objets i_1 et i_2 et i_3 représentant des voitures

(i_1, [**Nom :** R4, **Marque :** Renault, **Année :** 1978, **Châssis :** i_4])

(i_2, [**Nom :** R4, **Marque :** Renault, **Année :** 1978, **Châssis :** i_4])

(i_3, [**Nom :** R4, **Marque :** Renault, **Année :** 1978, **Châssis :** i_5])

les objets châssis

(i_4, [**Type :** XF330, **Poids :** 200])

(i_5, [**Type :** XF330, **Poids :** 200])

Les objets i_1 et i_2 et i_3 ne sont pas identiques.

Les objets i_1 et i_2 sont égaux superficiellement, puisqu'ils ont la même valeur.

Les objets i_2 et i_3 ne sont pas égaux superficiellement, leurs valeurs diffèrent pour le châssis, mais ils sont égaux en profondeur car si on les développe en on remplaçant les identificateurs par les valeurs d'objets qu'ils représentent, on retrouve deux valeurs égales.

[DELERI91]

3.3.3. *Persistance*

La persistance signifie que la durée de vie d'un objet dépasse la durée d'exécution du programme qui l'utilise. Il existe plusieurs formes de persistance :

- Persistance attachée à un type : tous les objets d'un type persistant sont persistants.
- Persistance attachée à une variable : une variable particulière est désignée persistante.
- Persistance attachée à un objet : un objet particulier est désigné persistant.
- Persistance dynamique : un objet peut passer du statut temporaire à celui de persistant.

Les racines de persistance dans les systèmes orientés objets peuvent être les différents éléments du schéma : classes, objets, types ou variables.

Chapitre 4

Définition

Ce chapitre définit les SGBD orientés objet, en décrivant les fonctionnalités communes des SGBD ainsi que les fonctionnalités spécifiques des SGBDOO.

4.1. Systèmes de gestion de bases de données

Un SGBD est un logiciel qui permet d'interagir avec une base de données. Il offre les services suivants.

4.1.1. *Persistance des données*

Le SGBD gère un ensemble de données persistantes. La persistance des données signifie qu'il existe de façon permanente, un ensemble de données : la base de données.

4.1.2. *Modélisation des données*

Un SGBD doit permettre de gérer des données et des liens complexes entre ces données. Ces liens correspondent à des associations entre les objets de l'application qui sont représentés.

Le SGBD doit s'appuyer sur un modèle de données qui permet de définir la structure des données avec leurs liens, et offre un ensemble d'opérateurs destinés à manipuler ces données.

4.1.3. *Gestion du disque*

Un SGBD doit avoir accès à de volumineux ensembles de données, d'une manière efficace. Les stratégies de stockage et d'accès aux données physiques sur disque doivent être considérées.

4.1.4. *Partage des données*

Plusieurs utilisateurs, à travers différentes applications, doivent pouvoir accéder, simultanément, aux mêmes données sans avoir à se soucier du fait qu'ils ne sont pas les seuls à opérer sur ces données. Il est nécessaire de contrôler le partage des données, de détecter d'éventuels conflits d'accès et de les résoudre.

Le SGBD doit offrir une gestion efficace et cohérente des accès concurrents.

4.1.5. *Fiabilité des données*

Dans un volumineux ensemble de données à la structure complexe, le respect de la cohérence sémantique des données stockées est primordial.

Le SGBD doit garantir la fiabilité des données en offrant la possibilité de définir des règles de maintien de la cohérence de la base. Ces règles définissent les contraintes d'intégrité des données. Les contraintes d'intégrité des données définissent les propriétés que les données doivent satisfaire.

Le respect de la cohérence de la base est également conditionné par la gestion des autorisations, qui permet de limiter l'autorisation de certaines manipulations à des utilisateurs responsables.

4.1.6. *Sécurité des données*

Le SGBD doit protéger les données qu'il gère contre les agressions extérieures. Les agressions peuvent être d'ordre physique, comme celles provoquées par une panne logicielle ou matérielle, ou d'ordre humain, comme une manipulation délibérément malveillante d'un utilisateur.

Les agressions d'ordre physique sont provoquées par des pannes logicielles ou matérielles. Ces agressions peuvent altérer la cohérence des données. Des mécanismes doivent permettre de restaurer la base dans un état cohérent. Le SGBD doit garantir le stockage des données dans un état cohérent.

Les agressions d'ordre humain sont provoquées par des manipulations délibérément malveillantes de la part d'un utilisateur. Le SGBD doit permettre la journalisation des modifications faites sur les données, afin de pouvoir défaire ou refaire ces modifications. Le SGBD doit aussi permettre d'affecter différents droits d'accès sur les données en fonction des utilisateurs.

4.1.7. *Interrogation adéquate de la base de données*

Les utilisateurs doivent pouvoir interroger interactivement et par des langages déclaratifs le contenu de la base.

4.1.8. *Indépendance des données*

Un SGBD doit permettre d'écrire des applications sans se soucier de la structure physique des données et des méthodes d'accès associées. Il permet ainsi de prendre en compte les évolutions des structures de données ou des méthodes d'accès aux données sans remettre en cause les applications existantes.

On distingue deux niveaux d'indépendance :

- l'indépendance physique,
- l'indépendance logique.

L'indépendance physique permet de modifier les structures de stockage ou les méthodes d'accès aux données sans que cela ait d'influence sur les applications. On pourra ainsi changer un index sur une collection, ou changer de méthode de tri pour permettre au système de s'adapter aux données et optimiser ses performances en prenant en compte les besoins de telle ou telle application particulière.

L'indépendance logique doit permettre d'enrichir l'organisation des données sans répercussions sur les applications existantes.

L'indépendance des données est un idéal difficile à atteindre et l'on constatera, selon les systèmes, différents niveaux d'indépendance.

4.2. Systèmes de gestion de bases de données orientés objet

De nombreuses définitions sont données sur les SGBD orientés objet, la définition donnée par le groupe de standardisation Object Database Management Group **[ODMG93]** synthétise bien ces différentes définitions.

Les systèmes de bases de données orientées objet sont le résultat de l'intégration des fonctionnalités classiques des SGBD et d'un langage orienté objet.

[ODMG93]

Un SGBDOO réunit les fonctionnalités d'un SGBD et d'un langage de programmation orienté objet. Nous allons définir les spécificités des SGBDOO.

Les SGBD orientés objet ont donné lieu à de nombreuses propositions, parmi les plus marquantes celle de Atkinson, Bancilhon, De Witt, Dittrich, Maier et Zdonik est celle qui revient le plus souvent dans la littérature. Cette proposition est appelée « Le manifeste » **[ABDDMZ89]**.

Le manifeste a été proposé par un groupe de la communauté des bases de données qui s'est attaché à concevoir et à construire de nouveaux systèmes.

Le manifeste énonce des règles classées en trois catégories :

– les règles obligatoires,

– les règles facultatives,

– les règles ouvertes.

4.2.1. *Les règles obligatoires*

Les règles obligatoires représentent l'ensemble des fonctionnalités que doit impérativement remplir un SGBD pour mériter le qualificatif d'orienté objet.

Les objets complexes

L'ensemble des constructeurs offerts par le modèle doit contenir au moins les constructeurs ensemble et n-uplet, liste et/ou tableau. Des opérations de manipulation de ces objets doivent être offertes.

L'identité d'objet

L'identité d'objet doit être partie intégrante du système. Les identificateurs doivent être gérés par le système.

L'encapsulation

L'encapsulation doit être offerte, mais le langage de requêtes doit avoir la possibilité de passer au travers.

Type ou classe

Un SGBDOO doit offrir soit la notion de classe, soit la notion de type. Le concepteur de SGBDOO est libre de choisir le concept qui lui convient.

L'héritage

L'héritage simple doit être offert.

La liaison dynamique

La surcharge dynamique doit être offerte.

Le langage de requêtes

Tout SGBD doit offrir un langage de requêtes. Aucun formalisme n'est imposé à priori, mais le langage d'interrogation doit être de haut niveau d'abstraction, efficace (donc optimisable) et indépendant des applications.

La complétude du langage

L'intégration du langage de requêtes dans un langage de programmation doit être préférée à son interfaçage dans ce langage car l'interfaçage suppose des modèles de fonctionnement déphasés, alors que l'intégration impose des modèles homogènes.

L'extensibilité

Le modèle adopté doit permettre la définition de nouveaux types d'objets.

La persistance

La gestion de la persistance des données doit être assurée.

La gestion du disque

L'optimisation du stockage des données doit être assurée.

La concurrence

La gestion des accès concurrents doit être assurée.

La reprise sur panne

Le système doit gérer des points de reprises, pour restaurer la base dans un état cohérent, en cas de panne.

4.2.2. *Les règles optionnelles*

Les règles optionnelles proposent des améliorations du SGBD de base qualifié d'orienté objet.

L'héritage multiple

Cette fonctionnalité est un atout supplémentaire, mais ne constitue pas un point indispensable.

La vérification de types

Opérer les vérifications de types à la compilation est présenté dans le manifeste comme une meilleure solution que la vérification à l'exécution. Néanmoins, cette fonctionnalité n'est pas obligatoire.

La répartition

L'architecture du système informatique, particulièrement l'architecture distribuée, est indépendante de l'approche objet et ne constitue pas un élément significatif.

Transactions longues et imbriquées

Le modèle de transactions « plates » est mal adapté à la nature des applications prises en compte par les SGBDOO. Ces applications peuvent conduire à des transactions de très longue durée, (en CAO par exemple). La notion de transactions longues ou imbriquées est un avantage, mais ceci ne constitue pas un prérequis obligatoire.

Les versions

Offrir un mécanisme de gestion des versions est un avantage, mais n'est pas une obligation.

4.2.3. *Les règles ouvertes*

Les règles ouvertes correspondent à des options pouvant être indifféremment choisies par l'architecte du système.

Ces règles sont les suivantes :

- le style du langage (impératif, logique, fonctionnel),
- l'extension du noyau minimal du système de types (généricité du second ordre),
- l'uniformité.

Chapitre 5
Méthodologie

De nombreuses méthodes de conception orientée objet existent, ce chapitre présente une synthèse succincte de ces méthodes.

Les différentes méthodologies orientées objet proposent un formalisme de modélisation. Ce chapitre propose un formalisme qui est un consensus des différentes représentations méthodologiques existantes.

5.1. Cycle de conception

Il existe de nombreuses méthodologies de conception orientée objet. Nous allons, dans ce chapitre, décrire une méthodologie de conception orientée objet et proposer une représentation graphique de modélisation orientée objet.

Caractéristiques générales des méthodes

La démarche méthodologique de conception orientée objet repose sur le principe de l'itération. Le système est conçu par affinements successifs au cours desquels on répétera le même processus. On illustre cette méthode par une spirale.

Cette méthode conduit à analyser les problèmes en les décomposant en sous-ensembles homogènes de complexité maîtrisable.

Chaque tour de spirale constitue une itération qui permettra d'affiner la réalisation au fur et à mesure. Un tour de spirale correspond au cycle de vie d'un module logiciel.

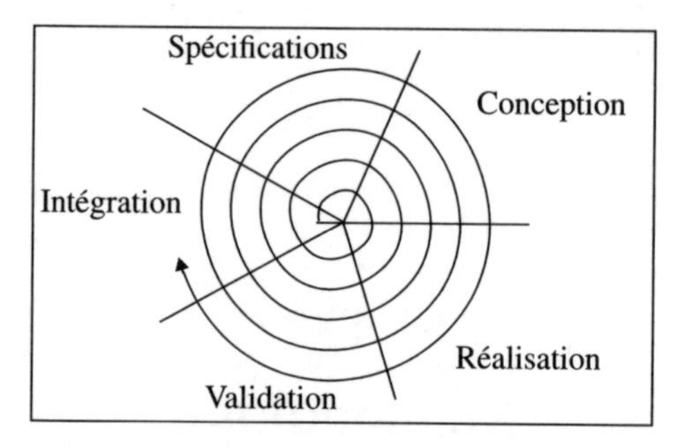

Le cycle de vie en spirale

La phase de conception comprend les phases suivantes :

1. Identifier les classes et former les domaines fonctionnels au fur et à mesure des itérations.
2. Identifier les attributs de chaque classe.
3. Identifier les relations entre les classes.
4. Identifier les opérations applicables sur les classes.
5. Identifier les communications entre les classes.

La phase de conception est suivie par une phase de réalisation. L'application sera réalisée au fur et à mesure de sa conception. Cette démarche revient à réaliser un prototype de l'application qui va évoluer en fonction du développement des modules jusqu'à devenir une application finie.

On peut définir trois vues principales pour modéliser une application :

1. La vue structurelle

C'est la vue des données. Elle décrit les classes d'objets et les relations statiques entre les classes.

2. La vue comportementale

Elle décrit, sous forme de diagrammes d'états, le comportement du système.

3. La vue architecturale

Elle permet de décomposer le système en sous-ensembles fonctionnels.

Le chapitre suivant propose un formalisme de modélisation objet qui permet de décrire la vue structurelle. La vue comportementale peut être décrite par des diagrammes d'états. La vue architecturale est obtenue en décomposant et en organisant la vue structurelle en sous-ensembles fonctionnels.

5.2. Modélisation

Il existe de nombreux modèles capables de décrire le schéma d'une application orientée objet. Nous proposons une modélisation, capable de représenter ce schéma. Cette modélisation est fortement inspirée des modélisations existantes.

5.2.1. *Représentation d'une classe*

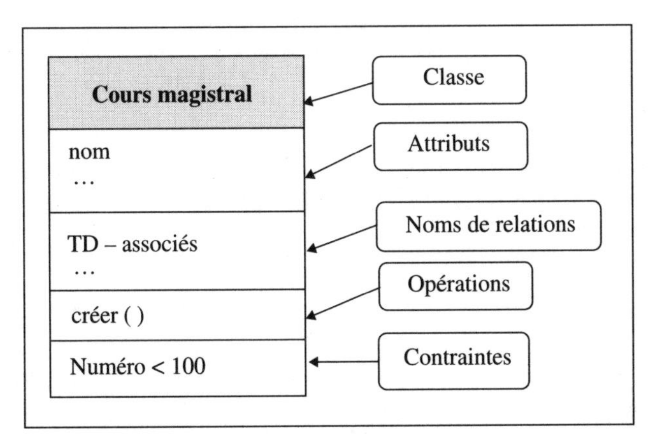

Représentation d'une classe

On représente une classe par un rectangle décomposé en cinq parties :

1. La première partie est grisée et contient le nom de la classe en caractères gras.
2. La deuxième partie contient le nom des attributs associés à cette classe.
3. La toisième partie contient le nom des relations impliquant cette classe.
4. La quatrième partie désigne les opérations associées à cette classe.
5. La cinquième partie définit les contraintes sur la classe.

5.2.2. *Attributs*

Les attributs peuvent être atomiques, n-uplet ou ensemble.

– Les attributs atomiques sont représentés par leur nom.

– Les symboles [ ] désignent le constructeur n-uplet. Un attribut n-uplet est représenté par son nom suivi du constructeur n-uplet, à l'intérieur duquel la structure n-uplet est décrite.

– Les symboles { } désignent le constructeur ensemble. Un attribut ensemble est représenté par son nom suivi du constructeur ensemble dans lequel apparaît le type des éléments de l'ensemble.

nom id–étudiant adresse–u [université, chambre]

5.2.3. *Les contraintes*

Les contraintes sont définies par des prédicats sur les propriétés. Elles permettent de définir des contraintes d'intégrité et de spécialiser des classes en classes dérivées.

5.2.4. *Les relations*

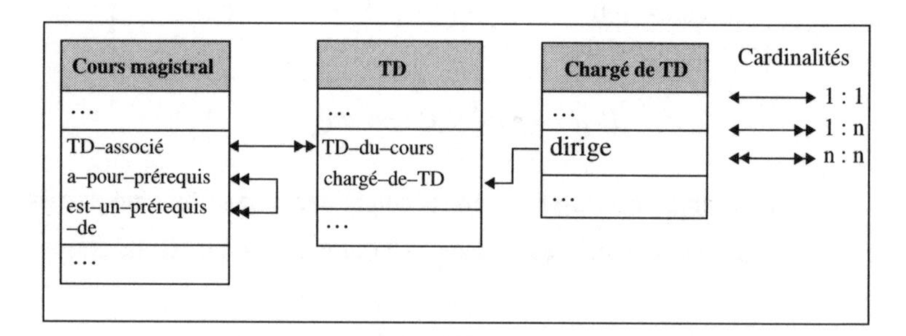

Représentation des relations

Les relations sont représentées à chaque extrémité par un nom significatif du sens de parcours et par des arcs fléchés. La cardinalité de la relation est indiquée par les flèches placées aux extrémités des arcs.

Les relations permettent de représenter les objets complexes, en effet une relation vers une classe peut être considérée comme un attribut de l'objet. L'agrégation, c'est-à-dire le lien de composition, peut être représentée par ces relations, et n'est donc pas distinguée. On peut la considérer comme une relation nommée « agrégation ». Les relations permettent également de représenter les objets cycliques.

5.2.5. *Les méthodes et les messages*

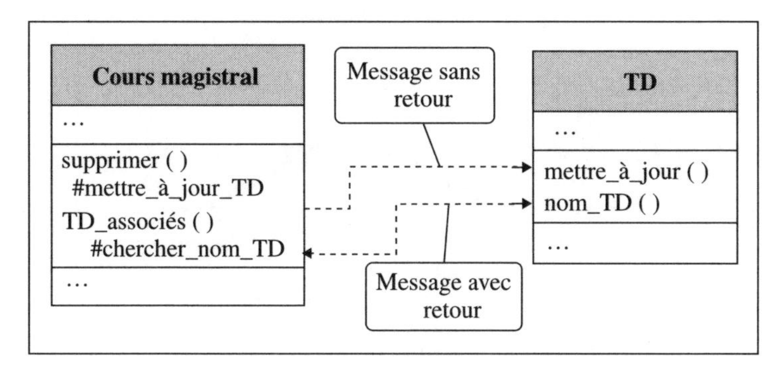

Représentation des méthodes et des messages

Les méthodes sont représentées par leur nom suivi d'arguments entre parenthèses. Les arguments désignent des paramètres de la méthode.

Les méthodes peuvent envoyer des messages vers des méthodes d'autres objets. Les envois de messages peuvent être avec ou sans retour.

5.2.6. *Héritage*

L'héritage est représenté par des liens fléchés dans le sens sous-classe → superclasse.

Les propriétés héritées sont représentées en caractères gras italiques.

L'héritage multiple est modélisé en représentant plusieurs liens vers les superclasses héritées.

En cas de conflit de nom, il est possible de renommer une des propriétés. Un lien pointillé permet d'identifier la propriété renommée.

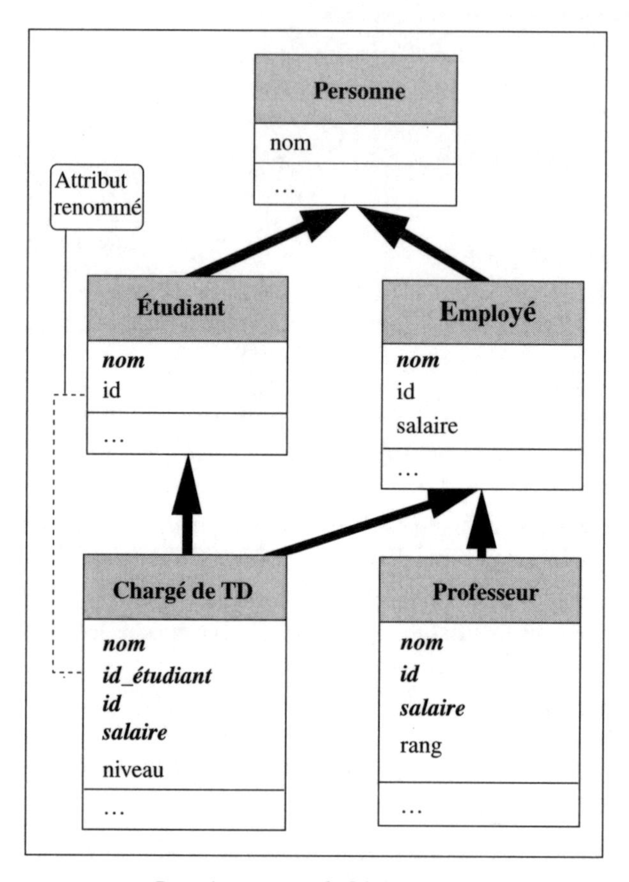

Représentation de l'héritage

5.2.7. *Classes abstraites*

On appelle classe abstraite, une classe qui ne possède pas d'instances propres.

On peut la distinguer des autres classes par un double trait :

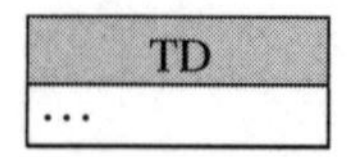

Chapitre 6

Technologie et technique

Ce chapitre présente l'architecture générale d'un SGBDOO telle qu'elle est définie par le standard ODMG-93.

Le fonctionnement des gestionnaires d'objet est décrit, la représentation physique des données ainsi que les langages de programmation sont ensuite présentés.

6.1. Architecture

ODMG-93 V1.1 définit les constituants principaux d'un SGBD orienté objet comme étant les suivants :

– le Langage de Définition Objet,

– le Langage de Requêtes Objet,

– l'intégration du langage de programmation.

Le programmeur écrit les déclarations du schéma de l'application, ainsi qu'un programme source pour l'implémentation de l'application. Le schéma de l'application est déclaré à l'aide du Langage de Définition Objet. Le programme source est écrit dans un Langage de Programmation qui a été étendu en un Langage de Manipulation Objet incluant les transactions et les requêtes objet.

Le langage de définition objet peut être une extension du langage de programmation ou indépendant.

Les déclarations et le programme source sont compilés et liés avec le SGBD orienté objet pour produire une application exécutable. Les types des données de la base de données doivent se conformer aux déclarations pour pouvoir être accédés par l'application.

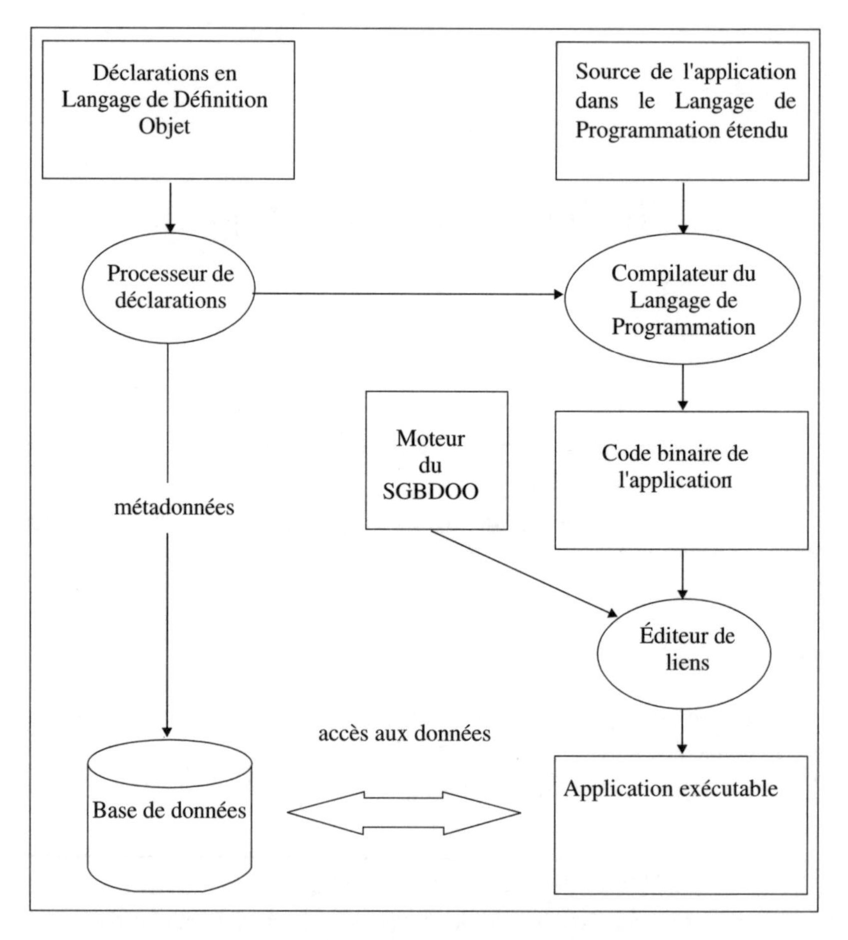

Architecture d'un SGBD orienté objet **[ODMG93]**

6.2. Gestionnaire d'objets

Delobel, Lécluse et Richard imaginent une architecture fonctionnelle pour décrire les différentes étapes qui permettent, à partir d'un objet défini au niveau du langage, d'aboutir à la localisation de l'objet sur un support mémoire. Cette architecture est composée de 6 modules fonctionnels.

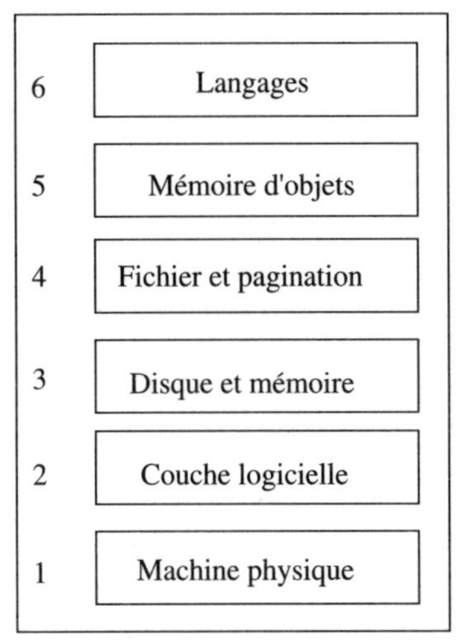

Architecture d'un gestionnaire
d'objets [DELERI91]

1. La machine physique fournit la mémoire centrale, une mémoire secondaire stable et une interface de communication pour le réseau.
2. La couche logicielle est l'interface qui permet l'accès aux différentes composantes de la machine physique.
3. La couche disque et mémoire correspond à la représentation de la mémoire stable (le disque) en un ensemble de blocs de taille fixe. Les blocs peuvent être organisés en unités de regroupements contigus ou disjoints, selon le système.
4. La couche fichier et pagination assure le transport des blocs entre la mémoire principale et le disque.
5. La mémoire d'objet est la couche essentielle du gestionnaire d'objets car elle implémente le modèle de données. Elle assure la gestion du mécanisme d'envoi de messages, l'exécution des méthodes déclenchées par les messages, la gestion des objets temporaires, l'accès aux valeurs des objets, la modification et la création d'objets, etc.
6. La couche langage ne fait pas partie du gestionnaire d'objets. Sa fonction est de compiler les expressions du langage et de maintenir le schéma logique de la base de données.

Les relais entre chaque étape sont appelés *descripteurs*. Ils définissent les paramètres d'entrée pour l'étape suivante.

6.2.1. *Limites fonctionnelles du gestionnaire d'objets*

Cette architecture correspond à un large spectre de systèmes. Une partie de ces modules fonctionnels constitue le gestionnaire d'objets.

Frontière supérieure

Il apparaît que la frontière supérieure du gestionnaire d'objets est l'interface entre la couche langage et la mémoire d'objets.

Frontière inférieure

Il est moins évident de situer la frontière inférieure.

- Certaines réalisations ont utilisé tout ou partie d'un SGBD existant pour gérer les objets.
- D'autres ont supposé l'existence d'un système de gestion de fichiers assurant les fonctionnalités des couches 3 et 4.
- Néanmoins, les réalisations récentes montrent que la mise en œuvre d'un gestionnaire d'objets performant nécessite une adaptation importante des couches 3 et 4.

Nous considérons donc qu'un gestionnaire d'objets intègre les modules fonctionnels 3, 4 et 5.

6.2.2. *Mécanismes d'adressage*

Le rôle d'un mécanisme d'adressage se décompose en deux grandes étapes.

1. La première est la transformation d'un nom externe, défini au niveau du langage de programmation, en un nom interne. Cette opération est liée à la compilation ou l'interprétation du langage. Cette étape correspond au module 1 de la figure précédente. Elle conduit à la construction d'un répertoire, géré par le système, qui associe le nom interne et le nom externe.
2. La deuxième étape consiste à localiser physiquement l'objet dans la mémoire.

Le mécanisme d'adressage doit permettre l'accès le plus efficace possible aux objets. On distingue deux catégories de systèmes.

6.2.2.1. *Les systèmes à deux niveaux de représentation*

Les données sont représentées de manière différente sur le disque et en mémoire centrale. Les objets peuvent être référencés dans deux référentiels distincts.

Cette technique présente l'inconvénient de nécessiter des conversions de données du disque vers la mémoire. L'accès à des sous-composants nécessitera de nombreuses indirections. En revanche une fois chargées en mémoire, les données persistantes et temporaires apparaissent sous une forme homogène.

6.2.2.2. *Les systèmes à un niveau de représentation*

Le format des données en mémoire ou sur disque est le même. On utilise pour cela un mécanisme de mémoire virtuelle. Les références entre les objets sont des adresses de mémoire virtuelle.

Les mécanismes d'adressage virtuel nécessitent des adaptations pour répondre aux exigences de sécurité et de performances des bases de données. Le volume d'adressage virtuel est fonction de la technologie employée. Les avantages de cette solution sont qu'elle ne nécessite ni copies, ni conversions de format.

6.2.3. *Représentation de l'identité d'objet*

L'identité d'objet est unique et permet de distinguer et de localiser l'objet. Il est essentiel qu'elle ne varie pas durant la vie de l'objet. L'implémentation de celui-ci peut être réalisée de différentes façons.

Une unité d'information est un couple :

id	donnée

L'adressage d'un objet peut être réalisé de différentes formes :

- *Adresse physique en mémoire centrale* : ce mécanisme est le plus utilisé par les langages de programmation. Il permet la gestion uniforme des objets persistants et temporaires.
- *Adresse physique en mémoire secondaire* : ce mécanisme est très utilisé dans les bases de données. La structure de l'identificateur reflète la structure logique de la mémoire.
- *Indirection* : l'identificateur est une entrée dans une table d'objets locale ou globale. Cette table établit une correspondance avec l'adresse physique réelle de l'objet. Cette technique assure une bonne indépendance entre l'identité de l'objet et son implémentation. L'inconvénient est qu'il faut effectuer des recherches dans une table.
- *Identificateur structuré* : des informations sur le chemin d'accès à l'objet sont codées dans l'identificateur. L'identificateur peut contenir un code représentant la classe de l'objet, ou le site de l'objet dans le cas d'une architecture distribuée.

– *Identificateur interne* : un identificateur interne indépendant de toute localisation est généré au moment de la création de l'objet. Cet identificateur est géré par le système. Il ne sera jamais réutilisé, même après la disparition de l'objet. Cette solution offre une indépendance physique des données idéale. Néanmoins, elle diminue les performances.

6.3. Représentation d'une struture de données

Ce chapitre décrit une technique de représentation de données complexes dans les SGBDOO.

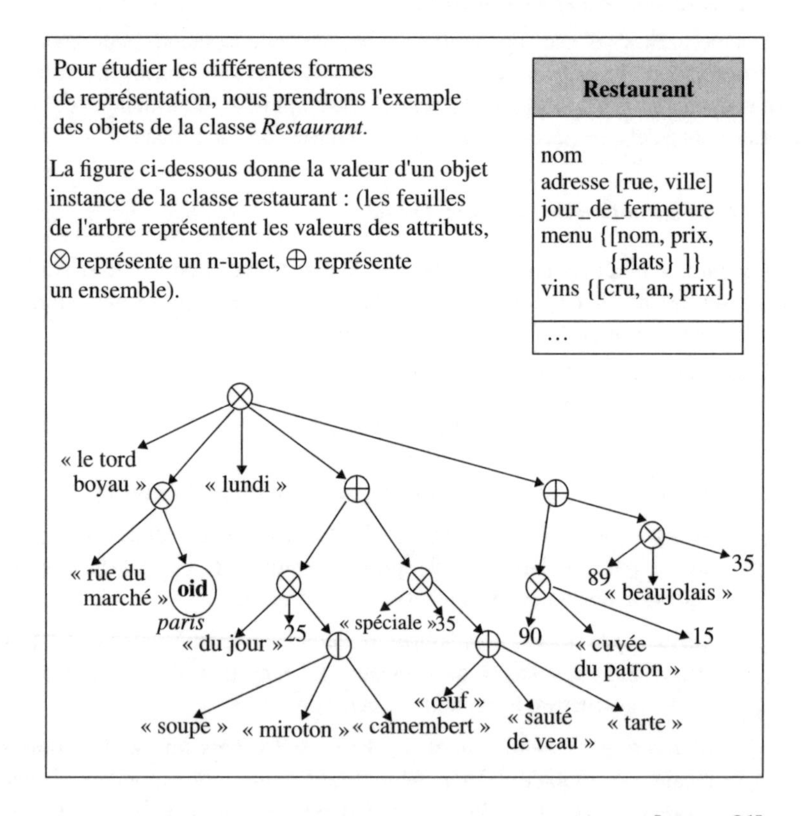

[DELERI91]

6.3.1. *Implémentation d'un n-uplet*

Le n-uplet peut être représenté par un tableau dont la dimension est définie par le nombre d'attributs, chaque élément contenant un lien interne vers la valeur de l'attribut.

L'attribut adresse correspond, par exemple, au deuxième élément du tableau. Le lien ne pointe pas directement sur la valeur relative à l'adresse, mais à nouveau sur une structure de n-uplets qui permet de retrouver sa valeur.

6.3.2. *Implémentation d'un ensemble*

L'ensemble peut être implémenté par un tableau de pointeurs ou une liste.

Le tableau de pointeurs est une structure contenant une entrée pour chaque élément de l'ensemble.

6.3.3. *Représentation normalisée*

Une représentation est dite normalisée si toute l'information n'apparaît que dans les feuilles, les autres nœuds ne contenant que de l'information sur la structure et sur les liens.

Cette représentation correspond à la fragmentation maximale de la structure car chaque unité d'information peut être accédée de manière indépendante.

Une grande fragmentation facilite les évolutions et les mises à jour. Elle peut être utilisée en mémoire, mais elle n'est pas adaptée à une représentation des données sur le disque, dans la mesure où elle risque de répartir la structure sur des enregistrements physiques distincts.

Les liens peuvent être comparés à des adresses physiques, des adresses indirectes ou des identificateurs. L'adressage indirect et les identificateurs d'objets nécessitent la mise en œuvre d'un répertoire intermédiaire permettant la traduction des adresses.

Il existe deux types de liens. Pour utiliser les deux types de liens, il faut mettre en œuvre un codage différent pour chacun afin de les distinguer :

Les liens internes

Ce type de lien ne peut être interprété qu'à l'intérieur d'un environnement donné. Dans notre figure ci-dessus, les différents composants d'un restaurant ne pourront être interprétés que localement à ce restaurant.

Les liens externes

Le lien vers la ville *paris*, représenté dans la figure ci-dessus, est un lien externe. Il correspond à un identificateur d'objet. Sa portée est globale à la base de données.

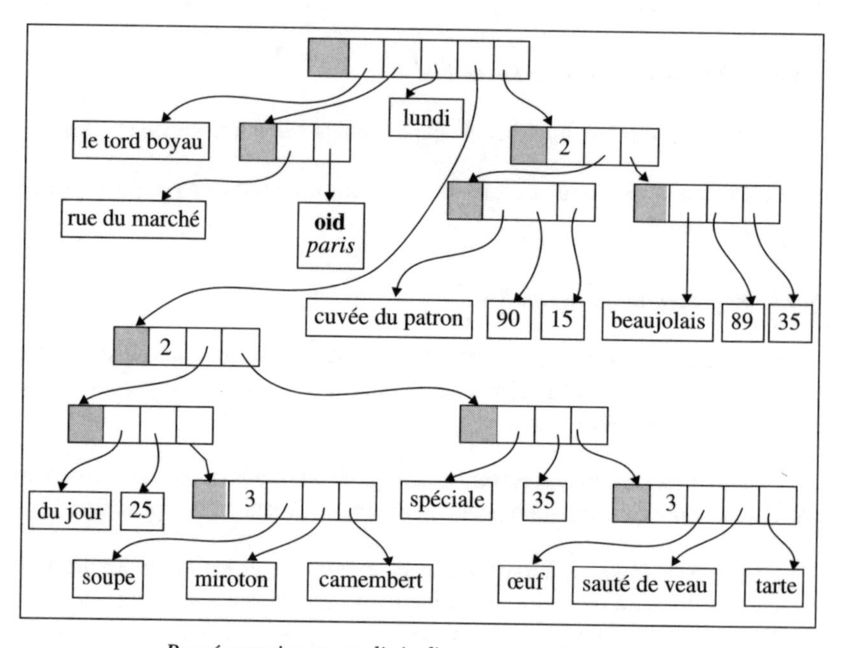

Représentation normalisée d'un restaurant **[DELERI91]**

6.4. Représentation physique en mémoire secondaire

Pour éviter un morcellement trop important de la structure en mémoire secondaire, il faut définir une représentation adéquate en mémoire. Cette représentation s'obtient en remontant l'information des feuilles de la représentation normalisée, vers la racine. On obtient une représentation *linéaire*.

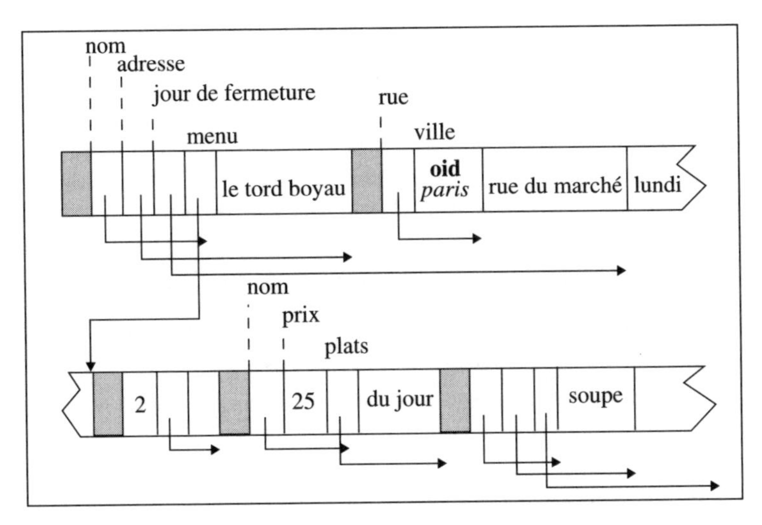

Représentation linaire d'un restaurant **[DELERI91]**

6.4.1. *Taille des objets*

L'inconvénient principal de la représentation présentée ci-dessus est que la longueur totale d'un objet peut dépasser la taille d'une page. La page étant l'unité d'entrée-sortie. La longueur de certains objets tels que les données multimédias : son, images, etc, peuvent atteindre plusieurs méga-octets et plus, soit une taille dépassant largement celle d'une page qui varie en moyenne de 512 octets à 4 096 octets.

Il est important de trouver le découpage optimal en faisant tenir l'information dans un ensemble de pages.

Une solution consiste à définir deux types d'objets qui sont représentés différemment :

– Un objet court est un objet dont la taille est inférieure à la taille d'une page.

– Un objet long est un objet dont la taille est supérieure à la taille d'une page.

6.4.1.1. *Représentation des objets courts*

Un n-uplet court est composé de trois parties :

– l'en-tête composé d'une information sur le type, de sa longueur totale et d'indicateurs de présence d'attributs optionnels ;

– la partie de longueur fixe composée d'une entrée relative à chaque attribut, la valeur de l'attribut pour les attributs atomiques de longueur fixe, un déplacement et la longueur de l'attribut pour les attributs de longueur variable ;

– la partie de longueur variable traitée comme une représentation linéaire pour autant que la longueur de cette zone soit inférieure à la taille d'une page.

Un ensemble court est structuré de la manière suivante :

– l'en-tête composé d'une information sur le type des éléments de l'ensemble, de sa longueur totale et de sa cardinalité ;

– la partie de longueur fixe composée d'une liste de déplacements relative à chaque élément ;

– une troisième partie de longueur fixe ou variable représente les atomes de longueur fixe sous leur forme élémentaire, et les atomes de longueur variable par la longueur de l'atome suivie de sa valeur.

6.4.1.2. *Représentation des objets longs*

Tous les objets longs sont regroupés dans un fichier.

Chaque objet long est identifié par un identificateur d'objet long. Ces identificateurs permettent l'accès au catalogue d'objets longs. Ce catalogue donne le type de l'objet long et des informations complémentaires d'accès à ses composants.

Un n-uplet est représenté par une séquence dont les éléments sont de longueur différente.

Un ensemble long est implémenté sous forme d'un B-arbre. Si l'un des éléments de l'ensemble est lui même un objet long, la zone des données correspondante dans le B-arbre contient l'identificateur de l'objet.

Un B-arbre est une structure de données particulièrement adaptée à la recherche dichotomique.

Un atome long est représenté par une séquence d'éléments de même longueur.

Dans la représentation ci-dessous, nous retrouvons la structure des objets courts : en-tête, partie de longueur fixe et partie de longueur variable.

Dans cette représentation, le nom du restaurant « le tord boyau » et l'ensemble de ses menus, sont supposés être de grande longueur. La valeur de ses attributs est accédée par une indirection avec identificateur d'objet long. L'attribut nom est organisé comme une séquence de caractères. L'attribut menu est organisé sous forme d'un B-arbre dont la clé est le nom du menu.

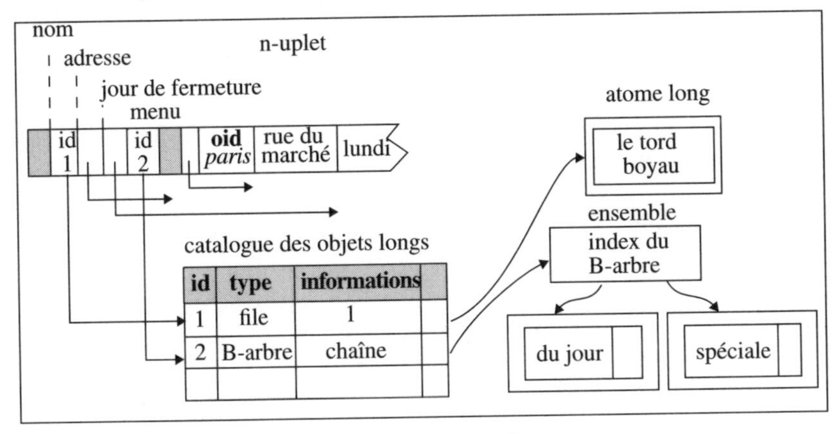

Représentation linaire d'un objet long **[DELERI91]**

6.5. Représentation de l'héritage

Il existe 4 grands modes de représentation de l'héritage :

– représentation en vrac ou universelle, avec ou sans extension de classe,

– représentation selon une répartition horizontale,

– représentation selon une répartition verticale,

– répartition selon la technique Attribut Objet Valeur (AOV).

Pour illustrer ces quatre modes de représentation de l'héritage, nous prendrons l'exemple de la relation d'héritage suivante. Dans cet exemple, la classe Où-aller se spécialise en deux sous-classes : Restaurant et Monument. La classe Restaurant-Historique hérite des deux classes Restaurant et Monument.

Où-aller
Nom
Ville

Restaurant
héritage
jour
cuisine

Monument
héritage
date

Restaurant-Historique
héritage multiple
quoi_voir

[DELERI91]

6.5.1. *Organisation en vrac*

Les données sont stockées sous forme d'un unique tableau de valeurs construit sur tous les attributs. Le tableau possède une entrée pour chaque attribut de la classe et autant de lignes que d'objets. Lorsqu'un attribut n'est pas défini pour une classe, la valeur correspondante n'existe pas et une valeur nulle doit être insérée.

Exemple de représentation en vrac :

oid	**nom**	**ville**	**jour**	**cuisine**	**date**	**quoi_voir**
001	la concorde	paris	∅	∅	∅	∅
002	flo	paris	2	alsacienne	∅	∅
003	tour eiffel	paris	∅	∅	1890	∅
004	coupole	paris	1	traditionnelle	1935	peinture

6.5.2. *Répartition horizontale*

Exemple de la classe Où-aller avec répartition horizontale :

oid	**nom**	**ville**
001	la concorde	paris
002	flo	paris
003	tour eiffel	paris
004	coupole	paris

Un objet est placé dans le fichier relatif à la classe auquel il appartient.

Les instances des sous-classes sont aussi instances des super classes. Ceci peut être traité, soit en copiant la valeur des attributs existant dans la super classe, soit en construisant une extension. La duplication de l'information facilite l'accès à l'information, mais impose la répercussion des mises à jour dans les copies. Si l'information n'est pas dupliquée l'accès à l'information des objets d'une classe nécessite le parcours de toutes les sous-classes.

6.5.3. *Répartition verticale*

L'information est fragmentée sans aucune perte. Pour chaque classe, les valeurs de l'identificateur et des attributs spécifiques sont enregistrées.

La représentation de la classe Où-aller sera identique à celle présentée ci-dessus. La représentation des sous-classes ne contiendra que les informations spécifiques aux sous-classes.

Exemple de répartition verticale :

Restaurant

oid	jour	cuisine
002	2	alsacienne
004	1	traditionnelle

Monument

oid	date
003	1890
004	1935

Restaurant-Historique

oid	quoi_voir
004	peinture

6.5.4. *Attribut Objet Valeur (AOV)*

Exemple de répartition AOV :

oid	attribut	valeur
001	nom	la concorde
001	ville	paris
002	nom	flo
002	ville	paris
002	jour	2
002	cuisine	alsacienne
...	...	...

Chaque valeur d'attribut est codée sous forme d'un triplet de valeurs : Identificateur, Attribut Valeur.

Conclusion

Nous classons les méthodes par ordre croissant de coût en espace mémoire :

1. Représentation horizontale sans copie.
2. Représentation verticale.
3. Attribut Objet Valeur (AOV).

L'efficacité d'accès d'une méthode dépend des besoins d'accès : retrouver toutes les instances d'une classe, retrouver un objet, retrouver la valeur de l'attribut d'un objet.

> Pour retrouver toutes les instances d'une classe, la représentation horizontale est la plus efficace.
> Pour retrouver la valeur de l'attribut d'un objet, la structure AOV est la plus adaptée.

6.6. Techniques d'optimisation de stockage

6.6.1. *Indexation*

Un index est une structure de données qui accélère les recherches de données. Son objectif est d'optimiser les performances.

Le principe de l'indexation consiste à trouver l'expression équivalente à une requête exprimée, mais dont le coût en termes de manipulations en mémoire ou d'opérations d'entrées sorties est plus faible.

Actuellement, pour les modèles orientés objet, les techniques d'optimisation des requêtes sont encore dans une phase de recherche. Les règles de transformation des requêtes sont très complexes et l'étude d'un ensemble exhaustif de règles n'a pas encore été faite.

6.6.2. *Le regroupement*

Le regroupement de données est une technique de répartition des données sur le disque de manière à minimiser les accès physiques aux enregistrements lors de l'exécution des traitements.

L'objectif d'un algorithme de regroupement est de placer sur le disque, aussi près que possible, les objets qui sont utilisés en même temps.

On distingue deux formes de regroupement :

- Regroupement statique : le placement des objets est fait au moment de leur création et aucune réorganisation n'est effectuée lors des mises à jour.
- Regroupement dynamique : le placement des objets peut être fait à tout moment, et le système s'adapte aux changements. Ce principe est beaucoup plus intéressant dans un environnement où les opérations d'écriture sont plus nombreuses que les opérations de lecture. [YU74] [YUSILATA81].

La structuration en objets longs, objets courts est aussi une stratégie possible pour le regroupement des objets complexes.

Les algorithmes mis en œuvre sont des heuristiques recherchant une solution quasi optimale. Le principe général est de mesurer, au cours d'un traitement, les positions relatives des objets manipulés. Les positions des objets accédés simultanément seront rapprochées au détriment des autres. Le principal inconvénient est que ces systèmes adaptatifs sont instables, les fréquentes réorganisations pénalisent les performances.

Le paramètre d'entrée essentiel est la fréquence des accès, cette information doit être stockée avec chaque objet et mise à jour. Cette solution est coûteuse en cas de modifications fréquentes. Une alternative consiste à n'enregistrer que la fréquence des accès entre types de données en la stockant dans le catalogue des types.

6.6.3. *Gestion des transactions*

Un ensemble de processus peut opérer simultanément sur une même donnée, en lecture ou en écriture. Des règles de coordination strictes doivent être mises en œuvre.

> Si deux processus P1 et P2 incrémentent, en parallèle, la même donnée X = 0 et que l'on ne gère pas la concurrence, la valeur finale de la donnée sera X = 1 alors qu'elle devrait être X = 2.

La solution à ces problèmes consiste à regrouper l'ensemble des opérations à effectuer dans des transactions. Une transaction doit être considérée comme une unité atomique de traitement. Ce qui signifie que ses effets sont soit intégralement répercutés sur la base de données, soit intégralement annulés. Une transaction qui s'exécute jusqu'à la fin est « validée » ; une transaction qui ne termine pas « avorte ».

Les transactions possèdent les propriétés suivantes :

- *l'indivisibilité* : vue de l'extérieur, une transaction ne possède pas d'états intermédiaires ;
- *le recouvrement* : tous les objets traités au cours d'une transaction peuvent retrouver leur état initial. La validation d'une transaction constitue un point de reprise.

Les systèmes orientés objet sont souvent utilisés dans des applications de conception. De par la nature des données manipulées, la durée des transactions peut être très longue. L'optimisation de la gestion des transactions est donc d'un grand intérêt. Différentes voies de recherches sont ouvertes.

6.6.3.1. *Les modèles à transactions imbriquées*

Une transaction imbriquée correspond à la décomposition d'un traitement en une arborescence de sous-traitements ; chaque sous-traitement pouvant, lui-même être décomposé.

6.6.3.2. *Les modèles à base de données publiques et privées*

Dans cette approche, une transaction longue ne peut s'exécuter que sur une base privée, après copie des données à traiter de la base de données publique à la base de données privée. En fin de transaction, les données traitées sont copiées de la base privée à la base publique.

6.6.3.3. *Les modèles à versions*

Une transaction longue est modélisée comme une séquence de transactions courtes qui agissent chacune sur des versions d'objets de la base de données. Les versions d'un objet étant indépendantes les unes des autres, les conflits d'accès sont très limités.

6.6.4. *Gestion des versions*

Les nouvelles applications telles que la CAO, le génie logiciel ou la bureautique, nécessitent de conserver, au cours du temps les états successifs d'un objet. L'ensemble de ces états constitue l'ensemble des versions d'un objet.

Les versions d'un objet peuvent être ordonnées suivant un *arbre des versions*.

La problématique de la gestion des versions a ouvert plusieurs voies de recherche ou de développement.

6.6.4.1. *Référence statique et référence dynamique*

Un objet o peut référencer un objet *o'*. Si l'objet o possède plusieurs versions, la référence peut être *statique* ou *dynamique*.

– La référence statique identifie une seule version.

– La référence dynamique identifie l'ensemble des versions.

6.6.4.2. *Percolation*

Les mises à jours des versions des objets composites mettent en œuvre des mécanismes complexes de propagation en cascade. Ce phénomène appelé *percolation*, ainsi que les moyens d'en limiter le recours, ont été particulièrement étudiés.

6.6.4.3. *Versions de bases de données*

Cette approche consiste à définir à la place des versions d'objets, des versions de la base de données. Ces versions de base de données sont également créées par dérivation. Un système d'estampilles permet d'éviter de stocker les versions redondantes d'un objet existant dans deux versions différentes de la base.

6.7. Langages

6.7.1. *Langage de définition des données*

Le langage de définition de données doit offrir des primitives permettant de modéliser l'application en utilisant toutes les abstractions offertes par le modèle.

6.7.2. *Langages de manipulation des données*

Il existe plusieurs modèles pour exprimer les calculs dans la programmation :

- la programmation impérative,
- la programmation fonctionnelle,
- la programmation logique.

Programmation impérative

La programmation impérative consiste à décrire explicitement l'algorithme à l'aide d'instructions. Les langages tels que *Fortran*, *Pascal* et *C* appartiennent à cette catégorie **[BENDOU93]**.

Programmation fonctionnelle

La programmation fonctionnelle consiste à décrire les calculs à l'aide de fonctions. *Lisp* en est l'exemple le plus connu **[BENDOU93]**.

Programmation logique

La programmation logique est fondée sur la logique formelle, les programmes sont décrits par des prédicats. Le principal langage logique est *Prolog* **[BENDOU93]**.

6.7.2.1. *Langages d'interrogation de données*

Les langages déclaratifs sont basés sur le paradigme de programmation logique et offrent un grand confort d'utilisation. Ils permettent de décrire directement le résultat à obtenir sans s'inquiéter du moyen de l'obtenir. En revanche, ils n'offrent pas la puissance des langages impératifs qui permettent de formuler des itérations.

Le paradigme déclaratif est le mieux adapté aux langages d'interrogation des données.

6.7.2.2. *Langages de programmation*

Il n'y pas d'indication particulière concernant le paradigme de programmation à adopter pour les langages de programmation.

Les langages orientés objet respectent les trois paradigmes de programmation.

- *Langages orientés objet impératifs* : C++, Objective C, Eiffel.
- *Langages orientés objet fonctionnels* : CLOS, Flavors, Galileo.
- *Langages orientés objet logiques* : Yafool, Objlog.

Chapitre 7
Normalisation

Il existe différents standards qui s'appliquent aux objets, tels que CORBA, OMTF et OSTF qui ont été spécifiés par l'Object Management Group (OMG).

Il n'existe pas aujourd'hui de norme définissant les bases de données orientées objet. En revanche, un organisme à entrepris de combler cette lacune. Il s'agit de l'Object Database Management Group (ODMG), affilié en février 94 à l'OMG.

La version actuelle du standard ODMG-93 est la version 1.2. Ce chapitre présente le standard ODMG-93.

7.1. Standard ODMG-93

L'ODMG est un organisme qui a choisi de développer un standard pour permettre aux utilisateurs de SGBDOO d'écrire des applications portables d'un SGBDOO à l'autre. L'ODMG est composé de conseillers et de représentants de sociétés qui se sont engagées à promouvoir le standard.

7.1.1. *Propriétés d'un SGBD orienté objet respectant le standard ODMG-93*

Les SGBDOO intègrent de manière transparente les fonctionnalités d'une base de données avec un langage de programmation orienté objet.

Le système de typage des objets du SGBDOO est homogène avec celui du langage de programmation. Il n'est pas nécessaire de traduire les données entre leur base et leur représentation dans le langage de programmation, ce qui évite les dysfonctionnements.

Le SGBDOO possède un langage de requêtes déclaratif.

Les objets de la base de données apparaissent comme des objets du langage de programmation. Le SGBD ajoute au langage le stockage permanent des données, le contrôle concurrent, la récupération des données, les requêtes associatives, etc.

7.1.2. *Caractéristiques du modèle objet ODMG-93*

Ce paragraphe présente les caractéristiques du modèle objet ODMG-93 et les compare aux différentes notions évoquées dans ce document.

Le modèle ODMG-93 respecte les principes déjà évoqués d'objet, encapsulation, types, classes, héritage, surcharge sémantique et résolution tardive, objets complexes, uniformité, identité d'objet, persistance, transactions. Nous ne présenterons ici que ceux qui diffèrent de ce qui à déjà été présenté et ceux qui méritent des précisions.

7.1.2.1. *Types ou classes*

Dans le modèle ODMG-93 la notion de type prédomine sur celle de classe.

Un type est défini par les caractéristiques suivantes : opérations, attributs et relations.

7.1.2.2. *Le type object*

Le type *object* du modèle ODMG-93 correspond aux notions désignées par *types abstraits* ou *classes* dans les paragraphes 2.5. Systèmes de types et 3.2. Concepts orientés objet applicables aux bases de données.

7.1.2.3. *Classes*

Un type possède une interface et une ou plusieurs implémentations.

Dans le modèle ODMG-93, les *classes* correspondent à l'association de l'interface d'un type et d'une de ses implémentations.

7.1.2.4. *Héritage*

Les types objet forment un graphe défini par la relation sous-type/supertype. Ces relations respectent le concept d'héritage simple et multiple.

Un mécanisme permet de résoudre les conflits de noms qui peuvent se produire lors de l'héritage multiple.

7.1.2.5. *Types abstraits*

Un type abstrait dans le modèle ODMG-93 est un type qui n'est pas directement instanciable. Il ne fait que définir des caractéristiques héritées par ses sous types et ne définit pas d'implémentation. On peut comparer les types abstraits du modèle ODMG-93 aux classes abstraites citées dans le paragraphe 5.2. Modélisation.

7.1.2.6. *Uniformité*

Le modèle objet offre une uniformité totale. Toutes les abstractions manipulées par le modèle : objet, littéraux, attributs, relations, opérations, types, etc., sont des objets typés.

7.1.2.7. *Persistance*

La durée de vie d'un objet modifiable dépend de son type. Trois durées de vie sont reconnues dans le modèle de base :

- Un objet dont la durée de vie est *coterminus_with_procedure* est typiquement celui qui est déclaré dans une procédure. Sa durée de vie est celle de la procédure.
- La durée de vie d'un objet *coterminus_with_process* est égale à la durée de l'exécution de l'application.
- Un objet dont la durée de vie est *coterminus_with_database* est un objet persistant stocké dans la base de données.

7.1.3. *Le langage de requêtes Object Query Langage (OQL)*

Le langage OQL supporte le modèle ODMG-93.

OQL n'est pas un langage de programmation à part entière, mais il peut être imbriqué ou imbriquer les langages de programmation intégrés par l'ODMG–93.OQL est un langage déclaratif basé sur la paradigme de programmation logique.

OQL possède une syntaxe concrète proche de *Structured Query Language* (SQL), le langage de requêtes normalisé des bases de données relationnelles.

OQL fournit des primitives de haut niveau, pour traiter les constructions complexes, mettant en œuvre les constructeurs ensemble, n-uplets, etc.

OQL ne fournit pas explicitement d'opérateurs de mise à jour. Il exploite les opérations définies sur les objets à ce propos.

7.1.4. *Les langages de programmation intégrés*

Le modèle ODMG-93 et le langage de requêtes OQL offrent une intégration avec les langages de programmation orientés objet C++ et *Smalltalk*.

Chapitre 8
Aspects socio-économiques

Ce chapitre présente dans une première partie, les points de vue subjectifs du public sur les SGBDOO et apporte des arguments fondés sur des faits pour démentir les préjugés.

La deuxième partie de ce chapitre présente un état du marché des SGBDOO.

8.1. SGBD orientés objet et mythes

De nombreux mythes gravitent autour des SGBDOO. David Taylor a exposé ces mythes et les a démentis par des faits dans *Object Magazine* de mars 1996 **[OBJMAR96].**

Le salon RealWare Awards qui s'est tenu au DB/Expo en mai 1995 à San Francisco a organisé un concours sur le développement d'applications industrielles orientées objet. Les trois finalistes de ce concours ont utilisé des SGBDOO.

Les trois finalistes étaient : Northwest Natural Gas, Celestica Inc et Ameritech Advanced Data Services. Ces trois sociétés ont utilisé pour leurs applications les SGBDOO, respectivement, ObjectStore de Object Design, Versant de Versant Object Technology et Gemstone de Gemstone Systems. Celestica fut désigné vainqueur.

Les résultats de ces applications démentent quelques-uns des préjugés qui affectent les SGBDOO.

Les SGBDOO ne sont pas adaptés aux applications traditionnelles.

Un des mythes courants est que les SGBDOO ne sont pas utilisés pour des applications traditionnelles. Northwest Natural Gas utilise le SGBDOO ObjectStore de Object Design, pour gérer le système d'information clients. Le système stocke les informations de service sur 400 000 clients. 250 représentants des services clients les consultent dans 7 bureaux du district ouest de l'Oregon et sud-ouest de Washington.

Celestica utilise les SGBDOO Gemstone, de Gemstone Systems, pour le contrôle des ouvriers de fabrication et les systèmes de rapport. Le système supporte plus de 500 utilisateurs allant de l'ouvrier d'atelier à l'encadrement moyen et aux groupes de support d'ingénierie.

Ameritech Advance Data Services utilise le SGBDOO Versant de Versant Object Technology, pour gérer un système d'information de management global qui regroupe la comptabilité, l'entrée des commandes, la définition des prix et le support avant-vente. Plus de 200 personnes utilisent le système dans 5 états.

Ces applications (système d'information clients, contrôle du personnel ouvrier de fabrication et système de rapport, ainsi que le système d'information de management) font partie des applications traditionnelles. Elles montrent que les SGBDOO sont adaptés aux applications traditionnelles.

Les SGBDOO ne fonctionnent pas à grande échelle.

Un second mythe est que les SGBDOO ne fonctionnent pas à grande échelle. On entend dire : « ils sont corrects pour une petite application avec peu d'utilisateurs, mais ne pensez même pas à les utiliser pour une plus grande application avec beaucoup d'utilisateurs. » L'ensemble des applications finalistes présentées au RealWare gère une base de données dont le volume tourne autour du gigaoctet. Chacune avait des centaines d'utilisateurs. Ces applications démontrent que les SGBDOO s'appliquent très bien à un nombre important d'utilisateurs et à de grands volumes de données.

Les SGBDOO ne sont pas interrogeables.

Le quatrième mythe est qu'on ne peut pas interroger un SGBDOO. Toutes les applications présentées par les finalistes du RealWare utilisent les requêtes.

Conclusion

> Ces faits montrent que les SGBDOO ne sont pas seulement en phase de maturation, mais que de nombreuses applications traditionnelles existent. Des systèmes critiques pour le fonctionnement de la compagnie, qui impliquent des centaines d'usagers et des gigaoctets de données, font partie des grandes applications.
>
> Ces mythes n'incitent pas les utilisateurs à se servir des SGBDOO qui peuvent leur être d'un grand secours. A cause de ces mythes, les gens prennent des décisions qui ne vont pas forcément dans le sens de leur intérêt. Un SGBDOO n'est pas toujours la meilleure réponse à un problème technique, mais fonder une décision sur un préjugé n'est pas non plus la meilleure réponse.

David Taylor **[OBJMAR96]**

8.2. Le marché

Les paragraphes suivants présentent quelques applications existantes. Ils donnent une liste des fournisseurs et présentent la répartition du marché entre les fournisseurs les plus représentés.

8.2.1. *Applications dans les télécommunications*

La société Motorola commercialise des produits de télécommunications mobiles. Elle a lancé le projet Iridium. Ce projet consiste à bâtir un réseau de télécommunications dans l'espace. Ce réseau sera supporté par 66 satellites en orbite basse. Le SGBDOO Objectivity/DB a été choisi pour gérer les données relatives aux communications qui passeront par ce réseau. On présente ce projet en disant qu'il manipulera le plus grand volume de données au monde.

Infoseek/Netscape a développé un service de navigation présenté comme le plus rapide, le plus puissant et le plus utilisé sur Internet à ce jour avec près de 5 000 000 de demandes d'information par jour. Le SGBD Matisse va être utilisé pour la gestion des données de facturation, la mémorisation des requêtes utilisateurs et comme moteur de recherche.

British Telecom, Nippon Telephone Telegraph utilisent le SGBDOO Ontos pour gérer leurs systèmes de communication.

AT&T utilise l'interface Persistence et le SGBD relationnel Sybase pour gérer les communications de son réseau mondial intelligent.

8.2.2. *Applications dans l'industrie*

La compagnie hydroélectrique British Columbia Hydro a développé un système d'information de maintenance de son outil industriel. La base de données contient toutes les informations de maintenance relatives à l'outil industriel. Cette application utilise le SGBDOO Gemstone. Elle gère plus de 300 000 éléments, 150 utilisateurs simultanés répartis sur 7 sites. L'objectif de ce projet est de gérer 1 000 000 d'éléments, 1 100 utilisateurs simultanés répartis sur 60 sites.

8.2.3. *Application à la gestion de documents multimédias*

La société italienne Italtriest est spécialisée dans la réalisation, la production et la gestion de panneaux publicitaires. Elle produit et gère 18 000 panneaux publicitaires destinés à 7 000 stations services réparties sur le territoire national. Cette société à développé une application de gestion géographique des messages publicitaires et des points de vente. Cette application permet de localiser les messages publicitaires et les points de vente sur une carte géographique, de visualiser les panneaux publicitaires par simple click sur la carte, et de gérer l'historique des points de vente. Cette application utilise le SGBDOO O_2.

8.2.4. *Applications dans la finance*

Nomura International, la division investissements bancaires de Nomura Securities Co Ltd a choisi le SGBDOO ObjectStore dans le cadre du projet Hoodini. L'objectif est de fournir les informations financières à jour à 300 courtiers répartis dans 15 villes de 12 pays.

8.2.5. *L'état du marché*

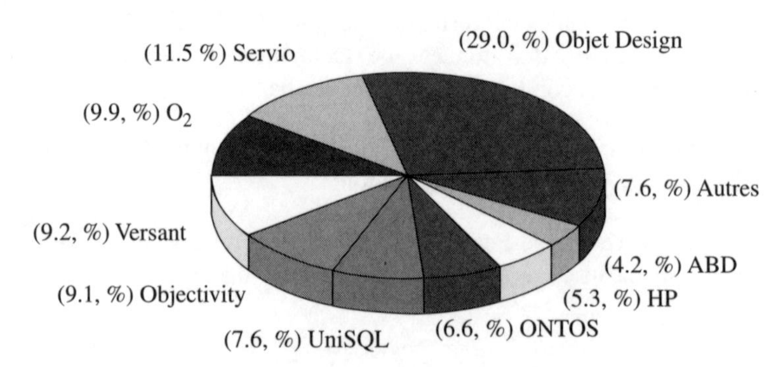

Le marché mondial des SGBDOO en 1993 ***[IMAGmai95]***

Année	M $
90	10
91	22
92	43
93	76
94	169
95	354

Le tableau ci-dessus donne les chiffres (en millions de dollars) de l'évolution du marché des SGBDOO. Les chiffres sont vérifiés jusque 1993 **[ADICO93]**.

8.2.6. *Les offres*

Nous présentons, dans ce chapitre, une liste non exhaustive des différentes offres du marché en précisant leur positionnement par rapport au standard ODMG-93 et leur modèle (O : objet, RE : relationnel étendu, O/R : Interface gérant des objets dans un SGBD relationnel).

Produit	**Fournisseur**	**Version du standard ODMG–93 respectée**				**Type**
		Modèle	Objet Query Language	Intégration C++	Intégration Smalltalk	
Gemstone	Gemstone Systems,Inc (Servio	1.1	/	/	1.2	0
	ADB,Inc					
	Micram Object Technology GmbH	1.2	/	1.2	/	
	O_2 Technology, Inc	/	1.2	1.2	1.1	0

Produit	Fournisseur	Version du standard ODMG–93 respectée				Type
Objectivity/ DB	Objectivity,Inc	1.2	1.2	1.2	1.2	0
	Object Design, Inc	/	/	1.2	1.2	0
	CV Software Construction	/	/	/	1.1	
	Omniscience Object Technology, Inc	1.2	1.2	1.2	/	
	Ontos					0
	Hewlett Packard					0
	MCC					
	POET Software, Inc	/	1.2	1.2	/	
	UniSQL, Inc	/	1.2	1.1	1.2	
	Versant Object Technology	/	/	1.2	/	0
	Persistence Software, Inc					O/R

Chapitre 9

Conclusion

Nous concluons cette étude en présentant le domaine d'application des SGBDOO, en apportant une critique sur les arguments préconçus concernant les SGBDOO et en proposant une réflexion sur leur avenir.

9.1. Le modèle objet

Les SGBD relationnels ne sont pas adaptés aux données complexes des nouvelles applications telles que la CAO, la bureautique, le génie logiciel, les données géographiques, et les données multimédias. Un marché potentiel important est ouvert.

Les nouveaux systèmes peuvent répondre aux besoins de ce marché. Ces systèmes sont issus de deux courants. On distingue un courant de type évolution avec les systèmes relationnels étendus et un système de type révolution avec les SGBDOO.

Les systèmes relationnels étendus offrent l'avantage de réutiliser les acquis issus des systèmes relationnels en termes de maturité de technologie et ne provoquent pas de révolution dans le monde des utilisateurs. En revanche, ils conservent certains désavantages liés au modèle relationnel comme la limitation du pouvoir de modélisation. Ces systèmes ne sont pas à même de prendre pleinement en compte les besoins des nouvelles applications.

Les SGBDOO proposent des modèles nouveaux offrant une richesse et une liberté totale d'expression. Ne bénéficiant pas d'acquis technologiques mûrs et éprouvés, le développement de ces systèmes a été difficile : de nombreux problèmes ont été résolus, mais d'autres n'ont pas encore trouvé de solution satisfaisante. Ces systèmes constituent une technologie entièrement neuve qui prend en compte de manière pleinement satisfaisante les besoins de nouvelles applications.

Cette étude montre que la technologie objet bénéfice aujourd'hui d'outils adaptés pour le stockage de données persistantes. Ces outils offrent les mêmes fonctionnalités que les SGBD conventionnels. Ils apportent une solution aux limitations des systèmes relationnels grâce à la richesse de modélisation qu'apporte le modèle objet.

9.2. Le passé

Les éditeurs de SGBD relationnels critiquent les SGBDOO tout en annonçant à court terme, la mise sur le marché de leur propre SGBDOO.

Les arguments principaux contre ces systèmes sont la baisse des performances dès qu'ils s'agit de partager les données entre un grand nombre d'utilisateurs et leur inadaptation aux applications de gestion.

Cette mauvaise réputation est sans doute issue de l'arrivée prématurée des premiers systèmes sur le marché. On constate, pour les systèmes précédents un délai d'une dizaine d'années entre la proposition des concepts et la mise sur le marché des produits correspondants. Les recherches sur les SGBDOO ont commencé vers 1985 et les premiers produits ont été commercialisés vers 1990, soit 5 ans, c'est-à-dire la moitié de la période de gestation des systèmes précédents.

En supposant que ces arguments soient encore vrais aujourd'hui, on peut répondre que ce n'est pas l'adaptation des SGBD au modèle objet qui est la cause de ces mauvaises performances, mais que c'est l'adaptation des SGBD à un nouveau modèle. En effet, les performances sont liées à la technique et non au modèle utilisé. En revanche le développement d'une nouvelle technologie exige de nombreuses mises au point et optimisations. On considère que pour les générations précédentes de SGBD il a fallu 10 ans pour transformer les concepts en une technologie aux performances satisfaisantes. Les concepts des SGBDOO ont été proposés vers le milieu des années 80. En généralisant ces informations, on peut penser qu'avec l'évolution des recherches dans le domaine, les SGBDOO offriront des performances satisfaisantes dans un futur proche.

Les nombreuses applications des SGBDOO, dans des domaines de pointe comme les télécommunications où les schémas de données sont complexes, démentent les arguments négatifs avancés.

On peut imaginer que les SGBDOO ne posent pas de problèmes insurmontables. Cependant, ces systèmes sont récents et l'on peut supposer qu'il reste des améliorations à apporter.

9.3. Le présent

Le domaine d'application des SGBDOO comprend les applications de gestion traditionnelles, la gestion de données techniques, l'administration de réseaux de télécommunications, la gestion de la documentation, la cartographie, etc.

Le contexte économique actuel n'invite pas à prendre de risques par l'acquisition d'outils très avancés. Seules, les entreprises pour lesquelles l'optimisation et la modélisation précise de données sont un élément stratégique, n'hésitent pas à se lancer dans l'aventure. C'est le cas des nombreux opérateurs téléphoniques qui constituent la majorité des utilisateurs de SGBDOO.

9.4. Le futur

La question de savoir si les nouveaux systèmes vont remplacer les systèmes relationnels est difficile. On peut répondre en disant que chaque système apporte des solutions à des problèmes de nature différente. On peut donc penser que ces systèmes sont complémentaires et que chacun aura sa place dans un marché où les besoins sont très divers :

- les systèmes relationnels étendus répondent bien aux besoins des entreprises qui souhaitent élargir le champ de leur système d'information sans révolutionner leur système informatique ;

- les SGBDOO répondent aux besoins des nouvelles applications et permettent de modéliser précisément des structures de données complexes. Ils séduisent les entreprises pour qui la gestion précise des données des nouvelles applications ou des structures de données complexes constituent un point stratégique.

La réussite de ces systèmes est conditionnée par la mise en place d'une normalisation. L'ODMG propose un standard élaboré auquel adhèrent la plupart des constructeurs de SGBDOO. On peut penser que la promotion de ce standard en norme donnera une grande impulsion aux SGBDOO.

La pénétration des SGBDOO sur le marché des SGBD est délicate. L'approche objet nécessite un travail de refonte des applications existantes, ainsi qu'un effort de formation.

Une solution pour percer le marché sera d'assurer la communication de ces systèmes avec les SGBD existants.

D'autres produits qualifiés d'*hybrides*, sont des passerelles entre SGBD relationnels et objet, ils pallient les limites des SGBD relationnels tout en les utilisant comme support de stockage. Cette démarche manque d'homogénéité et risque de poser des problèmes. Ils offrent néanmoins une solution intermédiaire qui permet de récupérer les outils existants.

Glossaire

Attribut : Un attribut correspond à la colonne d'une relation caractérisée par un nom [GARDARIN89].

B-Arbre : Un B–arbre est une structure de données particulièrement adaptée à la recherche dichotomique.

Langage de programmation déclaratif : Un langage déclaratif est un langage avec lequel l'utilisateur décrit le résultat et non pas le moyen d'obtenir le résultat par opposition aux langages impératifs.

n-uplet : La structure d'un n-uplet est celle d'une relation. Un n-uplet correspond à une ligne de la relation. Nous employons le terme « n-uplet » d'une manière générale, dans tous les modèles, alors que nous utilisons le terme « relation » dans le contexte relationnel.

ODMG : Object Data Management Group.

OMG : Object Management Group.

Programmation fonctionnelle : La programmation fonctionnelle consiste à décrire les calculs à l'aide de fonctions. *Lisp* en est l'exemple le plus connu [BENDOU93].

Première forme normale : Une relation est en première forme normale si tout attribut de la relation contient une valeur atomique [GARDARIN89].

Programmation impérative : La programmation impérative consiste à décrire explicitement l'algorithme à l'aide d'instructions. Les langages tels que *Fortran*, *Pascal* et *C* appartiennent à cette catégorie [BENDOU93].

Programmation logique : La programmation logique est fondée sur la logique formelle, les programmes sont décrits par des prédicats. Le principal langage logique est *Prolog* [BENDOU93].

Relation : Une relation est le produit cartésien d'une liste de domaines. Une relation peut être vue comme un tableau à deux dimensions appelé *table* [GARDARIN89].

SGBD : Système de Gestion de Bases de Données.

SGBDOO : Système de Gestion de Bases de Données Orienté Objet.

Bibliographie

[ABDDMZ89] : M. Atkinson, F. Bancilhon, D. De Witt, K. Dittrich, D. Maier, S. Zdonik, « The object oriented database system manifesto », *in Deductive an object oriented database systems*, 1989.

[ABIGRU88] : S. Abiteboul, S. Grumbach, « A logic based langage for complex objects », *in Proceedings of EDBT international conference*, 1988.

[ABIKAN89] : S. Abiteboul, P. Kanellakis, « Object identity as query language primitive », *in Proceedings of the ACM SIGACT-SIGMOD Symp*, 1989.

[ADICO93] : M. Adiba, C. Collet, *Objets et bases de données : le SGBD O2*, Hermès, 1993.

[BANKHO86] : F. Bancilhon, S. Khoshafian, « A calculus for complex objects », *in Proceedings of the ACM SIGACT-SIGMOD Symp*, 1986.

[BENDOU93] : V. Benzaken A. Doucet, *Bases de données orientées objet : origines et principes,* Armand Colin, 1993.

[CHEN76] : P. P. Chen, The Entity-Relationship Model : Toward a Unified View of Data*;* *ACM Transactions on database systems,* 1976.

[CODD70] : E. Cood, A relationnal data model for large shared data banks, *Communications of the ACM,* 1970.

[DELERI91] : C. Delobel, C. Lécluse, P. Richard, *Bases de données : des systèmes relationnels aux systèmes à objets*, InterEditions, 1991.

[GARDARIN89] : G. Gardarin, *Bases de données : les systèmes et leurs langages,* Eyrolles, 1989.

[IMAGmai95] : *Informatiques magazine*, mai 1995.

[KUVAR85] : G. M. Kuper M. Y. Vardi, « On the expressive power of the logical data model », *in Proceedings of the ACM SIGACT-SIGMOD International conference,* 1985.

[MAKINOUCHI 77] : A. Makinouchi, « A consideration on normal form on not-necessarily normalized relations in the relationnal model ». *in Proceedings of VLDB Int. Conf.*, 1977.

[MALLORDY9] : L. Mallordy, *Répartition d'objets dans les bases de données*, Hermès, collection Cnam, 1995.

[OBJmar96] : D. Taylor, « ODBMS : Debunking the myths », *Object magazine*, mars 1996.

[ODMG93] : R. G. G. Catell, *ODMG-93 Le standard des bases de données objet,* International Thomson publishing, 1995.

[YU74] : C. Yu, « A clustering technique based on user queries », *Journal of American Society for information sciences*, 1974.

[YUSILATA81] : C. Yu, M. Siu, K. Lam T. Tai, « Adaptative clustering schemes : General framework », *IEEE Computer software and application conference,* 1981.

[ZANIOLO85] : C. Zaniolo, « The representation and deductive retrieval of complex objects », *in Proceedings of VLDB Int. Conf.*, 1985.

Contacts

GemStone
GemStone Systems, Inc
15400 NW Greenbrier Parkway
Suite 280
Beaverton, OR 97006 USA
Tél. + 1 503 629 8383
Fax + 1 503 629 8556
email : info@gemstone.com
web : http://www.gemstone.com

IDB Object Database
Persistent Data Systems, Inc
PO Box 38415
Pittsburg, PA 15328 USA
Tél. + 1 412 963 1843
Fax + 1 412 963 1846
email : info@persist.com

Illustra
Illustra Information Technologies, Inc
1111 Broadway, Suite 2000
Oakland, CA 94607 USA
Tél. + 1 510 6542 8000
Fax + 1 510 869 6350
email : info@illustra.com
web : http://www.illustra.com

ITASCA
IBEX Computing, SA
International Business Park
4th Blvd, Building Hera
F74160 Archempe, France
Tél. + 33 50 31 57 00
Fax + 33 50 31 57 01
email : ibexcom@iprolink.ch

MATISSE
ADB SA
« Le Dôme » 3, rue de la Haye
BP 10919
95731 Roissy-Charles-de-Gaulle
Tél. + 33 (1) 48 64 72 73
Fax + 33 (1) 48 64 39 11
email : info@adb.fr

MICRAM
MICRAM Object Technology GmbH
Universitaetsstrasse 142
D-44799 Bochum Allemagne
Tél. + 49 234 9708 305
Fax + 48 234 9708 301

O2
O2 Technologie
7, rue du parc de Clagny
78035 Versailles
Tél. + 33 (1) 30 84 77 77
Fax + 33 (1) 30 84 77 90
email : info@o2tech.com
web : http://www.o2tech.com

Objectivity/DB
Objectivity, Inc
301 B E.Evelyn Avenue
Mountain View, CA 94041 USA
Tél. + 1 800 767 6259
Fax + 1 415 254 7171
email : info@objy.com
web : http://www.objectivity.com

ObjectStore
Object Design, Inc
25 Mall Road
Burlington, MA 01803 USA
Tél. + 1 800 962 9620/1 415 254 7100
Fax + 1 617 674 5019
email : info@odi.com
web : http://www.odi.com

Odapter
Hewlett-Packard Company
19111 Pruneridge Avenue
Cupertino, CA 95013 USA
Tél. + 1 408 447 5051
Fax + 1 408 447 0956
email : odapter@cup.hp.com

ODB-II
Fujitsu Open Systems Solutions, Inc
3055 Orchard Drive
San Jose, CA 95134 USA
Tél. + 1 800 545 6774
Fax + 1 408 456 7050
email : info@ossi.com
web : http://www.ossi.com

ODBMS
VC Software Construction
Petritorwall 28
3318 Braunschweig, Allemagne
Tél. + 49 531 24240 0
Fax + 49 531 24240 24
email : 100111.2316@com-puserve.com

ODMG
Object Database Management Group
13504 Clinton Place
Burnsville, MN 55337 USA
Tél +1 612 953 7250
Fax +1 612 397 7146
email : info@odmg.org

OMG
Object Management Group
Framingham Corporate Center
492 Old Connecticut Path
Framingham, MN 01104 USA
Tél +1 508 820 4300
Fax +1 508 820 4303
email : omg@omg.org

Omniscience
Omniscience object Technology, Inc
3080 Olcott Street, Suite 100C
Santa Clara, CA 95054 USA
Tél. + 1 800 888 8489
Fax + 1 408 562 0757
email : info@oot.com
web : http://www.omniscience.com

ONTOS DB
ONTOS, inc
900 Chelmsford Street
Lowell, MA 01851 USA
Tél. + 1 800 436 6867
Fax + 1 508 323 8101
email : info@ontos.com
web : http://www.ontos.com

Persistence
Persistence Software, Inc
1700 S.Amphlett Blvd
Suite 250
San Mateo, CA 94402 USA
Tél. + 1 415 341 7733
Fax + 1 415 341 8432
email : info@persistence.com

POET
POET Software, inc
999 Baker Way
Suite 100
San Mateo, CA 94404 USA
Tél. + 1 415 286 4640
Fax + 1 415 286 4630
email : info@poet.com
web : http://www.poet.com

UniSQL
UniSQL, Inc
8911 Capitol of Texal Highway North
Suite 2300
Austin, TX 78759-7200 USA
Tél. + 1 800 451 3267
Fax + 1 512 343 7383
email : info@unisql.com
web : http://www.unisql.com

VERSANT
Versant Object Technology
1380 Willow Road
Menlo Park, CA 94025 USA
Tél. 1 800 837 7268
Fax + 1 415 325 2380
email : info@versant.com
web : http://www.versant.com

Windward Solutions Smalltalk Broker
Windward Solutions, Inc
PO Box 819
Redwood City, CA 94064 USA
Tél. + 1 415 369 1504
Fax + 1 415 369 1504
email : windward@cerfnet.com

Index

A

adressage 54
agrégation 25
AOV 63
applications 75
applications traditionnelles 75
architecture 51
association 25
attributs 47
autorisations 40

C

C++ 72
classes 24, 34, 47, 70
classes abstraites 50
conception 45
concepts orientés objet 32
concurrence 43
conflit d'héritage
contraintes 48

D

dysfonctionnements 18

E

encapsulation 33, 42
Entité / Relation 26
extensibilité 43
extension 24, 34

F

fiabilité des données 40
finance 76

G

Gemstone 76
généralisation 29
gestion du disque 40, 40
gestionnaire d'objets 54
groupement 26

H

héritage 35, 43, 49, 70
– multiple 35
– simple 35

I

identité d'objet 21, 37, 42, 55
implémentation 33, 56
indépendance des données 41
indexation 64
industrie 76
instances 28, 34
intégration de bases de données et de langages de programmation 29, 51, 71
intégrité des données 40
interface 33
interrogation de données 41

L

Langages
– Ada 27
– d'interrogation de données 67
– de définition de données 67
– de manipulation de données 67
– de programmation 18, 68
– de requêtes 33
– de requêtes OQL 72
– déclaratifs 16, 41
– orientés objet 32
– persistants 29
liaison dynamique 36, 43

M

Matisse 75
messages 34, 49
méthodes 45
modèle
– hiérarchique 15
– identité d'objet 21
– NF2 18
– Non First Normal Form 18
– objets complexes 20
– orienté objet 18
– relationnel 15, 17
– relationnel étendu 18
– réseau 15, 26
– sémantique 24, 31
modélisation 39, 47
multimédia 76
mythes 73

O

O_2 76
Objectivity/DB 75
ObjectStore 76
objets
– complexes 20, 36, 42
– courts 59
– cycliques 22
– longs 60
offres 77
Ontos 75
optimisation 64
organisation en vrac 62

P

partage des données 40
percolation 66
persistance 38, 39, 71
programmation
– fonctionnelle 67
– impérative 67
– logique 67

R

receveur 34
regroupement 64
relations 48
répartition 44
répartition horizontale 62
répartition verticale 63
représentation de l'héritage 61
représentation physique en mémoire secondaire 58
reprise sur panne 43
résolution tardive 35

S

sécurité des données 40
SGBD
– orientés objet 16
– relationnels 15
signature 33
Smalltalk 72
spécialisation 25
spécification 33
standard ODMG 93 34, 69
surcharge sémantique 35

systèmes de gestion de fichiers 13

T

taille des objets 59
télécommunications 75
transactions 44, 65
types 26, 44, 70
types abstraits 28, 71

U

uniformité 36, 71

V

versions 44, 67

CET OUVRAGE A ÉTÉ COMPOSÉ
PAR LES ÉDITIONS HERMÈS
REPRODUIT ET ACHEVÉ D'IMPRIMER
PAR L'IMPRIMERIE FLOCH À MAYENNE
EN MARS 1997.

DÉPÔT LÉGAL : MARS 1997.
N° D'IMPRIMEUR : 41217.

Imprimé en France

Unity of the Church in the New Testament and Today

Lukas Vischer†
Ulrich Luz
Christian Link

Translated by
James E. Crouch

William B. Eerdmans Publishing Company
Grand Rapids, Michigan / Cambridge, U.K.

First published 2009 in German under the title
Ökumene im Neuen Testament und Heute
by Vandenhoeck & Ruprecht

Published 2010 by
Wm. B. Eerdmans Publishing Co.
2140 Oak Industrial Drive N.E., Grand Rapids, Michigan 49505 /
P.O. Box 163, Cambridge CB3 9PU U.K.

Printed in the United States of America

16 15 14 13 12 11 10 7 6 5 4 3 2 1

Library of Congress Cataloging-in-Publication Data

Vischer, Lukas.
[Ökumene im Neuen Testament und heute. English]
Unity of the church in the New Testament and today /
Lukas Vischer, Ulrich Luz, Christian Link; translated by James E. Crouch.
p. cm.
Includes index.
ISBN 978-0-8028-6376-8 (pbk.: alk. paper)
1. Church — Unity. 2. Church — Unity — Biblical teaching. 3. Church history.
I. Luz, Ulrich. II. Link, Christian, 1938- III. Title.

BV601.5.V5713 2010
262′.72 — dc22

2010023279

www.eerdmans.com

Contents

Abbreviations ix

Translator's Preface xi

In Memory of Lukas Vischer xiii

Introduction 1

Lukas Vischer

PART ONE

Difficulties in Looking to the New Testament for Guidance 7

Lukas Vischer

1. Scripture and Tradition 8
2. Scripture: Witness of an Active History 12
3. Unity Today 15
4. Concepts of Unity 18

PART TWO

On the Way to Unity: The Community of the Church in the New Testament 29

Ulrich Luz

Introduction 29

1. Jesus: The Origin of the Community of the Church 34

The Apostolic Age 43
2. The Beginnings of the Church after Easter 43
2.1. Tensions and Divergences 44
2.2. Unity-promoting Forces 47
3. The Beginnings of Ecclesiology 54
4. The First Basic Conflict: The Church's Unity with Israel 57
4.1. The Apostolic Council 58
4.2. James and the Church's Unity with Israel (by Christoph Knoch) 61
4.3. Paul and the Church's Unity with Israel 64
4.3.1. The Antioch Conflict (by Peter Lampe) 66
4.3.2. The Conflict between Strong and Weak in Rome (by Peter Lampe) 68
4.3.3. Paul and His Opponents 69
4.3.4. The Collection (by Andreas Karrer) 71
4.3.5. Paul's Last Journey to Jerusalem (by Andreas Karrer) 73
4.3.6. Church vis-à-vis Israel and for Israel 74
5. The Church as the Reality of Christ in Paul's Thought 76
5.1. The Basic Gift of Unity: Christ 76
5.2. The Whole Church and the Local Church 79
5.3. Christ's Effectiveness in the Whole Church (with Corinna Diestelkamp) 81
5.4. Christ's Effectiveness in the Local Church 84
5.4.1. The Parties in Corinth (1 Corinthians 1–4) (by Peter Lampe) 85
5.4.2. Meat Sacrificed to Idols (1 Corinthians 8–10) 86
5.4.3. Divided Lord's Supper? (1 Corinthians 11:17-34) 87
5.4.4. Tensions in Worship (1 Corinthians 12–14) 88
5.4.5. Conclusion 89
The Post-Apostolic Age 91
6. Developments in the Church after the Death of the Apostles 91
6.1. Tensions and Divergences 91
6.2. Unity-promoting Forces: Overview 95

6.3. Christianity as an Independent Religion 96
6.4. Tradition as a Unity-promoting Factor (with Joachim Diestelkamp) 100
6.5. The Apostles as Primary Figures of Unity 106
6.5.1. James 107
6.5.2. Peter 108
6.5.3. Paul (with Joachim Diestelkamp) 113
6.6. Ministerial Offices as a Unity-promoting Force (with Jürg Liechti) 118
7. The First Ecclesiological Concepts of Church Unity 126
7.1. The Epistle to the Ephesians 127
7.2. The Apocalypse of John 129
7.3. The Gospel of Luke and Acts 132
7.4. The Gospel of John (with Anne Liedtke) 136
8. The Second Basic Conflict: Church Fellowship in the Controversy with Christian Gnosticism 142
8.1. Introduction 142
8.2. The Gnosticizing Opponents as Seen by Church-Christians (with Andreas Karrer) 147
8.3. The Church-Christians as Seen by Their Christian-Gnostic Opponents 153
8.4. Final Observations 159

PART THREE
The Unity Movement: Church Fellowship in the Oecumene 163

Christian Link

1. On the Way to Unity 163
1.1. Unity as Process 164
1.2. Which Fellowship Do We Mean? 170
1.3. Dealing with Church Schisms: Basic Conflicts 173
2. The Church's Unity with Israel 179
2.1. With Which Israel Is the Church Dealing? 179
2.2. Christian Identity in the Mirror of the Jewish-Christian Dialogue 184

2.3. Israel and the Oecumene 189
3. Flash Points of Unity 193
3.1. Scripture 195
3.1.1. Scripture and Tradition 196
3.1.2. The Authority of Scripture 199
3.1.3. The Differences 202
3.2. Confession 204
3.2.1. Church Confessions 205
3.2.2. Contextual Confessing 207
3.3. Lord's Supper 209
3.3.1. The Fellowship Meal 212
3.3.2. The Lord's Supper as Rite 214
3.3.3. Lord's Supper and Ministry 217
3.3.4. The Social Location of the Lord's Supper 220
3.4. Ministerial Office 222
3.4.1. The Problem 223
3.4.2. Foundations of Church Law 226
3.4.3. Institution and Ministry 230
4. Conciliar Fellowship 235
4.1. The Council 237
4.2. Characteristics of Conciliarity 239
4.2.1. Worship 240
4.2.2. Conflict Orientation 241
4.2.3. The Search for Truth 243
5. Church Unity and Missions 245

Index of Subjects and Names 249

Index of Selected New Testament and Other Ancient Texts 252

Abbreviations

BEM	*Baptism, Eucharist and Ministry*, Faith and Order Paper No. 111 (Geneva: WCC, 1982)
BG	Biblische Gestalten
BiKi	*Bibel und Kirche*
BThSt	Biblisch-theologische Studien
BU	Biblische Untersuchungen
BZNW	Beihefte zur Zeitschrift für die neutestamentliche Wissenschaft
CA	*Confessio Augustana* (Augsburg Confession)
CD	Karl Barth, *Church Dogmatics*, 5 vols. in 14 (Edinburgh: T&T Clark, 1936-1977)
CSEL	Corpus scriptorum ecclesiasticorum Latinorum
CV	*Communio Viatorum*
DBW	Dietrich Bonhoeffer Werke
DV	*Dei Verbum*. Dogmatic Constitution on Divine Revelation
EKK	Evangelisch-katholischer Kommentar zum Neuen Testament
ET	English translation
EvTh	*Evangelische Theologie*
FRLANT	Forschungen zur Religion und Literatur des Alten und Neuen Testaments
GCS	Die griechischen christlichen Schriftsteller der ersten drei Jahrhunderte
GNT	Grundrisse zum Neuen Testament
GSL	Geistliche Schriftlesung
HFTh	*Handbuch der Fundamentaltheologie*
HST	*Handbuch systematischer Theologie*
IKZ	*Internationale kirchliche Zeitschrift*

KuD	*Kerygma und Dogma*
LG	*Lumen Gentium* (Dogmatic Constitution of the Church of the Second Vatican Council)
LThK	*Lexikon für Theologie und Kirche*
LXX	Septuagint
NHC	Nag Hammadi Codices
NHS	Nag Hammadi Studies
NT	*Novum Testamentum*
NTD	Das Neue Testament Deutsch
NTS	*New Testament Studies*
OiC	*One in Christ*
ÖR	*Ökumenische Rundschau*
PuP	Päpste und Papsttum
QD	Questiones disputatae
SBS	Stuttgarter Bibelstudien
StANT	Studien zum Alten und Neuen Testament
Str-B	Hermann L. Strack and Paul Billerbeck, *Kommentar zum Neuen Testament aus Talmud und Midrasch*, 2nd ed. (4 vols. Munich: Beck, 1956)
TB	Theologische Bücherei
TEH	Theologische Existenz Heute
ThV	*Theologische Versuche*
ThZ	*Theologische Zeitschrift*
UR	*Unitatis Redintegratio* (Decree on Ecumenism of the Second Vatican Council)
VIEG	Veröffentlichungen des Instituts für Europäische Geschichte
VuF	*Verkündigung und Forschung*
WCC	World Council of Churches
WCS	World Council of Churches. Studies
WdF	Wege der Forschung
WMANT	Wissenschaftliche Monographien zum Alten und Neuen Testament
WPKG	*Wissenschaft und Praxis in Kirche und Gesellschaft*
WUNT	Wissenschaftliche Untersuchungen zum Neuen Testament
ZMiss	*Zeitschrift für Mission*
ZNW	*Zeitschrift für die neutestamentliche Wissenschaft*
ZThK	*Zeitschrift für Theologie und Kirche*

Translator's Preface

One of the most important concepts of this book, *Vorgabe,* has no easy English equivalent. Look in a good German dictionary and you may find that in sports it refers to a handicap or to points or odds given in betting. German-language theologians use it as a technical term for what is given before and apart from human effort. It is close to the idea of prevenient grace, but translating *Vorgabe* literally as "pre-gift" would not be satisfactory since, among other reasons, the prefix *vor* indicates rank as well as time. I have settled on the translation "basic gift." For more on *Vorgabe,* see Part Two, footnotes 8 and 27.

By contrast, the other technical term in this book, *Gemeinschaft,* suffers from an embarrassment of riches. One can, and I do, translate it as "community" or as "fellowship." It corresponds to the Latin *communio* and the Greek *koinonia.* It can also have the sense of communion, sharing, and participation, as, for example, in 1 Corinthians 10:14-22.

The book includes extensive discussions of *Amt,* or "office," in the church, what one generally thinks of as the ordained clergy. Usually I follow the practice of translating it with "ministry," as in the Lima document *Baptism, Eucharist and Ministry.* Occasionally I leave it as "office" or use "ministerial office."

JEC

In Memory of Lukas Vischer

Lukas Vischer died on March 11, 2008. For the last year of his life he struggled against an unrelenting and destructive case of pancreatic cancer. He resisted this illness as long as he could, without bitterness, calmly and peacefully, often even cheerfully. He rejected any kind of resignation because he was looking forward to what the coming years would bring: to the great Calvin Jubilee of 2009 for which he had prepared with an inspiring international conference in the John Knox Center (Geneva), to an increasing human sensitivity about climate change, to a growing fellowship among Christian churches, especially at the base level, and therefore also to the new edition of this book. He was looking forward to the appearance of an English edition; on one of his last days he signed the contract with Eerdmans Publishing Company. And he was delighted that Vandenhoeck & Ruprecht would bring out the new German edition.

His death is a great loss for theology and the ecumenical movement. Lukas showed us what it means to do theology in and for the church. For him, theology and church were inseparable. Conversely, he continuously reminded the ecumenical movement and his own Reformed Church of their biblical and theological roots. He was for them both inspirer and admonisher.

Above all, he was filled with the conviction that God, the creator of the world and the redeemer and liberator of his human children, is always ahead of us and therefore is the sustaining ground of all human action. This faith kept him from being depressed even, and especially, about the condition — which he himself strongly criticized — in which the ecumenical movement finds itself today almost fifty years after the Second Vatican Council. When writing the new introduction to our book he refused to speak of ecumenical stagnation or even of an ecumenical ice age. The difficulties were already well known; now it was time to look back to the Bible's beginnings and in this way to look forward into the future.

Thus this new-old book is also a legacy of Lukas Vischer. The revision of the introduction and the continuation of his own "Part One" are among the last texts he wrote. He made only modest changes to "his" texts, and in that way he remained true to himself. With gratitude we look back on the mutual journey with him that finds its expression in this book.

Berne and Bochum
April 2008

ULRICH LUZ
CHRISTIAN LINK

Introduction

Lukas Vischer

> There may be good grounds for the rise of these divisions. There may be serious obstacles to their removal. There may be many things which can be said by way of interpretation and mitigation. But this does not alter the fact that every division as such is a deep riddle, a scandal. . . . For the matter itself . . . demands always, and in all circumstances, *unam ecclesiam.* And if history contradicts this, then it speaks only of the actuality and not the truth. Even under the fatherly and effective providence of God which can cause it to work for good, a scandal is still a scandal. The disunity of the Church is a scandal.
>
> Karl Barth[1]

> When the church says that she is one, she says just as emphatically that she has been injured by the rupture in her heart and in her maternal body, that she bears open wounds that are constantly bleeding and that make her life poorer and her witness in the world more cumbrous.
>
> Abbé Paul Couturier[2]

These are only two of the many quotations one might find that say essentially the same thing. While in every age there have been people who have experienced

1. *CD,* vol. IV/1, pp. 675, 677.

2. "Téstament œcuménique," in Maurice Villain, *L'Abbé Paul Couturier,* 3d ed. (Tournai: Casterman, 1959), pp. 356-57.

division in the church as a contradiction of the gospel of reconciliation, the radical and increasingly rapid changes to which all areas of human life are subjected today have made that contradiction intolerable. For our witness to the gospel to be credible we must overcome the separation and bring to clear expression our common life in Christ. There was a time when the separated churches did not shrink from this task; in the nineteenth and especially in the twentieth century they made a beginning. They drew closer to one another. They replaced polemic with dialogue. They began to bear a common witness and to work together in shared structures. The ecumenical movement was born.

The movement gave rise to great hopes. For many people, the World Council of Churches, established in Amsterdam in 1948, was a foretaste of the unity they were hoping to make real. As great as were the differences among the participating churches, there was unanimity about one thing: we shall stay together. After the horror of the Second World War a new future opened up for the churches. With the Second Vatican Council (1962-1965) there was an unexpected expansion of the ecumenical movement. Now the whole range of denominational traditions was participating in the movement. The dams appeared to be broken. Christians of all confessions were able to come together without prejudice, to pray together, and to come to a common understanding of what discipleship means today.

The sense of community permeated all levels. With theological dialogue came the recognition that it was possible to see many differences in doctrine and practice in a new light. The joint Lutheran-Catholic declaration on the doctrine of justification represented a high point in this development. Increasingly, biblical scholarship became a common enterprise. Above all, however, contact among the separated churches gave rise to a deepening of spiritual life. Spiritual traditions of other churches that previously had been regarded as "foreign" came to be at home in one's own church. The great challenges of our day — poverty, the use of power, the destruction of the environment — came to be seen as common tasks.

It is true that in recent days this movement has stagnated. Within the past few decades there has been a renewed emphasis on denominational identity. Anyone who believed that the denominational age was over must be disappointed. Once again each church is emphasizing the profile of its own tradition. To be sure, the churches continue to proclaim their commitment to the ecumenical movement. There is scarcely any church that would not speak of the imperative of unity. They even declare their solemn obligations to unity. Yet this ecumenical discourse has little credibility. In reality, the churches have retreated into their denominational shells. The ecumenical movement continues to be celebrated, but actual cooperation is stagnant.

For many people this development is deeply disappointing. It stands in direct contradiction to the fellowship they have experienced. What they had in common seemed to them to be so much greater than what separated them that it is difficult for them to return to their earlier positions. Why not risk plunging wholeheartedly into community? Why do we go our separate ways at the Lord's table when in so many areas we are able to share what is essential? For many people this disappointment leads to a disappointment in the gospel as a whole. What are they to do with churches that focus their attention on their own distinguishing features rather than on their central message?

One could cite many reasons for this development. Doubtless one of the most important reasons is the churches' helplessness in the face of the great questions of our age. Whether it is the Orthodox churches of the East, the Roman Catholic Church, or the Protestant churches, each church in its own way feels forced on the defensive by its dealings with the modern world. It is extraordinarily difficult to share this helplessness with other churches. To do so would call into question those pretensions inherited from the past that until now appeared to offer security. It is easier to gloss over them with a renewed emphasis on one's own fundamentals. This is also why the ecumenical movement is especially constrained when ecumenical commitment appears to jeopardize the institutional independence of the individual churches. One simply is not permitted to give up the symbols of continuity.

Why does it make sense in this situation to bring out a study about the unity of the church? In the late 1980s, when we were working on the first edition of this volume, one could still hope for common initiatives. In 1983 the World Council of Churches had summoned the churches to a conciliar movement for justice, peace, and the integrity of creation, and in those days it was by no means clear yet that the proposal would founder on the resistance of the churches. Why, however, does it make sense today to invite people to consider a unity that would include all churches?

For us there is no doubt about the answer. Precisely because the ecumenical movement appears to be stagnant, it is important to take a fresh look at the New Testament. Even a brief look in its pages reveals that in fact God in Christ does want to create a community that is united in love. Every rupture indicates a failure on the part of the church. Paul calls out to the conflicted church at Corinth: "Is Christ divided?" The community of the church is not an incidental matter; it is the gift and favor of Christ. Ecumenism is not optional; it belongs to the essence of the church. Bishop Charles Brent, the founder of the movement for faith and order (1862-1929), once said, "If unity has slipped away from our grasp, it is the common fault of the Christian world. If it is to be regained it must be by the concerted action of all Christians." Concerted action! As long as the separated churches confront one another like *chiens de fayence,*[3] as long as each demands that the others conform to and join its ideas of unity, one can hardly expect further progress. No tradition can create unity by itself; it is an enterprise that must be done together. Brent continued: "Every section has shared in shattering unity. Every section must share in the effort to restore it."[4]

Our study has grown out of an inter-denominational Protestant, Old Catholic,[5] and Roman Catholic discussion led by professors and students of the Old Catholic–Reformed theological faculty of the University of Berne and the Roman Catholic faculty of Fribourg in Switzerland. It is a theological rough draft. After a thorough discussion of the general perspectives, individual members of the working group were commissioned to examine and report on various aspects of the theme. It took nineteen sessions, some of them lasting more than one day, to cover all of the relevant questions. Three members of the working group (Lukas Vischer, Ulrich Luz, and Christian Link) accepted the responsibility for recording the results of the sessions. That none of the Catholic members of the group — Heinrich Stirnimann and Hermann Venetz and, representing the Old Catholic side, Kurt Stalder — served as coauthors was due to technical rather than theological reasons. Since we were in agreement on all the essential matters, the denominational membership of the "writers" was not all that important. Student members of the working group also contributed to Part Two of the book. Their offerings contain the summary of studies they had prepared as seminar papers. They are Christoph Knoch (pp. 61-64), Andreas Karrer (pp. 71-74, 150f.), Peter Lampe (pp. 66-69, 85f.), Corinna Diestelkamp (pp. 83f.), Joachim Diestelkamp (pp. 104f., 116f.), Jürg Liechti (pp. 121f., 123, 124-26), and Anne Liedtke (pp. 137-39).

More than fifteen years after the appearance of the first edition, it was clear to us that we had to rework the book. Indeed, parts of many sections needed to be rewritten. Thus in many ways the study we offer today has a new appearance.

Our point of departure is the New Testament. Instead of spending time on general matters, we have asked ourselves what can be inferred on this theme from the various witnesses of the New Testament. How did early

3. *Chiens de fayence* are porcelain dogs with a particular kind of glazing. A close English-language equivalent might be "china dogs." The point here is that the figurines simply sit there smiling at each other without doing anything. — Trans.

4. H. N. Bate, ed., *Faith and Order: Proceedings of the World Conference, Lausanne, August 3-21, 1927* (New York: Doran, 1927), p. 4.

5. The term is *christkatholisch,* the name by which the Old Catholic Church is known in Switzerland. — Trans.

Christianity deal with the call to unity? And what can we derive from the evidence of the New Testament for the task of the churches today? We know, of course, that the Bible cannot directly solve our modern problems, but it can show how earliest Christianity dealt with the tensions that already existed in the New Testament period and how it made community real. That serves as a guide for us, for we can follow the earlier example. The Bible is all the more important for ecumenism since it is one of the few bonds of unity that has lasted through all the centuries of Christian division and was never completely "denominationalized" by churchly interpretations. The underlying thesis of this book is that unity is a permanent and never-ending task of the church. Unity is never conclusively established. It is true, of course, that it is something given us and that we therefore do not need to invent it. Christ's work and message are its firm starting point. At the same time, however, it is something that is constantly in the making. The New Testament already bears witness to us of this movement toward unity. The apostolic preaching is a singular call to unity. The apostles also had to deal with centrifugal forces, and they emphatically resisted them. Today we must carry forward this movement toward unity. From generation to generation the horizons shift, and we must deal with new presuppositions. Yet the thrust remains the same. The *communio* in Christ must be established by means of "bonds of love."

Unity as movement! Unity as process! On the one hand, it is clear that unity does not mean uniformity. The church we meet in the witness of the New Testament is marked by a multiplicity of expressions of the gospel. Unity need not do away with differences. That cannot mean, on the other hand, that, as is increasingly the case today, differences and contradictions are simply accepted as unavoidable. The church's schism remains a scandal that must be eliminated, and every generation must step up to the task of helping to bring God's gift to fruition. The New Testament continually summons us to enter the struggle on behalf of the visible *communio* in Christ.

Our book consists of three parts. First, we will offer a few general reflections about what one can learn from the New Testament and what this witness can mean in the life of the church today. The second part attempts to recapitulate in the form of a survey how the Christian movement struggled for unity in the first century. The third part is a systematic-theological reflection on what was said in the second part, and it draws some conclusions for today's discussion about the unity of the church.

It only remains to offer our thanks — first of all to our excellent translator, James E. Crouch, and then to the staff of the William B. Eerdmans Publishing Company.

The first edition was dedicated to the memory of a member of our working group, Michael Zenger. We want to remember his name in this edition as well. He departed this life in the summer of 1986. Michael suffered much because of the church's barrenness and divisiveness, and his desire and hope were for its living unity.

PART ONE

Difficulties in Looking to the New Testament for Guidance

Lukas Vischer

All churches appeal to Scripture. They regard it as the necessary foundation of their doctrine and life. They know that they are obligated to listen to its witness.

Should it then not be the case that if the separated churches would examine Scripture together and give heed to its witness in their midst they would remove the barriers to unity? In the course of the ecumenical movement people have often made this assumption. They hoped that going back to the original witness would make it possible to achieve a breakthrough. The common study of Scripture would bring together the representatives of the various traditions. It would, so to speak, have a cleansing effect by making it possible to distinguish between what is primary and what is secondary. Confronting the biblical witness would make visible the true foundation and the appropriate form of the church's unity.

To a degree the assumption proved to be right. Returning to the original witness did indeed often lead to positive results. The ideas of unity that the representatives of various churches brought from their tradition were called into question when they had to be justified in a joint discussion before the witness of Scripture. Thus Protestant Christians discovered anew the significance for unity of the worshiping community, and Roman Catholic Christians had to see for themselves that certain ecclesiastical structures they regarded as an absolute precondition for church unity had not been ordained by Jesus himself but were the result of historical developments. On both sides, working with the biblical witness led to a new emphasis on the work of the Holy Spirit in the life of the church.

At the same time, however, the assumption was too naïve. Looking to Scripture for guidance about unity proved to be much more complicated than was originally assumed.

1. Scripture and Tradition

The inquiry is difficult first of all because the churches are not able to start from a uniform understanding of Scripture and its meaning for the church's life and witness. As much as they regard it in general as a necessary foundation, their ideas differ widely in the details. The meaning and the role of Scripture are circumscribed by differing theological and ecclesiological presuppositions. For example, the different traditions define the relationship between the authority of Scripture and the authority of the church in fundamentally different ways. Scripture also plays different roles in the life of the individual churches. One thinks, for example, of the position Scripture occupies in worship. It makes a difference whether the emphasis lies on the regular reading of selected passages of Scripture or on their interpretation in the sermon.

Thus from the very beginning the presuppositions that are accepted in the various traditions influence the study of Scripture. Scripture does not stand above the differences among the individual traditions as a neutral referee. It is, rather, read and heard unavoidably in the context of each tradition. Of course, it is possible to agree about the proper exegesis of certain texts on the basis of historical-critical study, but when it comes time to interpret the text's original sense discovered by this method in its meaning for the life of the church, the differences in understanding Scripture and its authority come once again to the fore.

The difference becomes especially clear when it comes to defining the relationship between Scripture and tradition. One can read Scripture under the assumption that finally there can be no disagreement between its witness and the church's tradition preserved through the centuries. A special form of this opinion is the claim that the witness of Scripture has been understood in an exemplary manner in the tradition of the ancient church. Scripture can also be understood, however, as a critical court of appeal. It contains the original witness on which the church is dependent if it is to be preserved from distortion and error. God always speaks anew to his church through the testimony of Scripture. Tradition is always under the suspicion of having deviated from the original message. The churches of the Reformation were forced to this understanding of Scripture by their own experience. The tension between Scripture and ecclesiastical conditions had become so obvious that the protest against tradition was unavoidable.

For a long time the different understanding of the relationship between Scripture and tradition appeared to be one of the unbridgeable contrasts among the churches. Thus it is no wonder that in the ecumenical conversation special attention was focused on this question. And the efforts were not fruitless. The World Conference for Faith and Order in Montreal (1963) was able to offer the following jointly formulated statement:

> Our starting-point is that we are all living in a tradition which goes back to our Lord and has its roots in the Old Testament, and are all indebted to that tradition inasmuch as we have received the revealed truth, the Gospel, through its being transmitted from one generation to another. Thus we can say that we exist as Christians by the Tradition of the Gospel (the *paradosis* of the *kerygma*) testified in Scripture, transmitted in and by the Church through the power of the Holy Spirit. Tradition taken in this sense is actualized in the preaching of the Word, in the administration of the Sacraments and worship, in Christian teaching and theology, and in mission and witness to Christ by the lives of the members of the Church.[1]

This text is so important because it looks at the question of the relationship between Scripture and tradition from a new perspective. The usual emphasis is turned on its head. One could say that instead of "Scripture and tradition" it speaks of "tradition and Scripture." It makes it clear that in all ages and even today the church draws the good news from the living tradition that from the beginning has been passed on from generation to generation. The transmission of the gospel is the precondition for the church's existence and life. For its part Holy Scripture is nothing other than the mirror of this tradition. At the same time, however, it is the criterion that permits us to distinguish between the true tradition and stunted or even distorted traditions, for in it is indelibly fixed the original witness of the tradition. "For the post-apostolic Church the appeal to the Tradition received from the apostles became the criterion. As this Tradition was embodied in the apostolic writings, it became natural to use those writings as an authority for determining where the true Tradition was to be found."[2] Thus the question has shifted. The primary question is no longer to what degree Scripture and to what degree tradition bear witness to God's revelation. The question is rather how one can distinguish between true tradition and distorted tradition and what role the witness of Scripture plays in this task.

Somewhat later, the Second Vatican Council made a similar pronouncement when it gave up the traditional idea of two independent sources of reve-

1. P. C. Rodger and Lukas Vischer, eds., *The Fourth World Conference on Faith and Order, Montreal 1963* (New York: Association, 1964), pp. 51-52.

2. Rodger and Vischer, eds., *Montreal*, p. 52.

lation. “There exists a close connection and communication between sacred tradition and Sacred Scripture. For both of them, flowing from the same divine wellspring, in a certain way merge into a unity and tend toward the same end” (Dogmatic Constitution on Divine Revelation, *Dei Verbum*, 9). In view of this change in the way the question is put, one can at least raise the question whether applying the term “authority” to Scripture is really appropriate. Does this term do justice to the close connection, indeed, the blending of Scripture and tradition? Or does it instead deceive us into thinking that Scripture is completely separate from tradition and stands over against the church as a self-contained court of appeal? If Scripture bears witness to the true tradition in the church’s tradition, it does matter whether the church, the community that has grown out of the tradition, has a living relationship with that original witness. It must allow itself to be inspired, corrected, and led in a continuous conversation with those first witnesses. In this role Scripture can be described with the catchword “authority.” The witness of Scripture carries so much weight that in no circumstances can the church ignore it. Indeed, its weight is so great that in certain circumstances one can, or even must, speak of the sole authority of Scripture. Yet one may never forget how closely and inseparably Scripture and tradition are allied.

As one can see in these texts, the differing positions have moved closer together. Yet, differences remain. Although the contrast is seen in a new perspective, it has not been eliminated. Scripture continues to be read from different presuppositions. The primary difference is that a different value is accorded to the tradition of the ancient church. To what degree is Scripture a court of appeal even for the earliest tradition? To what degree are they so interwoven that they interpret one another reciprocally? To what degree are Scripture and the tradition of the ancient church normative for the church of all ages?

The different presuppositions have radical consequences precisely when we are talking about the unity of the church, consequences that three examples will illustrate.

What significance does the credo of the ancient church have for the unity of the church? How are Scripture and credo related?

What importance are we to attribute to the development of the ecclesiastical ministries in the first centuries? What stage of the development is binding for the following ages?

What significance does the role of Peter have for the unity of the church? Is the idea of a Petrine office a legitimate development of the biblical testimony about Peter?

These examples show that the appeal to Scripture does not alone make unity possible. The theological and ecclesiological presuppositions of the various traditions complicate the effort to come to a common understanding of the biblical witness. Even if the joint effort to discover the original sense should be successful, the question remains how one is to make use of the results.

Thus appealing to Scripture does not by itself enable us to move beyond the differing conceptions of the unity of the church because the differing conceptions of unity influence how Scripture is read and interpreted. The result is a contradiction: all churches acknowledge that Scripture is a criterion for distinguishing between true tradition and distorted traditions, yet this criterion is embedded in the context of the traditions. For this reason even the text of the declaration of Montreal ends with the open question, "How can we overcome the situation in which we all read Scripture in the light of our own traditions?"[3]

Of course, to recognize this dilemma is not to say that the attempt to come to a common understanding of Scripture's witness is inevitably hopeless. The mutual study of Scripture is fundamental to every ecumenical conversation. At the same time, however, one must examine critically one's own presuppositions. One must constantly ask whether the theory and practice of one's interpretation really agree or whether it turns out that in view of the challenges of one's age the theory no longer does justice to Scripture's witness. One must ask whether certain criteria of interpretation that proved to be of value in given historical situations have become a "pre-judgment" that in a new historical situation makes it difficult to hear the witness of Scripture without bias. One thinks, by way of example, of the way Paul's statements in Romans 13 on the role of authorities are used. His call to the Roman church to obey the authorities may in many situations prove to be the central instruction to which other statements about one's relationship to political power are to be subordinated or indeed even connected. If it is understood as a principle, however, and applied without distinction to all situations, one does violence to the diversity of the biblical witness. The problem becomes even greater when the interpretation that was valid in a given situation becomes a part of one's denominational heritage. In any case, the task of gaining clarity about the witness necessary in one's own historical situation will inevitably lead to a clash among the differing starting positions of the denominational traditions.

3. Rodger and Vischer, eds., *Montreal*, p. 54.

2. Scripture: Witness of an Active History

The attempt to learn what Scripture, and especially the New Testament, has to say about the unity of the church comes up against a further difficulty, one that lies in the nature of the New Testament texts themselves. The New Testament contains a variety of writings that, although revolving around the same center, in many other ways differ from one another. They are all born of different occasions, and in their content as well as in their form they reflect the presuppositions, purposes, and emphases of certain authors and situations. Only later were they brought together in the collection in which we read them today. For this reason, whoever consults the New Testament inevitably is faced with a multiplicity of voices and statements that cannot simply be reduced to a common denominator.

It is, therefore, not proper to expect from the New Testament a consistent doctrine of the unity of the church. Given the nature of the New Testament, it is not able to provide a coherent theology, and the attempt to bring together the various statements of the New Testament like the pieces of a mosaic is from the very beginning a futile endeavor.

Yet the difficulty goes even deeper. The diversity of statements about the nature of the church and its unity, which on closer examination are obvious in the writings of the New Testament, raises the question whether the nascent church actually lived in unity or whether even this first age was characterized by controversies and conflicts. In the ecumenical movement the assumption is often unthinkingly expressed that the first Christians were "of one mind." Yet closer examination of the New Testament writings shows that they bear witness to an active history full of conflict. It is time to abandon once and for all the image of harmonious agreement. Clearly, the gospel could be appropriated and proclaimed only by working through controversies.

For this reason, the task can be simply to re-tell the active history we know from the New Testament witnesses. How did the Christians of the first generation deal with the gospel's impulse? What tensions arose as a result? In what interplay of forces did various interpretations develop? What forms of Christian faith and life emerged? How were conflicts overcome — or not overcome? The New Testament does not first and foremost exhibit a coherent concept of the unity of the church; rather, it shows how people struggled in the multiplicity of interpretations and concepts on behalf of community in Christ.

Indeed, one can ask whether the term "unity" already creates false expectations and thus blocks access to the New Testament witness. To begin with, one must recognize that the word "unity" appears relatively infrequently in the New Testament. One finds it only in late writings, and even there not in connection with "church." The author of Ephesians speaks of the "unity of the Spirit" (4:3) and of the "unity of faith and of the knowledge of the Son of God" (4:13). He uses the word "unity" to develop the confession to the *one* Lord. Because Christians have been called to hope through the one Spirit, they are to maintain the bond of peace in the unity of the Spirit. Later, in Ignatius, the term "unification" *(henosis)* takes on greater importance.

The term is especially encumbered by a long philosophical tradition. Its use in Platonic philosophy has left its mark on the word. Wherever the word is used, the idea of multiplicity is implied as its opposite. The "one" denotes what is real, and one must reason a posteriori to it from the "many."

When the term is used against this background, the emphasis is unavoidable that the church can exist only in the singular, and the multiplicity of churches must stand in contradiction to Jesus Christ, the one reality. Admittedly, this consideration makes sense in the present situation. In view of the multiplicity of churches that mutually exclude one another, we must be reminded that in Christ God has chosen *one* people.

Yet the difficulty is that, in its philosophical sense, the term misses the personal character of community in Christ. The fellowship of the church is firmly bound to the person of Jesus Christ. One can speak of the church's unity only because it is founded in the one Lord. If this bond is overlooked, a too static understanding of the church can easily become associated with the idea of unity. The character of the movement that belonged to the Christian community in the earliest period can no longer come into its own.

Thus, as much as the idea of unity emphasizes an important aspect in the understanding of the church, it also constricts the inquiry. The idea of community/fellowship *(communio)* is without doubt more appropriate to the New Testament witness. In that day the issue around which the controversies raged was not how one could achieve unity (in the sense of a singular number or especially of uniformity); it was how the fellowship in Christ could be preserved as a living reality.

From these findings one may draw two important conclusions. The picture that emerges from a closer examination of the New Testament witness most certainly requires us to ask anew to what degree community in Christ has room for a multiplicity of interpretations, expressions, and forms. To what extent is the diversity we meet in the New Testament also a model for the church today? The ecumenical movement has often been led by the view that the original unity was shattered over the centuries — that the guilt of Christians led to increasingly diverging separations. Against this background the ecumenical movement could be understood as the effort of the churches to recover that original condition. "If unity has slipped away from our grasp it is the common fault of the Christian world. If it is to be regained it must be by the concerted action of all Christians" (Charles Brent).[4] The biblical witness offers hardly any support for this view. To be sure, this conception is the basis for the image of the first church that Luke presents in Acts. The community is of one heart and soul; later it is afflicted by ravenous wolves that destroy its unity. A closer reading of the New Testament, however, soon shows that this picture is the expression of an ideal view of the church. From the very beginning the community had to struggle for its unity. For this reason, the question we must ask today is how in the present ecumenical movement we can recover and continue the struggle for fellowship in Christ, a struggle that was characteristic of the early church. Unity shatters when this struggle ceases. It is destroyed primarily by the hardening of positions, by exclusivity and self-contented isolation. It will be restored when the fronts start to move and the living discussion begins anew.

On the other hand, the observation that the New Testament reflects a multiplicity of ecclesiological perspectives does not permit us to conclude that the differences among the denominations are already present in the New Testament. The diversity of the New Testament period is not to be compared with the differences among today's denominations. The diversity we meet in the New Testament is the diversity of living debate, but the denominations are characterized by the institutional hardening of given positions. The confessional statements one finds in the New Testament are acts in which one sees something of the active history of the earliest church. They are part of the effort to make community real. The confessional statements characteristic of denominational traditions are the signs of institutional identity. They define community.[5]

The diversity in the New Testament is not to be misunderstood as a static condition any more than unity may be understood as something static. Otherwise the misunderstanding to which the term "unity" so easily gives rise would simply return as its distorted mirror image. It is so difficult today to recognize and understand Scripture as bearing witness to an active history because it appears to be present in a self-contained whole. The writings, which according to the judgment of the church bear witness to the true tradition, have been selected by the formation of the canon. In the process they have been divorced

4. H. N. Bate, ed., *Faith and Order: Proceedings of the World Conference, Lausanne, August 3-21, 1927* (New York: Doran, 1927), p. 4.

5. Cf. here Ernst Käsemann, "The Canon of the New Testament and the Unity of the Church," in Käsemann, *Essays on New Testament Themes* (Philadelphia: Fortress, 1982), pp. 95-107.

from the historical context in which they originated. For this reason the modern reader is tempted to read them as a timeless text. To be sure, the formation of the canon is of the greatest significance for the church. By distinguishing between the primary and secondary witnesses, the church laid the groundwork for identifying the true tradition within the church's tradition, and today's church cannot ignore this fundamental decision. Therefore, it is important to remember that the formation of the canon itself is part of the "active history" to which the New Testament bears witness. Differentiating among the witnesses did not take place overnight. A protracted process was necessary before the boundaries of the canon were finally established. This reality suggests to us how important it is to read the writings of the New Testament in their historical context.

3. Unity Today

This last consideration suggests a third limit with which the study of the New Testament has to deal. To what extent are the New Testament statements about the unity of the church really able to answer the questions churches in the ecumenical movement are asking? Assuming that we are able to describe the different conceptions of unity one finds in the New Testament and to trace their interplay, what would we gain for the question of the unity of the church today? Is it not the case that today's situation is so radically different that the example of the New Testament age is relevant only to a limited extent?

Of course, our point of departure has not changed. The reasons that compelled the first generations to struggle for community are still valid today. What was true for the authors of the New Testament is still true for the modern ecumenical movement — that with his reconciling work in Christ God has laid the foundation for a community in love, and that obedience to God involves giving visible expression to this unity. The call to unity is the same, and it is therefore not surprising that the great texts of the New Testament in which the drive to unity has been formulated are also relevant today. Some of these texts recur in ecumenical worship services with such regularity that they come close to evoking a feeling of satiety (John 17:20-21; Rom. 15:7; Eph. 4:1-6).

It is true that already in the earliest age the task of making unity real did not appear everywhere in the same way. It makes a great difference whether the call to unity confronted the community in Jerusalem, the one in Antioch, or those that grew out of Paul's mission. Above all, however, the question of unity was posed in a new way when the living witness of the apostles died out and the church no longer had access to it in its preaching. The church of the "post-apostolic" age had to demonstrate the authenticity of its witness in a different way. It had to find ways of laying claim to the apostles' witness for themselves. We see this process already at work in the writings of the New Testament. Without doubt, the most important and influential event in the process is the formation of the canon.

The situation becomes complicated, however, when we ask how the unity of the churches is to be realized today on the basis of the biblical witness. Then it becomes very clear how the presuppositions have changed. The church has been led a long way since those lively beginnings. New questions have been raised. Controversies have led to conflicts and schisms, and while these schisms were hardening the churches have been led in the direction of new horizons with new questions. Simply describing how the first generation dealt with the call to unity cannot answer this question. We must take seriously the principle formulated in Montreal. Holy Scripture lets us look, as through a window, into the first phase of the tradition that flows from God's revelation in Jesus Christ. Yet the tradition did not end with this first phase. It continues throughout the centuries. Four considerations may illustrate how the questions have changed.

(1) With our reference to the canon we have already suggested the first difference. In that earliest period, Scripture was not yet seen as an authority. The Christians struggled for unity on the basis of the proclamation they had received. Scripture was not a factor in the controversies that characterized the earliest period. Only later did the various writings with which we can trace the earliest history become the "Holy Scripture" to which the church appealed when dealing with controversial issues. "As this tradition was embodied in the apostolic writings, it became natural to use those writings as an authority for determining where the true Tradition was to be found."[6] The appeal to Scripture was possible only after the canon had been established in its broad outlines. Only then for the first time could one ask what *the* Scripture has to say about the unity of the church. Scripture thus has taken on a new role in the church. It now becomes a factor of the church's unity. No longer can unity be realized without at the same time according to Scripture its due place. Now the question is what relationship this witness, recognized as apostolic, has to other authorities whose task it is to keep the community in the true tradition. One cannot decide this question on the basis of Scripture alone.

(2) The worldwide expansion of the church that has taken place throughout the centuries, and especially in recent times, can serve as a second example. The church's missionary effort has always extended the boundaries.

6. Rodger and Vischer, eds., *Montreal*, p. 52.

Today the gospel has gone to all continents. As a result, the separated churches are faced with the task of giving shape to this worldwide fellowship. The horizon of the ecumenical world has expanded. Just as the church had to prove the unity it had received from Christ in the *oecumene* of the Roman empire, today it must give appropriate shape to this unity in the human *oecumene*. What does unity mean when the most distant parts of the world live in mutual dependence? What does a genuine common witness to reconciliation in Christ mean in a world of unrighteousness and repression? How much agreement in word and deed is necessary beyond the borders of countries and continents? What significance do the modern possibilities of communication have for the unity of the church? What structures are appropriate for promoting the necessary exchange? What would the apostles say about it today? None of these questions can be answered directly on the basis of Scripture. They have only been raised at all because of the church's success in fulfilling the missionary task.

(3) And to what extent is the church on all levels of its life also charged to be involved in the shaping of society? This question, too, cannot be answered on the basis of Scripture alone. We must also take into consideration that in many places the proclamation of the gospel made the churches not only an acknowledged religious fellowship but also the majority of the population. The responsibility of a minority is not the same as that of a majority. A theologian has pointed out, not without justification, that Scripture is the book of a minority that is read today in the context of a majority in society. It is precisely the church's social engagement that represents one of the decisive "burdens" of unity. Still, the church cannot evade this engagement. Today the unity of the church can be realized only on the basis of clear positions on social questions.

(4) Must we not take this consideration even a step further and ask whether in certain areas the earliest church made flawed decisions? One thinks, for example, of its attitude toward slavery and toward the role of women in the church. Both themes are addressed directly in the New Testament. It is becoming increasingly clear today that the solutions of that age did not reflect the gospel's deepest spirit. A sensitivity has developed in the course of the centuries that in retrospect must be critical even of the witness of the earliest church. In those days it obviously was not felt that the toleration of slavery and the subordination of women contradicted the community God wanted. Today the contradiction has become unmistakably clear.

In view of these new questions, of what use is it then to sketch out the course of the church's earliest history? Do we not have to conduct the debate about the unity of the church on a completely different level? Without doubt, such a conclusion would be precipitous. Although it is true that we must recognize the limits the church faces in consulting Scripture, it would be a mistake if the church saw in Scripture nothing more than a general call to unity. The effort to trace as faithfully and completely as possible the complex development of the early church from the perspective of fellowship in Christ can also provide important impulses for the task one faces in the present ecumenical movement.

First of all, we must say that the attempt to re-tell that early history does greater justice to the character of the biblical witness. Narrating the history makes it clear that both in the early periods and today unity has been nothing more than lived community. We see the picture of a community that carries the treasure of the gospel in earthen vessels and therefore never has unity as a secure possession. When we tell the story, Scripture becomes the mirror in which we recognize ourselves.

Above all, however, dealing with Scripture can open new perspectives for us about our present task. By keeping in view how the church dealt with the task of community in the beginning, the separated churches today can avoid many misunderstandings and false expectations. Limiting our examination of Scripture to the "classical" unity texts, however, will soon lead to a certain helplessness. How are we to make progress in realizing unity there? Nevertheless, a description exploring the details of the struggle for unity can uncover unexpected aspects and provide new stimulation. Scripture will become, so to speak, a competent partner in fulfilling today's task.

And yet we must finally say that describing that history cannot by itself open the way to unity. It does not relieve the church of the responsibility of asking those questions which, under the promise of the Holy Spirit, the call to unity raises today. As much as the witness of the earliest period is able to inspire us, the churches are still faced with the task of carrying on together the tradition whose first phase we see in Scripture.

4. Concepts of Unity

It is against this background that we are to understand the joint efforts to gain clarity about the unity to be realized in the ecumenical movement. How can the unity given us in Jesus Christ be made visible? What shape must it have? We have seen that the separated churches are not yet able jointly to answer these questions. The answers every church has given and continues to give on the basis of its own tradition are simply too far apart. And even a joint study of Scripture does not necessarily lead to a concept that can be pursued jointly.

The common description of the goal can come about only through hard work done together in wrestling with the issues of a given age.

Since the beginning of the ecumenical movement, repeated efforts have been made in this direction, yet we are still — indeed, probably more than ever — far removed from a common vision that can be shared by all churches.

Initially, the ecumenical movement led to spontaneous alliances. The movements resulting from the conferences of Edinburgh (1910), Stockholm (1925), and Lausanne (1927) made it clear that the great themes of the ecumenical movement could be pursued and clarified only with the help of common structures. Regular cooperation began, and as it grew deeper and broader it became clear that more solid structures were also needed. The challenges of the period before and during the Second World War led to the establishment in 1948 of the World Council of Churches. The separated churches resolved to create a kind of alliance or federation. Even though they were not in agreement on numerous doctrines, especially on the understanding of the church and its unity — indeed, only in a limited sense were they able to acknowledge one another as churches — they were ready to bear a common witness. They had in common their confession of Jesus Christ as God and Savior. They were led by the conviction that the message laid out in this confession had to be carried jointly into today's world. From the very beginning it was clear that this alliance did not at all mean that church unity had been achieved. The World Council of Churches was nothing more than a "temporary community" that permitted the churches to raise the question of unity concretely — in some measure the scaffolding that made possible the construction of the common house. In common prayer, in mutual exchange, and especially in the common struggle with the major questions and tasks of the age, the contours of unity were to become clear step by step. There had been similar confederated alliances before, especially in the framework of the international missionary movement. In connection with the founding of the World Council of Churches, they became a foundational structure of the ecumenical movement. At all levels — continental, national, local — there sprang up "ecumenical councils," or sometimes less pretentiously named "working fellowships of Christian churches."

In the early years of the ecumenical movement, many people were of the opinion that such federative associations were already an adequate expression of unity in Christ. What more was needed? What is essential is that the churches come together on the basis of their common confession. They need not surrender their own unique character in order to make their unity visible. It is enough that they acknowledge one another as churches of Jesus Christ and let themselves be led mutually by the gospel's witness. It was asserted, especially by certain Protestant circles, that true unity is invisible anyway and will always remain so. The historical denominations are basically nothing more than shells not worth arguing about. Each represents part of the many-sided Christian truth. Each has its own contribution to make to the whole. The federation gives the churches the opportunity to develop it together.

It became increasingly clear, however, that the federation could be no more than a transitional goal. It is not enough to presume unity to be an "invisible reality"; it must become visible. It presupposes that the sacraments must be recognized reciprocally — above all, that the eucharist is celebrated together without qualification. The community in Christ must prove to be harmony in love. The image of visible separation that the churches have offered for centuries must be overcome by recognizable reconciliation. In this regard, the Second World War represents a turning point. Although at the conferences on Faith and Order in Lausanne (1927) and Edinburgh (1937) the relationship between invisible and visible church was still intensively discussed,[7] the call to visibility characterized the post-war period. Behind the formation of the World Council of Churches in Amsterdam stood the clear will to bring an end to division and to make a new beginning in unity.

In the last decades, three concepts of unity in particular have been developed and debated in the ecumenical movement. Initially, the concept of *organic unity* stood in the foreground. The claim here was that, in order to make visible the unity given in Christ, it was necessary for the churches to agree not only in confessing Christ but also in the main articles of faith. They must come together in the administration of the sacraments and be able to take joint responsibility for ordination to the ministries of the churches. In addition, they must work toward agreement on structures that make possible common doctrines and action. Where this concept is advocated it is at the same time emphasized that today's denominational separation is an intolerable violation of God's will. Unity can be expressed appropriately only when the individual denominations are ready to surrender their separate existence and sink into the background in favor of the one church. For the individual churches, the transition from separation into organic unity is in a sense a dying and rising. They leave behind their sinful separation and rise as a community that "sings to God a new song."

The debate over this concept goes back to the beginnings of the ecu-

7. Cf., e.g., Hermann Sasse, ed., *Die Weltkonferenz für Glauben und Kirchenfassung, Lausanne 1927* (Berlin: Furche, 1929), p. 534.

menical movement. It lay behind the founding of the movement for "Faith and Order," for this movement wanted nothing more than to produce the common basis in the areas of doctrine and the churches' sacramental structures that is necessary for unity. Those who consistently advocate this concept can a priori not be satisfied with a simple federation. In order to reach the goal of organic unity, one needs an actual union. Negotiations were then initiated among separated churches in a number of countries. As early as 1925 various Protestant churches came together to form the United Church of Canada. The Church of South India originated in 1947, a year before the founding of the World Council of Churches. Additional unions followed in North India (1970), Australia (1977), and other countries. They showed that the model of organic unity did not have to remain a mere vision; it can become a historical reality.

The concept was also accepted in the World Council of Churches. As we have seen, the question of the nature of the unity to be realized initially remained unanswered when the Council was formed. The common denominator holding the churches together was simply the confession of Jesus Christ as God and Savior. Of course, it was taken for granted that the churches that joined the Council were committed to working for the unity of the church. What unity meant in its details, however, was intentionally left open. The answer to the question was to come out of the dynamic discussion within the Council.

Early on, there was an initial attempt to give an answer. At the third full assembly of the World Council of Churches in New Delhi (1961), the assembly voted to approve the following text:

> We believe that the unity which is both God's will and his gift to his Church is being made visible as all in each place who are baptized into Jesus Christ and confess him as Lord and Saviour are brought by the Holy Spirit into one fully committed fellowship, holding the one apostolic faith, preaching the one Gospel, breaking the one bread, joining in common prayer, and having a corporate life reaching out in witness and service to all and who at the same time are united with the whole Christian fellowship in all places and all ages in such wise that ministry and members are accepted by all, and that all can act and speak together as occasion requires for the tasks to which God calls his people.[8]

This description of the "unity we seek" is on the whole determined by the concept of organic unity. In the background stands the experience of the un-

8. W. A. Visser 't Hooft, ed., *The New Delhi Report: The Third Assembly of the World Council of Churches* (New York: Association, 1962), p. 116.

ions, in particular the founding of the Church of South India. Lesslie Newbigin (1909-1998), the architect of the declaration, had worked in southern India and had participated in the negotiations that led to the formation of the Church of South India. First and foremost, the text speaks of "one fully committed fellowship." That means that the churches unite without reservations. The declaration then lists the elements belonging to the united church. In addition to baptism they are the common confession, agreement in the preaching of the gospel, the eucharistic fellowship, the mutual recognition of the ordained ministries and the members of the church, the common ordering in prayer, in witness, in service. As important as this declaration is, one must immediately add that the full assembly was not in a position to go beyond listing these elements. It was not possible to provide agreement on the details in New Delhi. The declaration merely makes clear to what aspects the separated churches need to give their special attention if they want to do justice to the business of unity given them by the ecumenical movement.

In the 1960s and 1970s, however, the debate took a new turn. The Second Vatican Council and the participation of the Roman Catholic Church in the ecumenical movement produced a new constellation. The Roman Catholic Church with its tradition and especially its understanding of church unity had to be included in the discussions about the nature of the unity we seek. New aspects had to be taken into consideration. As we have seen, the concept of organic unity was entirely realistic in the area of the Protestant churches, but would it do justice to the new situation? The member churches of the World Council of Churches were organized on a national or territorial basis; now, with the Roman Catholic Church, a church with a universal structure was entering the ecumenical movement. Its presence made unavoidable the question of how unity would have to be expressed on a universal level. The declaration of the full assembly of New Delhi puts the emphasis on the unity of the church at the local level. It speaks first of all of the unity of "all in each place." The unity of the church is constituted, so to speak, from below. There were only passing intimations of the unity of the church at the universal level. To the degree that the ecumenical movement encompassed wider circles, however, this question had to receive a clearer answer.

In this new situation the concept of *unity in reconciled diversity* began to be circulated, especially by the Evangelical-Lutheran side. This idea seeks to emphasize that today's confessional traditions will continue to maintain their significance in the future. Every one of them has unique experiences and insights to contribute to the whole. The move toward unity is to be understood primarily as an event of reconciliation. To be sure, it presupposes wide-ranging agreement. The churches must come to an understanding about confession; they must celebrate the sacraments together and be able to recognize mutually and completely the ordained ministries. They must also be in a position to speak and act jointly when the situation demands it. Thus none of the denominations existing today will be able to continue to exist in their present forms in the one church. Each will be changed by the experience of reconciliation. Yet, the identity of each — and this is what is essential in the new concept — will not be eradicated; it will still be recognizable. The unity of the church is the reconciled diversity of the previously separated churches.

The idea intentionally differs from the concept of organic unity. Unity in reconciled diversity is understood as an alliance of existing churches newly united by acts of reconciliation. By making room in their midst for God's gift of unity, the denominational differences are, so to speak, cleansed. Yet they do not have to die; they are included in the whole.

Of decisive significance for the concept of unity in reconciled diversity is the question of the relationship between unity and diversity. In the ecumenical movement it had been clear from the very beginning that unity is not the same as uniformity. There is room in the one church for differing expressions of the one truth. What is essential is not the identity of the declarations and forms but mutual recognition and the willingness to make a common witness. The New Delhi declaration allowed no doubt about that. And yet there is in this regard a difference between the concepts of organic unity and unity in reconciled diversity. Although the advocates of the first concept were interested primarily in the elements that establish unity, the advocates of reconciled diversity were primarily interested in freeing differences in the church from the stigma of illegitimacy. In a declaration formulated in the spirit of the concept, we read: "Diversities which are rooted in theological traditions, various cultural, ethnic or historical contacts *are integral to the nature of communion* . . . (italics added). In communion diversities are brought together in harmony."[9] Immediately the warning is added that diversity cannot be unlimited. It is illegitimate, it is said, "when, for instance, it makes impossible the common confession of Jesus Christ as God and Saviour the same yesterday, today and forever." Basically this brings us back to asking again what commonality is necessary for bearing witness to the gospel today.

The idea of "reconciled diversity" becomes more understandable when we remember that following the Second Vatican Council there was a new

9. Cf. the declaration on "The Unity of the Church as Koinonia: Gift and Calling," in *Signs of the Spirit: Official Report, Seventh Assembly,* ed. Michael Kinnamon (Grand Rapids: Eerdmans, 1991), p. 173.

form of ecumenical activity — bilateral dialogues at a worldwide level. As a universal community, the Roman Catholic Church could not join the community of the World Council of Churches. Its "natural" partners were the worldwide denominational unions. In the decades following the Council, an extended network of dialogues grew up. The hope was that careful theological work might broaden the common basis among the denominations. The dialogues were to clear the way for "reconciliation in diversity." As a matter of fact, noteworthy results were realized. Probably the most spectacular example was the common declaration of the Lutheran World Federation and the Catholic Church on the central issue of the Reformation, the doctrine of justification (1997). Yet, the question is whether this way can lead to a breakthrough to unity. The network of bilateral dialogues builds on the existing denominational traditions. When one faces off with denominational partners, one is compelled to deepen and solidify one's own denominational identity. For this reason the bilateral dialogues have led initially to consolidating the denominational reality of Christianity. The traditions face one another — admittedly, with a deepened understanding of what they have in common and of their differences — but they are hardly less separated than before. The dialogues clarified a great deal, but they did not make possible the kind of unity the churches could have in common.

And can it really be said that Christianity consists of "denominations" and that they are the decisive actors of the ecumenical movement? What is the significance of the movements that attempt to give new expression to the church's witness across denominational boundaries? What share in this do the spiritual impulses that break out from decade to decade have? What contribution can something like the Pentecostal movement make to realizing unity?

The obvious weakness of the concept of unity in reconciled diversity is the reality that the dimension of a common witness is missing in it today. The bilateral dialogues have contributed little to clarifying the major questions and tasks facing the churches today. Taken as a whole, it looks backward. Yet, the common struggles with the signs of the age are of decisive importance for the quest for unity. None of the churches has at its disposal the necessary answers. By facing the new challenges without prejudice they can even see themselves in new ways. What is considered to be a denominational characteristic takes on a new value in the common witness.

A third concept of unity was developed in the fifth full assembly of the World Council of Churches in Nairobi (1975). It described the unity we seek as *conciliar fellowship.*

> The one Church is to be envisioned as a conciliar fellowship of local churches which are themselves truly united. In this conciliar fellowship, each local church possesses, in communion with the others, the fullness of catholicity, witnesses to the same apostolic faith, and therefore recognizes the others as belonging to the same Church of Christ and guided by the same Spirit. As the New Delhi Assembly pointed out, they are bound together because they have received the same baptism and share in the same Eucharist; they recognize each other's members and ministries. They are one in their common commitment to confess the gospel of Christ by proclamation and service to the world. To this end, each church aims at maintaining sustained and sustaining relationships with her sister churches, expressed in conciliar gatherings whenever required for the fulfillment of their common calling.[10]

This description is built on the New Delhi declaration. It attempts to express more clearly how unity can become a reality not only for "all in each place" but also for "all in all places." It goes back to the church's conciliar tradition. Just as in the course of the centuries the church occasionally needed representative assemblies to call to remembrance the truth of the gospel and to determine the way into the future, so also today the churches must be able to come together as a council when the situation demands it. In order to be able to "celebrate" a council, there must be basic agreement about the apostolic faith as well as baptism and the eucharist and an unqualified recognition of the church's ministries. In addition, there must be an understanding of how common decisions can be made and how they can be received by the local churches.

A worldwide council that speaks in the name of all churches may well lie in the distant future; indeed, it is possible that it will never happen. In any case, however, the goal of conciliar fellowship — that is, a fellowship that is capable of calling a council — continues to exist. The ecumenical movement serves to fulfill the necessary presuppositions step by step both by means of theological dialogue and by means of joint witness in today's world. To a certain extent the ecumenical movement is to be understood as a "pre-conciliar" fellowship. By keeping its eye on the major goal, it can inspire people to make strides toward increasingly close community. All kinds of obstacles — differences in doctrine, past injuries that continue to fester in the present, conflicts about the church's witness in today's world — are named and cleared away. When the churches increasingly share a common

10. David M. Paton, ed., *Breaking Barriers: Nairobi 1975: The Official Report of the Fifth Assembly of the World Council of Churches* (Grand Rapids: Eerdmans, 1976), p. 60.

life, the community that binds them together in Christ becomes more visible to the world.

The concept of conciliar fellowship places the emphasis on the church's common task. The vision goes beyond the concept of reconciled diversity to the degree that it not only aims for reconciliation but also measures unity by how the church fulfills its task in today's world. In the here and now, the churches are challenged to be part of a common movement toward the one church in which God's gift can be reflected.[11]

Unity? It is interesting to note that in recent times one can detect a certain reserve toward the term "unity." When people speak of the goal of the ecumenical movement, there is a much greater tendency to use the term "fellowship," or *koinonia/communio.* As a matter of fact, the term "unity" does have obvious limits. It makes clear that there can be only one church of Jesus Christ. All the images used in the New Testament confirm it: the church is one body, one people, one temple, one bride. Separation is contrary to the nature of the church. That in the creed all churches profess their commitment to the one church emphatically reminds us of this. When it comes to describing their one church, however, new aspects must be taken into account. The separated churches that are on the way to unity face the task of making room in their midst for fellowship with Christ. They must open themselves to one another. They must communicate with one another. They must join together in following the leading of the Spirit of Christ. The term *koinonia* has the potential of expressing how unity can be lived. The concept of conciliar fellowship has already offered a first step in this direction. It describes the goal of the ecumenical movement as "fellowship." Yet the emphasis in the declaration of the seventh full assembly of the World Council of Churches in Canberra (1991) is even clearer. The title already indicates the direction: "The Unity of the Church as Koinonia: Gift and Calling." The text of the declaration then says: "The church is the foretaste of this communion with God and with one another. . . . The purpose of the church is . . . to point to the fullness of communion with God, humanity and the whole creation in the glory of the kingdom." And at another

11. The churches can contribute to this movement with common initiatives in the here and now. A good example of this kind of conciliar initiative was the appeal of the World Council on the occasion of the sixth full assembly in Vancouver (1983) to come together in a "conciliar process for justice, peace and the integrity of creation." The appeal was heard, and in the 1980s and early 1990s it gave rise to numerous joint actions, but the movement was not able to achieve long-term success. There was not enough energy to overcome denominational resistance, especially that of the Roman Catholic Church, and above all the lack of the churches' readiness to come to grips with the major issues of the age.

place one finds the lapidary sentence: "The unity of the church to which we are called is a koinonia."[12]

Without doubt, there are benefits to emphasizing the church as *communio.* It makes it possible for the call to unity to be more concrete. After decades of work, there are signs of fatigue in the ecumenical movement. Must the separation of the churches really be as intolerable as the fathers of the ecumenical movement claimed? In many circles one detects a retreat to denominational positions. It is therefore all the more important to present the goal of the movement in such a way that the churches will be tempted to move together and to become engaged as a *communio* for God's kingdom.[13]

* * *

How then are the concepts of unity that have been presented here to be seen in light of the New Testament? We must ask this question even if it is not possible to derive a description of the goal directly from Scripture. Every attempt to put into words the "unity we seek" has to justify itself before the witness of Scripture. Unity is more than simply the cross section of the convictions and claims of the individual churches. The unity in which the churches are to come together today must be a legitimate continuation of that earliest phase of the living tradition to which the New Testament bears witness.

This study is based on the understanding that, among the concepts presented thus far, the idea of conciliar fellowship best reflects the witness of the New Testament. Before we substantiate and elucidate this understanding more thoroughly, however, we turn our attention to the witness of the New Testament itself.

12. Kinnamon, ed., *Signs of the Spirit,* pp. 172, 173.

13. For additional material on the concept of conciliar fellowship, see *Councils and the Ecumenical Movement,* WCS 5 (Geneva: WCC, 1968); Reinhard Frieling, "Konziliare Gemeinschaft," in *Wandernde Horizonte auf dem Weg zur kirchlichen Einheit,* ed. Reinhard Groscurth (Frankfurt: Lembeck, 1974), pp. 137-47; Lukas Vischer, *Veränderung der Welt — Bekehrung der Kirchen* (Frankfurt: Lembeck, 1976), pp. 83-106; Harding Meyer, "'Einheit in versöhnter Vielfalt,' 'Konziliare Gemeinschaft,' 'Organische Union,' Gemeinsamkeit und Differenz gegenwärtig diskutierter Einheitskonzeptionen," *ÖR* 26 (1977): 377-400; Lukas Vischer, "Ist das wirklich die 'Einheit, die wir suchen'?" *ÖR* 41, no. 1 (1992): 7-24.

PART TWO

On the Way to Unity: The Community of the Church in the New Testament

Ulrich Luz

Introduction

Beginning with Constantine, for the Roman emperors the church was a decisive factor in the cohesion of the Roman Empire. It was able to be this because it was *one* church. In the late Roman Empire *one* church meant synods, intensive ecclesiastical communication, bishops, and metropolitan bishops. It also meant unity in the rule of faith and identical dogma. Finally, one church meant a common Bible, common worship identical in its principal features, a common calendar, and efforts to achieve a common practice in, for example, such matters as the questions of penance, of military service, or of divorce. After a long development, the unity of the church meant in the West a hierarchical organization with the pope at the top, and in the East the councils and the ecumenical patriarch as the central representative of the church.

All of this seems obvious to us, but we must keep in mind that in the context of the religions of late antiquity it was by no means self-evident. Christianity was only one of a number of religions that, beginning about 200 B.C., spread from the Orient throughout the entire Roman Empire. As was the case with all of them, at the local level Christianity was organized as a religious association analogous to the mystery religions. All the other Oriental religions in the Roman Empire, including the powerful religion of Mithras, remained at that stage of development. That is to say, they formed individual mystery communities that were only loosely connected. Christianity, however, was united in a church. Thus the church's visible unity made it relatively distinctive in the context of ancient religions. What we have here may well be something of the essence of Christian faith. To be concerned about the struggle for the church's visible unity in the New Testament period is to reflect on something that is essential to Christian faith. *That church unity must be visibly lived is at the heart of Christian faith.* That is the first supposition that guides this study.

Of course, we must immediately qualify what we have just said. Christianity's visible unity is not completely unique. Judaism offers an analogy precisely in this regard. It too has common institutions and rituals that are known to all Jews: the Temple, the Bible, the Torah, circumcision and Sabbath, calendar, and later, in a sense, the rabbis and the patriarchs. The Jews also struggled to achieve a common practice and a Halakah that was binding on all. Was the importance of visible unity in Christianity inherited from Judaism? It would certainly not be a mistake to say so. When it began, Christian faith simply wanted to be the final and definitive expression of Israel's faith in its God. In earlier times, as well as later, the biblical heritage was every bit as central for Christianity as was initially the connection of its own fellowship to the actual people of Israel or, as was later of paramount importance, to the idea of Israel. Even if one no longer wanted to have anything to do with actual Israel, one still understood oneself to be the people of God or the true Israel. Yet there were also differences early on. In Judaism visible unity is the expression of the election of a special people, Israel, whose institutions and laws clearly distinguish it from other nations. It was precisely this association with a special nation that the Christian church soon abandoned. Already in early Christianity Israel's faith made way for a *religion* for all nations. In late antiquity it became increasingly clear that *belonging to the people of Israel* was what was decisive for Judaism. By contrast, for Christianity, which understood itself to be a universal religion for all nations, special *doctrines* became the decisive characteristic that differentiated Christians from non-Christians or heretics.[1] Thus, even in comparison with Judaism, the struggle for unity in Christianity was something out of the ordinary; or, to be more precise, in the course of its historical development it became something out of the ordinary.

Yet we must extend the horizon even more. Is not the effort to achieve visible unity in a sense characteristic of every established religion?[2] If that is the case, Christianity's uniqueness in late antiquity would be that it was the only established religion that in that day prevailed throughout the world. One

1. Cf. Daniel Boyarin, *Border Lines: The Partition of Judaeo-Christianity* (Philadelphia: University of Pennsylvania Press, 2004).

2. Following Gustav Mensching (*Vergleichende Religionswissenschaft,* 2d ed. [Heidelberg: Quelle-Meyer, 1949], p. 151), I understand "established [*gestiftete*] religion" as a religion in which "a historically ascertainable personality with a characteristic religious way of looking at things has a decisive influence on the shaping and the spirit of concrete religion for an unforeseeable duration of its further development." Established religions have, in contrast to folk religions, universal and missionary tendencies.

cannot reject this suggestion out of hand, but we must differentiate. There is probably something in the nature of visible unity in every established religion, but its form and intensity vary widely. Among the Zoroastrian state religion; the monastic orders in Buddhism; Jainism; the hierarchically structured church of Manichaeism; the Islamic *ummah* (congregation/community) with its prescribed confession, scripture, sacred language, and religious law; and the Christian church or churches there are appreciable differences that express something of what is unique for each of these religions. Thus one cannot simply understand the unity of the church by subsuming Christianity under the heading of an established religion. One can comprehend what is unique about it only by re-telling and interpreting the distinctive history of the Christian struggle for unity. It begins with Jesus and the New Testament period.

This observation brings us to another problem, however, that forces us to differentiate. Christianity's unity has not always been understood in the same way. It has changed throughout history and has been — and still is — a matter of dispute among the several Christian communities. It is immediately obvious that church unity did not mean in the Constantinian age what it meant in the New Testament period. Less obvious is what the different understandings of church unity have in common. Even within the New Testament age, the differences are quite substantial, and there were considerable developments and changes precisely in this period. Not even the word "unity," which heads our book as a title, is found throughout the entire New Testament. It appears relatively late and in only a few New Testament works.[3] Earlier and elsewhere one did not speak of the church's unity. Thus we must ask: Were the efforts to achieve unity so different in different epochs and situations that in reality they did not have anything "Christian" in common? If that were the case, it would doubtless also mean the end of every attempt to get directions from the New Testament for our modern quest for unity. For the present, the only thing clear is that the wide range of diversity we find already in the New Testament keeps us from transferring our findings from the New Testament directly into the present.[4] For this reason we add to our first supposition a second: *Just as the struggle for church unity belongs to Christian faith, so the variety and the differences of these efforts also belong to Christian faith.*

Three levels are important for the following discussion.

(1) First of all, we will try to trace the course of the struggle for unity in New Testament times. We are interested in *history,* not merely in theology. It

3. Cf. above, pp. 12-13.

4. Cf. above, p. 11.

is our opinion that this is the best way to do justice to the texts.[5] We differ here from most of the (not very many!) existing studies of our theme.[6] As a rule they are interested primarily in "higher" theology and less in history as it is lived. Above all, however, we are of the opinion that only in this way can we do justice to what early Christianity experienced as the basis of unity, namely, the power of the exalted Lord Jesus. Thus we will give an account first of all of how Christians in the New Testament age sought church fellowship, how they struggled to achieve it, and how they realized it. The subject matter of the first level of this book is church history, not the history of theology.

(2) According to the testimony of the New Testament, however, the church is given a *basic gift,* called by different names in different works, to help in its struggle for church fellowship. Paul, for example, speaks of the "fellowship of his Son Jesus Christ" (1 Cor. 1:9), the presupposition of the fellowship of the believers, or of the "fellowship of the body of Christ" in the Lord's Supper on which the one body of the church is based (1 Cor. 10:16-17). Mat-

5. Cf. above, pp. 12-15.

6. Paul J. Achtemeier, *The Quest for Unity in the New Testament Church* (Philadelphia: Fortress, 1987); Raymond E. Brown, "The Unity and Diversity in New Testament Ecclesiology," *NT* 6 (1963): 298-308; Commission Biblique Pontificiale, *Unité et diversité dans l'Eglise: text officiel de la Commission biblique pontificale et travaux personels des members* (Città del Vaticano: Liberia Editrice Vaticana, 1989); Oscar Cullmann, *Unity through Diversity: Its Foundation, and a Contribution to the Discussion Concerning the Possibilities of Its Actualization,* trans. M. Eugene Boring (Philadelphia: Fortress, 1988); James Dunn, "Instruments of Koinonia in the Early Church," *OiC* 25 (1989): 204-16; Ferdinand Hahn, Karl Kertelge, and Rudolf Schnackenburg, *Einheit der Kirche: Grundlegung im Neuen Testament,* QD 84 (Freiburg: Herder, 1979); Ferdinand Hahn, "Die Einheit der Kirche nach dem Zeugnis des Apostels Paulus," in *Ekklesiologie des Neuen Testaments: für Karl Kertelge,* ed. Rainer Kampling and Thomas Söding (Freiburg: Herder, 1996), pp. 288-300; Ernst Käsemann, "The Canon of the New Testament and the Unity of the Church," in Käsemann, *Essays on New Testament Themes* (Philadelphia: Fortress, 1982), pp. 95-107; Ernst Käsemann, "Unity and Multiplicity in the New Testament Doctrine of the Church," in Käsemann, *New Testament Questions of Today* (Philadelphia: Fortress, 1969), pp. 252-59; Karl Kertelge, "Koinonia und Einheit der Kirche nach dem Neuen Testament," in *Communio Sanctorum: Einheit der Christen, Einheit der Kirche, Festschrift für Bischof Paul-Werner Scheele,* ed. Josef Schreiner and Klaus Wittstadt (Würzburg: Echter, 1988), pp. 53-67; Ulrich Luz, "Unity of the Church in Pauline Times," in *Agia Graphe kai synchronos Anthropos,* Festschrift Ioannis Karavidopoulos (Thessaloniki: Pournara, 2006), pp. 555-71; Ulrich Luz, "Das Problem der eucharistischen Gastfreundschaft in neutestamentlicher Sicht," in *Diakonia — Litourgia — Charisma,* Festschrift Georgios A. Galitis (Lebadeia: En plo, 2006), pp. 377-93; Franz Mussner, *Petrus und Paulus, Pole der Einheit: Eine Hilfe für die Kirchen,* QD 76 (Freiburg: Herder, 1976); Adolf Martin Ritter, "Die Einheit der Kirche als Problem des 1. Milleniums post Christum natum," *ThZ* 60 (2004): 43-61; Jürgen Roloff, *Die Kirche im Neuen Testament,* GNT 10 (Göttingen: Vandenhoeck & Ruprecht, 1993), esp. pp. 310-23; Gerd Theissen, "Die Einheit der Kirche: Kohärenz und Differenz im Urchristentum," *ZMiss* 20 (1994): 70-86.

thew speaks of the Risen One who is the Lord of the whole world and who sends forth his disciples (Matt. 28:16-20), Luke of the Spirit whom the Risen One sends (Luke 24:49), John of the unity of the Father and the Son "in" which the believers are (John 17:21). Ephesians speaks here of "one body and one Spirit . . . one Lord, one faith, one baptism, one God and Father of all" (Eph. 4:4-6). In the Pastorals the basic gift consists of the received tradition. In Ignatius it is the heavenly unity of the Father, the Son, and his apostles represented in the threefold ministry. In Tertullian it is the one immutable rule of faith. In Justin the prerequisite for participating in the eucharist is believing Christian doctrine, baptism, and a life lived in accordance with Christ.[7] There it is most clear how in time the basic *gift* of unity increasingly has taken on the characteristics of a *precondition* of unity. In each case tradition is in some way connected with the basic gift. No New Testament author speaks of the basic gift of unity without in some way making use of the story of Jesus of Nazareth. In all of the cases, however, the basic gift is a living reality and not *merely* identical with the received tradition, for, although the basic gift is an experience, it can be formulated and interpreted only in a concrete situation with human words as a theological statement. Thus the second level we must consider is the *basic gift of unity.* Of course, from the perspective of the New Testament witnesses it is the first level.

(3) Finally, the third level is then *theological reflection on church unity* in the New Testament. This level accompanies and thinks through the experiences of the unity that is both given and practiced. With our theological reflection on the process of unity initiated by Jesus we will discover repeatedly how ecclesiological concepts and narrative outlines originate. Thus theology is something secondary, or even tertiary — it is human response.[8] Of course, we will also see how theological outlines can become in turn ways of expressing the unity that is bestowed as a gift. That is to say, when they are transmitted to people who come later they can become expressions of the basic gift. They came into being as human efforts to express in words the gift of unity and one's own struggle to achieve it. For later generations they became the way of expressing the basic gift, and they pointed to the living Lord himself, Jesus Christ.

Yet history as it is lived is where Jesus Christ, the basic gift, is experienced and where the movement toward unity begins. It is where all theology

7. Tertullian, *De virginibus velandis* 1; Justin, *Apologia* 1.66.1-2.

8. Our distinction between basic gift and theology corresponds in principle to Rudolph Bultmann's distinction between kerygma and theology (*Theology of the New Testament,* trans. Kendrick Grobel [London: SCM, 1965], vol. 2, pp. 237-41). Of course, the level of history is largely obliterated in Bultmann's theology.

has its roots. By putting it in the center of the report we want to keep the New Testament ecclesiological statements from becoming an abstract "doctrine" about the unity of the church — a doctrine people then can believe to be true and can use in the present. Such doctrines are historically conditioned expressions of the power of Jesus Christ who has wanted and continues to want to move his church to fellowship and to unity.

After we briefly describe the significance of Jesus for the struggle for unity in the later church that appealed to him as its authority, we want to divide the New Testament age into two main epochs — the apostolic and post-apostolic periods. First of all, we want to give a general portrayal of the most important issues and the most important unity-promoting forces or ways of experiencing the "basic gift" for each epoch (sections 2 and 6). Then we will try to outline approaches to a theological analysis of the efforts to create church fellowship (sections 3 and 7). Then from each epoch we will describe the basic conflict that left its mark on the age — in the apostolic age the controversy over the church's relationship to Israel (section 4) and in the post-apostolic age the conflict (admittedly in its earliest stage) between Gnostic and so-called Early Catholic Christians (section 8). We will devote a separate section to a portrayal of Paul's thoughts on church fellowship (section 5).

1. Jesus: The Origin of the Community of the Church

Who, according to the New Testament, founded the church? There are two classic answers to this question. One of them is: "I believe that the Church . . . was instituted immediately and directly by the true and historical Christ himself and . . . was built on Peter, the first of the apostles."[9] This answer of the anti-modernists has been rejected by both Catholic and Protestant scholarship. Jesus almost never speaks of the church in his own words. The important saying of Matthew 16:18 speaks of the establishment of the church expressly in the future, and even then we are dealing with a saying that for a number of reasons can hardly be an authentic word of Jesus. Thus New Testament scholarship increasingly has come to the opposite conclusion and declared that the church was a post-Easter creation of the Risen One: "The Church has its origin and its beginning in the resurrection of Jesus Christ."[10]

9. For the Latin text, see Heinrich Denzinger and Adolf Schönmetzer, *Enchiridion Symbolorum,* 36th ed. (Freiburg: Herder, 1976), no. 3540.

10. Günther Bornkamm, *Jesus of Nazareth,* trans. Irene and Fraser McLuskey with James M. Robinson (New York: Harper, 1960), p. 186.

This second thesis has both historical and substantive difficulties. If taken as an absolute statement, it becomes historically difficult to explain the origin of the church at all. In twentieth-century Protestant scholarship it was long a widely accepted thesis that discontinuity prevailed between Jesus and the early church, in Christology as well as in ecclesiology. The general opinion was that Jesus himself had no explicit Christology — that it originated in earliest Christianity because of the resurrection, as a response to Jesus. Parallel to this view was the thesis of ecclesiological discontinuity — that Jesus founded no church, that he instead proclaimed the kingdom of God. What came after his death was not the kingdom but the church.[11] Yet the question is: How did the church happen to come into existence after Easter if there were no links to Jesus for such a development? In that case we would have to assume that when the disciples stayed together in the name of Jesus after Easter and carried on his proclamation they were trying to do something completely new — indeed, that in doing so they may even have been acting contrary to the Jesus in whose name they did it. That is historically improbable. In history there are developments and changes but no absolute breaks.

The thesis would cause severe substantive problems for today's churches. They could no longer claim Jesus as their authority. Or, if one wants to be somewhat less radical, when they did appeal to Jesus, they would no longer need to be concerned about the form of the church, since it wouldn't have had anything to do with Jesus anyway. Then the unity of the church, this great dream of so many Christians, would not be important as far as Jesus is concerned. The ecumenical movement would then be deprived of an important foundation, and in all probability even this book would not have needed to be written. If the church is founded only on the belief in the resurrection, it seems that it is in danger of losing its grounding in history. In that case there is no longer any historical basis for coming to an agreement about the shape of the church. Historically, Protestants have always exhibited a fatal tendency to regard the visible form of the church as unimportant. They have always found it relatively easy to pattern their church order after whatever political system happened to be dominant — for example, after a monarchy with the king or ruling nobleman as the supreme bishop or after a republican system with a synod that functioned like a secular parliament. They were able to do this since the *one true* church was invisible anyway. The visible state churches simply could not be the true church. One could call this Protestant tendency

11. Following an often-quoted statement from Alfred Loisy, *The Gospel and the Church*, trans. Christopher Home (1903; reprinted Philadelphia: Fortress, 1976), p. 166.

"ecclesiological docetism."[12] It is quite compatible with the historical thesis that Jesus did not want a church and that the church had no historical roots in Jesus.

On the other hand, however, it is clear that Jesus did not establish a church. There is no New Testament evidence that he did so. That the word "church" is almost completely absent from sayings attributed to Jesus speaks for itself.[13] By no means are we to understand that the Jew Jesus of Nazareth founded the post-Easter church, which consisted of Jews and Gentiles and very soon consisted almost solely of Gentiles. Jesus was certainly open to Gentiles in special cases, as his meetings with the centurion in Capernaum and the Syrophoenician woman show (Matt. 8:5-13; Mark 7:24-30), but those were exceptions. That the Gentiles would come to Israel was something he expected for the future kingdom of God, not for the present (Matt. 8:11-12). Christian theologians should be very suspicious of all attempts to understand the church as something established by Jesus, because to a great degree such a thesis reflects their own wishes and the needs of the church. In historical questions the wish is never permitted to be the father of the thought! Therefore, in view of the textual evidence, one can speak only of starting points or roots in Jesus that then after Easter led to the formation of the church.[14]

Who then founded the church is a question most New Testament witnesses do not even ask. The Gospels, which at least indirectly answer it, are for our understanding remarkably ambiguous. Admittedly, according to Luke the earthly Jesus already called and sent out apostles and disciples (Luke 5:1-11; 6:12-16; 9:1-6; 10:1-22), but it was the risen Lord who first made of them the church through the gift of the Spirit (Acts 1–2). According to Matthew, Jesus called his disciples in "Galilee of the Gentiles" (Matt. 4:15, 18-22) and sent them to Israel (chapter 10), but he relates the narrative in such a way that the future history of the church always shimmers through the story of Jesus. By contrast, the command "make disciples of all nations" (Matt. 28:19) comes first from the risen Lord. It is, therefore, a post-Easter command. Something similar is true of the Gospel of John. Like the Gospel of Matthew, John is also transparent regarding the experiences of the post-Easter church. Here Jesus calls his disciples in the same way that people be-

12. "Docetism" is the tenet that Christ only appeared to be human. One can call the view that the concrete-historical form of the church is irrelevant for faith "ecclesiological docetism."

13. The word "church" appears only in Matt. 16:18 and 18:17. It is highly probable that neither saying comes from the historical Jesus.

14. Jürgen Roloff (*Kirche*, p. 19) speaks of an "implied ecclesiology" in Jesus. He means by the term the same thing I am calling "starting points" or "roots."

came "disciples" later, after Easter. Not only are people called directly by Jesus; they are also won for Jesus and come to recognize who Christ is through the testimony of others (John 1:35-51). In both Matthew and John, the story of the historical Jesus and the deeds of the risen Lord after Easter are seen as if they were interwoven. If one were to ask New Testament witnesses who the church's founder was, they probably would not say who *has* founded the church; they would more than likely say that the risen Lord Jesus *is* its foundation. That means at one and the same time an element of freedom and of obligation. That Jesus is *risen* meant for them that as the living Lord he accompanies his church to new shores. That it is *Jesus* who is risen meant that, in this new beginning, all of them referred to *his* story. That it was a concrete human being, Jesus, who was risen made it both possible and necessary to come to an understanding after Easter about what it meant to believe in him. And since according to the witness of the New Testament the church is the church of the risen *Jesus,* it was also necessary and possible to come to an understanding about the church. All New Testament believers had to come together and stay together for the simple reason that they understood themselves to be disciples of the *same* Lord.

What, however, was the historical reality?

Jesus understood himself as God's messenger sent to Israel, perhaps as the coming Son of Man–World Judge. He inspired a missionary movement in Israel (cf. Luke 10:2-12). He understood his task to be to gather the people of Israel for the eschatological rule of God that was beginning to dawn with his activity.[15] The rule of God meant for him God's new and definitive turning to his people — a new, unsurpassable love. Thus God called his people to himself through Jesus, no longer on the basis of his previous saving deeds — the Exodus, the Sinai covenant, the Torah — but in a completely new way. He threw open the circle of the elect in Israel and called *all.* Especially Israel's people at the margin — the women, the unclean, the sick, the poor, the Samaritans, the tax collectors, and the children — entered the light of God's love. Jesus was interested in the entire nation of Israel, not simply in the righteous and not simply in a pious remnant. Thus Jesus was interested in God's people Israel and not in a new community separate from Israel. This new, entire people of God/Israel is based solely on God's love.

There were around Jesus two special groups, both of which were concerned with the gathering of God's people Israel and both of which consti-

15. On this point and on the entire chapter, see especially Gerhard Lohfink, "Jesus und die Kirche," *HFTh,* vol. 3: *Traktat Kirche* (Freiburg: Herder, 1986), pp. 49-96; Thomas Söding, *Jesus und die Kirche: Was sagt das Neue Testament?* (Freiburg: Herder, 2007), pp. 89-213.

tuted something of a bridge between Jesus and the later church: the group of the Twelve and the people who followed Jesus, that is, the disciples. In all probability they are not identical; the latter group is larger than the former. We can regard them as an inner circle and a somewhat wider circle of people who followed Jesus.

We turn first to the Twelve. Jesus gathered a group of twelve disciples "that they might be with him" (Mark 3:14). The historicity of this group has been contested, but in my judgment the arguments for that view are not very convincing. How could this group have originated after Easter, when precisely then — because of Judas's betrayal — it was no longer complete? How could one have invented the embarrassing fiction that a member of this closest circle had betrayed Jesus? Furthermore, nowhere after Easter do we see that the Twelve performed a real function — for example, in the leadership of the church.

Why did Jesus create this group? It is possible that it functioned as a sign. The twelve disciples in this circle represented the twelve tribes of God's people Israel (cf. Matt. 19:28) that Jesus was gathering. The group of twelve was a symbolic anticipation of the totality of Israel that Jesus wanted to restore. In a similar way it was a present sign of the coming kingdom of God, just as, for example, the demon exorcisms were a sign of the final victory over Satan or the fellowship meals with tax collectors and sinners were a sign of the heavenly banquet in God's kingdom. Perhaps we can add the following: there is wide agreement in the New Testament about the names of the disciples who belonged to the Twelve. Matthew the tax collector and Simon the Zealot, two extreme opposites in Israel, belonged to the group. In all probability Jesus intentionally formed the Twelve as a concrete example of his open understanding of Israel. The barriers in Israel will be overcome in the kingdom of God, and a new community will come into being.

In addition to the Twelve, there were others whom Jesus called to follow him. Jesus' call to follow him has nothing to do with rabbinic discipleship; it is directly patterned after the biblical model of Elisha's relationship to Elijah (1 Kings 19:19-21). To begin with, one sees in this group of followers similarities to the Twelve. Here, too, there is a connection to the task of gathering the eschatological people of God/Israel. The difference is that these followers do not represent the twelve-tribe nation. Their calling is rather to share in Jesus' task of gathering the people of God. The call to follow is the call to assume a task — namely, to be "fishers of men" (Mark 1:17) and to proclaim the kingdom of God (Luke 9:60). For this reason Jesus also sent his disciples to preach in Israel (cf. Mark 6:7-13; Luke 10:1-16), and he let them share his own authority (cf. Matt. 10:1). Even in the group of followers one can see something of the openness of the eschatological Israel: the name of a tax collector, Levi, turns up (Mark 2:14). Above all — and for the Jewish society of that day this is quite noteworthy — there are also the names of women who were disciples of Jesus, supported him, and at least to some extent shared his itinerant life (Luke 8:1-3; Mark 15:40-41).[16]

Yet there are also other characteristics of the group of followers — features that were to become important for the later church. Discipleship involves a personal bond with Jesus, the primary characteristic of which was that the followers shared Jesus' own itinerant life devoted to proclaiming the kingdom of God. Like Jesus, they also renounced vocation, family life, and possessions. The sayings about bearing one's cross (Mark 8:34; Matt. 10:38) and about saving and losing one's life (Mark 8:35; Matt. 10:39) are presumably not general maxims; they focus on the martyrdom facing Jesus and the disciples. "Cross" suggests execution, capital punishment; the metaphorical sense did not come into use until after Jesus' death. If we may assume that Jesus reckoned with his own death, discipleship involves suffering with Jesus already in his lifetime. Thus a personal bond with Jesus does not mean primarily having a close personal relationship to him. Nor does it simply mean affirming his teaching. It means joining him in proclaiming the kingdom of God with all the consequences that involves for one's own life.

What would that involve? The life Jesus lived in the light of the kingdom of God included his healings; his exorcisms (Luke 11:20); his renunciation of the orders of the world, of possessions, of structures of power and rank (Matt. 23:11); his renunciation of force in, for example, the passion narrative; and, above all, his association with outcasts, women, tax collectors, unclean people, and Samaritans. These things all belong to the life of the disciple-followers as well. They, too, practice nonviolence openly (Matt. 5:39-41), and in so doing they let a bit of the totally different world, the kingdom of God, shine through. They, too, travel about in obvious poverty (Luke 10:4), and in so doing they raise up a sign of the reversal of worldly power and worldly wealth in the kingdom of God. And above all they, too, live the fellowship of love that flows from God's love to the outcasts in Israel. It is no accident that there are so many reports of table-fellowship in the Gospels. In all of these things the group of followers is a sign of the dawning kingdom of God, much as the small mustard seed is already the beginning of the full-grown plant (cf. Mark 4:30-32). By taking over Jesus' own lifestyle, the fol-

16. This fact is important for the question of how women today should perform church ministries — more than ever a central question for the unity of the church.

lowers also become "parables" of the kingdom of God.[17] The existence of the group of followers is every bit as important for Jesus' proclamation as is his own life. When everything that is involved in the dawning of the kingdom of God is already lived and is already happening in a small circle of people, Jesus' proclamation is no abstract doctrine; it becomes something concrete people are able to experience.

Jesus then went to Jerusalem, and there he accepted — if he did not actually seek — his death.[18] In the judgment of today's scholarship, that again is something we can say with some confidence. Of special importance for our theme is the last meal Jesus ate with his disciples in Jerusalem. All the Synoptic witnesses tell us that there was such a meal. We can no longer say with absolute certainty what words Jesus spoke on that occasion. In all probability the early-sounding statement looking forward to the kingdom of God comes from that last supper: "Amen, I say to you, I will not drink again of the fruit of the vine until that day when I drink it new in the kingdom of God" (Mark 14:25). This saying shows that Jesus' anticipation of the coming of the kingdom of God was by no means shaken by the fact of his imminent death. It also confirms that wine was drunk at that farewell meal. All witnesses agree about *the* cup from which they all drank. That is noteworthy, since at Jewish meals as well as at the Passover feast every guest drank out of his own cup.[19] At that meal, however, a single cup, the cup of Jesus himself, made the round of all the disciples. That was so unusual that Jesus was forced to say something about it. The most immediately plausible suggestion is that this cup is to be understood as a sign of the community. Before his death Jesus wanted to strengthen the community of the disciples one more time, because he wanted them to stay together beyond his own death. That may also mean that he believed that he himself would have a special significance in the future. We no longer know for certain what Jesus said about this one cup, yet because there *must* have been an explanation of its meaning it is most probable that the cup saying transmitted to us (Mark 14:24; 1 Cor. 11:25) in some form also comes from Jesus. That would mean that in some form Jesus attributed soterio-

17. In his last Jesus book, Eduard Schweizer proposed understanding Jesus as a "parable of God." *Jesus, the Parable of God: What Do We Really Know about Jesus?* (Allison Park, PA: Pickwick, 1994).

18. Ulrich Luz, "Warum zog Jesus nach Jerusalem?" in *Der Historische Jesus: Tendenzen und Perspektiven der gegenwärtigen Forschung,* ed. Jens Schröter and Ralph Brucker, BZNW 114 (Berlin: de Gruyter, 2002), pp. 409-27.

19. See Heinz Schürmann, *Jesu Ureigener Tod: Exegetische Besinnungen und Ausblick* (Freiburg: Herder, 1976), pp. 76-77. There is an analogy in the bread ritual. Jesus breaks one loaf into pieces and divides it among his disciples.

logical significance to his death. That is not certain, however; here we can do no better than make educated guesses.

Thus Jesus wanted his community of disciples to continue beyond his death. Since this was related to the kingdom of God, that meant that they should continue to proclaim the kingdom of God until it finally arrived. We do not know with what period of time he may have reckoned or whether he thought the kingdom of God and the judgment would come in connection with his death (as Luke 12:49-50 appears to suggest).

In summary: the basic dimensions of what later became the church were already laid out in the group of the Twelve and the group of followers, although the intention of Jesus was not that the two groups should become the later church. It was that they should become the first germ-cell and the vanguard of the new Israel that God created with the beginning of his kingdom. Only historically, but not according to Jesus' intention, the church then evolved from this beginning when the disciples turned to the Gentile mission and when it became clear that they were rejected by Israel's majority. These primitive cells of the later church were essentially part of Jesus' proclamation of the kingdom of God. Their basic characteristics are:

1. looking *forward,* the relation to the kingdom of God. As a kind of parable, the disciples portrayed the kingdom of God and in so doing set up a countermark to the world — to its wealth, its relationships of domination and control, and its religious barriers.
2. looking *backward,* the relation to Jesus, who embodied the kingdom of God in his activity. The disciples took over Jesus' mission, his lifestyle, and his suffering.
3. *outwardly,* the relation to Israel as a whole, of which the group of the Twelve was a symbol. The proclamation of the kingdom of God was meant for this larger group.
4. *inwardly,* the love and the fellowship of the disciples among themselves and the inclusive power for outsiders and people at the margins as it reflected Jesus' proclamation of God's love.

Anticipating what is to come, we might say that from Jesus' perspective the later church has to portray and live its own gospel. Since Jesus' central concern was the gift of God's love, overcoming barriers, and integrating outsiders, *fellowship and love are the essential features of church that most clearly correspond to the gospel of Jesus Christ it proclaims.* Or, to say the same thing negatively, whenever in the church either the gospel or love is obscured, the church is in danger of losing itself. Thus from Jesus' perspective the task of combining gospel and love is the church's basic mission. The New Testament period will already show that sometimes the two are in danger of living in deep tension with one another.

What happened after Jesus' death? We know that initially the disciples fled and scattered. It was the Easter appearances that brought them together again. What did the Easter appearances and the belief in the Risen One mean for the church? They are not simply the church's primal date, but they effected more than a connection with what had existed before Easter.

The confession that God has raised Jesus from the dead is much more than belief in a miraculous resuscitation. When the disciples interpreted the Easter appearances this way, they probably were thinking of the praise of Israel's God they prayed daily: "Blessed art thou, O Lord, who quickenest the dead."[20] People expected that when the new age came God would raise the dead and thus demonstrate his divinity. Now when the disciples testified that God raised Jesus from the dead it meant for them that God has revealed himself definitively in Jesus. By aligning himself with Jesus and rescuing him from death, God has newly made known his name. From this point on, Israel's God was inseparably connected with this man, Jesus of Nazareth. From this point on, Jesus' followers could speak of God only in connection with Jesus. For the community of disciples that meant that because of Easter it was finally clear that Jesus was not simply one member of this community who was no longer present while the community as such continued on. Rather, Jesus is the continuing basis of this community. Without him this community could not proclaim God's kingdom. Without him it could not even exist — even, indeed, especially not after his death. He is living in his church. Of course, none of that had been foreign to the earlier fellowship with Jesus. Before Easter it had also been the case that Jesus himself called people to discipleship. It may be that at his farewell supper, when he broke the bread and passed the one cup around the circle, he had already intimated that he wanted to give his life for the sake of the disciples. Such intimations then became quite clear after Easter. Because God who raises the dead aligned himself with Jesus and raised him, Jesus became the foundation of his disciples' vital fellowship. They could live only because of him. They oriented their lives toward him. Because of him they continued to be called to the proclamation of the kingdom of God and to love.

We began by designating Jesus as the basic gift that always precedes the

20. Benediction 2 of the Eighteen Benedictions *(Shemoneh Esreh)*.

church's struggle for community and unity and that makes the effort possible. Precisely this basic gift has its basis in the Easter event.

THE APOSTOLIC AGE

2. The Beginnings of the Church after Easter

"Now the multitude of believers was one heart and one soul. . . ." These are the words with which Luke begins his portrayal of the primitive church in Jerusalem (Acts 4:32). The Lukan picture of the primitive church is well known. It was gathered in Jerusalem; Luke says nothing about other locations. It was united under the leadership of the twelve apostles, it prayed in the Temple, it broke the bread of the Lord's Supper together, it had possessions in common, and it praised God (Acts 2:42-47; 4:32-37). At the same time, it is equally well known that this is a Lukan ideal. Luke had a theological interest in Jerusalem; the primitive church in Jerusalem represented the church's continuity with Israel. Primitive Christian communism is an ideal image, although it is not without some historical basis.[21] Equally idealistic is Luke's portrayal of the group of the twelve apostles. It is probable that the linkage of the Twelve and the apostles, at least in part originally two separate groups, had already taken place before Luke.[22] We know almost nothing of earliest Christianity outside Jerusalem, perhaps because Luke knew nothing about it, perhaps because he did not want to talk about it. In all probability there were followers of Jesus elsewhere, especially in Galilee. Luke says nothing about what happened to them. He tells only about the Jerusalemites — that is, about the followers of Jesus who stayed in Jerusalem or went there after Easter. Luke also says nothing about the so-called itinerant charismatics. According to his description, traveling and doing missionary work is the task

21. Acts 4:36-37 conveys an early report that was well remembered. Joseph Barnabas sold a field and gave the proceeds to the apostles. Acts 5:1-11 presupposes that members of the community made available to the community the proceeds of property they sold, but not necessarily all the proceeds. (The charge against Ananias and Sapphira was merely that they had lied.) The practice of Jesus (Mark 10:17-27; disciples are called to leave their profession) and the situation of the Jerusalem church (the Galilean disciples had no way of supporting themselves in Jerusalem) both make it likely that the practice of holding possessions in common was widespread (a communism of consumption, not of production).

22. The earliest text, 1 Cor. 15:5, 7, presupposes that the Twelve and the apostles were at least partially two different groups, but Rev. 21:14 and Mark 6:7 already assume that the Twelve were apostles.

of the apostles, to whom one might add the evangelist Philip. Only occasional notes such as Acts 11:19 or the figure of the prophet Agabus, who appears more than once (cf. Acts 11:27-28; 21:10), suggest that Luke may have known more than he said. Above all, the uniformity of primitive Christian preaching was a basic concept of Luke's portrayal. One sees that, for example, when the Lukan Paul's preaching to Jews follows the same pattern that underlay Peter's sermons to Jews.[23] Not until Paul preached to the Gentiles did he follow a different pattern (Acts 14:15-17; 17:22-31). It is the addressees rather than the person of Paul or of Peter who determine for Luke the content of the preaching.

Very likely, the reality was not quite like that. Gerd Theissen summarizes a brief survey of primitive Christianity: "Life in primitive Christianity was quite Protestant-like. Where two or three were together they formed a divergent minority. It was precisely because of these many groups that people projected the ideal of an original church unity."[24] Luke, but also John or the author of Ephesians, were among the New Testament authors at the end of the first century who projected such ideals as a counterpoint to a completely different reality.

We offer two theses: (1) *From the beginning there were in primitive Christianity tensions and diverging tendencies.* (2) *From the beginning one senses a very strong tendency, the goal of which was that the followers of Jesus stay together.*

Since we have little actual knowledge of the earliest period, we will confine ourselves to rather general considerations.

2.1. *Tensions and Divergences*

Beginning with Acts 6:1, Luke tells of the tensions in Jerusalem between the Greek-speaking Jewish followers of Jesus (the "Hellenists"), who presumably had immigrated from the Diaspora, and the Aramaic-speaking disciples. These tensions must have had their roots in, among other things, a different interpretation of Jesus' understanding of the Jewish Law, the Torah. The Hellenists around Stephen criticized the Temple, and their understanding of the Torah was freer than was that of the Aramaic-speaking Christians (Acts 6:11, 14; 7:48-53). For this reason they, and only they, were persecuted in Jerusalem,

23. Acts 13:16-41; cf., for example, Acts 2:14-41.

24. "Die Einheit der Kirche: Kohärenz und Differenz im Urchristentum," *ZMiss* 20 (1994): 71.

and after Stephen was murdered they left Jerusalem.[25] At a very early date, therefore, the different attitude toward the Torah was a question that divided the followers of Jesus. It may be that the law-free Gentile mission was first carried on by such Greek-speaking Jewish followers of Jesus from the Diaspora (Acts 11:20).

Nevertheless, from the very beginning there must also have been other tensions in primitive Christianity. Gerd Theissen has called our attention to the phenomenon of primitive Christian itinerant charismatics.[26] What we have here is nothing more than the reality that after Jesus' death the Jesus movement continued literally as a movement of itinerant preachers. One is not to be misled here by the reality that in later Christianity (at the latest since the Gospel of Mark) "following Jesus" became a concept that could also be used metaphorically for a life in the service of Christ. Initially "following Jesus" meant the continuation of Jesus' itinerant life in the service of proclaiming the kingdom of God. Undoubtedly there were problems here. Who took care of the wives and children of those who went away to follow Jesus? Who took care of the wandering charismatics who became sick and old? What authority did these itinerant messengers of Jesus have who often understood themselves as prophets (cf. Matt. 23:34) and who appeared in the churches as representatives of the risen Lord (cf. Matt. 10:40-42)? Most of the conflicts we read about in Galatians, Philippians, and 2 Corinthians are conflicts with Christian emissaries who came into the Pauline churches from elsewhere. Later, Diotrephes (3 John 9-10) or Luke (Acts 20:29) also had to deal with such emissaries.

First Corinthians 1:12-17 suggests another problem, one that will not have been an isolated case. Where missionaries or apostles appeared, congregations became attached to personalities. In Corinth the groups of Paul, of Apollos, of Peter (and the mysterious "group of Christ"?) confronted one another. Obviously the members of the church honored in a special way those who had converted and baptized them, even as they rejected claims made by others. Paul, who in Corinth was clearly aware that he worked in cooperation with others (1 Cor. 3:9-10), still could not keep from boasting of his special position as the church's "father" (1 Cor. 4:15). Without the special role the apostles played as the founders of churches, it would be impossible to con-

25. According to Acts 6:1–8:3, the twelve apostles are also regarded as residing in Jerusalem. They, too, remain there after Stephen's death. In Gal. 1:18-19 Paul also expects to find Cephas and possibly other apostles in Jerusalem.

26. Gerd Theissen, *Sociology of Early Palestinian Christianity*, trans. John Bowden (Philadelphia: Fortress, 1978); Gerd Theissen, *Die Jesusbewegung: Sozialgeschichte einer Revolution der Werte* (Gütersloh: Gütersloher Verlagshaus, 2004).

ceive of the fundamental importance they had in retrospect in the second, post-apostolic generation.

Cultural factors in different regions could lead to tensions. There was doubtless a cultural factor in the different ways the Torah was understood by the "Hellenists" from the Diaspora and the Aramaic-speaking followers of Jesus in Palestine in Acts 6. Obedience to the Torah was more vigorously discussed in the Diaspora, and its consequences, separation from the Gentiles, were more noticeable than they were in Israel's heartland. That could have had different effects. Many Jews in the Diaspora laid special emphasis on exact obedience to the Torah, because in so doing they underscored their difference from the Gentiles. Others were more interested in being assimilated. The message of Jesus, which emphasized the love command rather than ritual laws, was more accommodating to such tendencies. It joined forces with the need of many Hellenistic Jews for assimilation, and thus in Antioch, for example, it led temporarily to table fellowship between the Jewish and non-Jewish followers of Jesus. The need for this kind of table fellowship was certainly greater in Antioch, where the Jews belonged to an ethnic and religious minority, than it was in Jerusalem, where there were few non-Jews. Thus the different cultural situation led to tensions. Different still was the situation for the church in Rome, where in Paul's day the Jewish followers of Jesus were an ethnic minority not only in the city but also in the church. The different practices in, for example, the question of food regulations led to tensions and conflicts.

There were also other tension-causing issues that were present especially in the local church. I offer here only a few suggestions. Many tensions have social causes, such as, for example, the tensions between poor and rich in Corinth. One sees also conflict between generations. At issue in Matthew 10:34-37 is the struggle between young people and (non-Christian?) parents. In later texts it is more the case that the young people (that is, the second Christian generation) are exhorted to be obedient to their elders *(1 Clement)*. Frequently there is evidence of conflicts between charismatics and non-charismatics (1 Cor. 14; Matt. 7:15-23; Mark 13:21-23). The ancient saying of Galatians 3:28 ("There is neither Jew nor Greek, neither slave nor free, neither male nor female"), known throughout Pauline Christianity, also reveals something about the potentials for conflict within the Christian communities as well as in the larger society of the day. They are important for our theme. Since in all New Testament texts "community" has both a local and a trans-regional dimension, and since in many cases the difficulties are the same in the local churches and the church at large, we have to look at the local level as well when we speak about the "unity of the church" and the things that threaten it. It is only the thematic arrangement of this present work, and not the subject matter itself, that justified placing the emphasis primarily on the transregional, "ecumenical" sense.

Soon, then, tensions caused by *different understandings of Jesus Christ as the basic gift* were added to these more general tensions. It is amazing how early Jesus Christ, the foundation that all followers of Jesus had in common, began to divide them as well as unite them. What ultimately separated Paul from his opponents was not social or cultural causes of tension; it was the "other Jesus" (2 Cor. 11:4). Why that was the case probably has something to do with the fact that Jesus himself had made very strong and very binding claims, indeed exclusive claims for his proclamation and his person. Whether one stands or falls in the last judgment depends on one's attitude toward him (cf. Luke 12:8-9). "Whoever hears and does *my* words" — not, for example, the words of the Torah as the rabbis said in similar images — "has built his house on the rock" (Matt. 7:24-27). The belief that God raised Jesus from the dead means that God had said yes to the man Jesus. As soon became obvious, that led to a fundamentally new orientation of Jewish monotheism. That, however, was not initially clear. Only gradually did it become clear that Jesus of Nazareth, who wanted to call Israel back to God, had the potential to become the gravitational center of a new religion — a religion that would burst the boundaries of the Jewish people. Of course, precisely that was a controversial issue, as the first basic conflict of the nascent church demonstrates. It was a conflict over the church's relationship to Israel. Was it to be part of Israel or separate from Israel? (See below, section 4.) Ultimately, it was precisely the "basic gift," Jesus Christ, the one who kept his followers together, who became the reason for their separation.

2.2. *Unity-promoting Forces*

From the very beginning there was a strong sense of the church's solidarity in primitive Christianity. It is amazing, indeed quite rare, how much primitive Christianity understood itself from its inception as a unity. From the very beginning unity-promoting forces were in play — forces that at best have only limited analogies in comparable contemporary religions.[27] These forces are as follows:

27. James Dunn ("Instruments of Koinonia in the Early Church," *OiC* 25 [1989]: 206-11) makes a distinction between "sources" and "instruments" of church unity. His distinction is similar to our distinction between "basic gift" and "unity-promoting forces." Among his "sources" are the Spirit, the story of Jesus, and the connection to Israel, and among his "instruments" are sacraments, confessions, and episcopacy. In the third part of this book, Christian

1. *Baptism.* As far as we can see, everywhere in the earliest churches new converts were baptized. In baptism the Jesus movement possessed a special rite of initiation that was the same for all — men and women, Jews and non-Jews. Why did baptism exist, presumably from the very beginning, as an entrance ritual? That is a difficult question. Of course, baptism goes back to John the Baptist, but he and his followers did not understand it as a ritual of entrance into a particular movement. Jesus was baptized by John, but whether he himself also baptized is an open question. It is reported in no early Christian writing, with the exception of the Gospel of John (John 3:22, 26). The Gospel of John contains some quite old information precisely from Israel's South, from Jerusalem and Judea, where John was also active. Thus it is quite possible that it passed on here something that is historically accurate, yet the silence of all other New Testament writings is quite strange. We can make no more than a cautious supposition that Jesus also might have baptized at the beginning of his activity. We can only say with some certainty that some, but not all, of Jesus' followers came from the groups around John the Baptist (cf. John 1:35-42).

The post-Easter disciples of Jesus did not simply take over John's baptism without changes. What remained of it was its relationship to Israel: baptism is the seal of those who belong to the eschatological people of God (cf. 2 Cor. 1:22). By taking over John's baptism, the followers of Jesus claimed to be the people of God/Israel whom John called and Jesus gathered. Thus the general acceptance of baptism presupposed an awareness of being God's people. What was new was the relationship to the risen Lord, Jesus. Baptism took place everywhere in his name. In contrast to the baptism of John, Christian baptism was associated with what God in his grace had done through Jesus. In baptism his followers experienced the power of the risen Lord.

Why did baptism establish itself in the Jesus movement so quickly and so universally as a rite of initiation? Whether Jesus himself baptized remains uncertain, and no New Testament witness says that Jesus ordained baptism during his lifetime. I suspect that the sense of the young Jesus movement that in its meeting with Jesus it had experienced God in an impressive and life-altering way was so strong that it had to be expressed in a new and unique rite of initiation. This rite had a fundamental significance that bound all followers of Jesus to one another. It is noteworthy that early Christian baptism was

---

Link speaks more of "flash points" of unity than of "forces" (below, pp. 168-69). I can agree with that as long as "flash point" *(Brennpunkt)* does not mean merely an empirical field where the question of unity is especially urgent. It must also mean a "burning point" *(brennender Punkt)* that not only makes unity necessary but also leads to it.

valid *everywhere* and did not have to be — indeed could not be — repeated. When Christians moved to another place, they did not need to be baptized again, as was said to be the case in mystery religions.[28] Conversely, a second baptism was also inconceivable. If persons baptized once had apostatized or had seriously broken the obligations they had accepted when entering the Christian community, no second baptism was possible. In short, baptism was radical, transforming, and uniting.

2. *The Lord's Supper.* It is less surprising that the Lord's Supper was spread throughout the entire Jesus movement, since it comes from Jesus himself. In the "for many" of the cup saying (Mark 14:24) there is at least implicitly a reference to the entire church. The words of institution that were probably found everywhere and the *maranatha* cry (1 Cor. 16:22; cf. Rev. 22:20; *Didache* 10.6) suggest that other ritual elements of the Lord's Supper were also found everywhere. The ecumenical aspect of the Lord's Supper is emphasized already in early interpretations of the Lord's Supper. Paul says, "The bread which we break, is it not a fellowship of the body of Christ?" And he explains: "If there is *one* loaf, the many are *one* body, for we all partake of the *one* loaf" (1 Cor. 10:16-17). The eucharistic prayer of the *Didache* contains the petition that the church be gathered from the four winds into God's kingdom (*Didache* 10.5).

3. *The confession.* In 1 Corinthians 15:3 Paul introduces his quotation of an early Christ confession with the words: "I delivered to you first of all what I also received." For him the confession is the basis for speaking to the Corinthian church about the common Christian belief in the future resurrection. It is a confession Paul has received. It is suggested in current scholarship — correctly, in my judgment — that we are to look for the origin of this confession in Palestine, since it is for Paul an expression of the faith he shares with the first apostles (cf. 1 Cor. 15:11). In any case, the text makes clear that there were confessional texts very early in the church. As a common basis of faith they have a uniting function. Also, at the beginning of Romans, the apostle Paul — personally unknown to the Roman church and perhaps a not uncontroversial figure — introduces himself with a Christ confession in order to establish the common basis of faith between him and the church (Rom. 1:3-4).

Of course, it is obvious in the New Testament that these early confessional formulas are worded quite differently. There is not *one* confession; there are many confessions, and in quite different ways they emphasize quite

28. Apuleius (*Metamorphoses* 11.27-29) states that the devotees of the Isis mysteries had to be initiated anew whenever they moved to a new location.

different aspects of Jesus' significance. There are no reasons to conclude, however, that there was ever a Christianity without enunciated confessions. They all point to the *one* Jesus Christ, but they do so in multiple ways. Both are important — the number of confessions that have been preserved and their common reference to the risen Lord Jesus. Both show that it was not the confessions themselves that bound the early Christians together; it was he to whom they point.

4. *The mission.* An unknown number of Jesus' followers continued his itinerant lifestyle, traveling without possessions throughout the land of Israel and proclaiming the kingdom of God with authority. The various forms of the sending discourse (Matt. 10:5-42; Mark 6:7-11; Q [= Luke] 10:2-16), with their tradition-historical antecedents, give us a glimpse of their life and their problems. Initially these wandering messengers of Jesus continued his mission in Israel. They viewed themselves as a movement in, not alongside, Israel (cf. Matt. 10:5-6, 23; 23:34-36, 37-39). Early on, however, they must have also taken on an important "inner-church" function: their preaching resulted in settled communities. The itinerant missionaries went out from and returned to these communities, and they were answerable to the communities as prophets and teachers. The Sayings Source Q[29] is full of the traditions of such itinerant prophets, but it also contains texts that reflect the problems of settled communities, and in the form in which it can be reconstructed today it most certainly was composed in such a community. It shows in an exemplary way how itinerant prophets and settled communities lived together. Especially in Palestine these itinerant prophets who moved from community to community must have played an important role in developing the consciousness of being part of the "whole church." They shared traditions and news with the communities. They provided contact among the communities. They created in the communities the awareness that they were part of a larger movement, the "whole church."

Already the sending discourse of the Sayings Source enunciated the principle that the worker is worthy of his pay (Q 10:7). This principle is quite old; obviously it was valid everywhere in the church. Paul presumes it, even when he forgoes the right of support for himself and Barnabas (1 Cor. 9:4-18) and must defend himself against the charge of not having done the same with others (2 Cor. 11:7). The significance of this right to be supported was that therein the communities acknowledged the itinerant missionaries as their "workers" for whom they had an obligation. With this support they assumed

29. Matthew and Luke probably used the Sayings Source Q as a source. It is generally cited as Q with Luke's chapter and verse numbers.

an element of "whole church" responsibility for the mission and for those who carried it out. They took their place in the whole of the Jesus movement. It is not unimportant that for one thing this becomes conspicuous in their physical support.

Our discussion of the itinerant charismatics showed that the communities understood mission as a joint task. Paul's life and missionary work make the same thing clear. What is noticeable right away about the apostolic council in Jerusalem (Gal. 2:1-10; Acts 15) is that those present had to come to an agreement about mission and that they were able to do so. That may appear to us to be self-evident, but in the context of ancient religions it is by no means a given. Seldom are ancient cults aware of a transregional missionary connection. Why should a Serapis devotee in Egypt care what happened with his god when he was proclaimed in the streets of Corinth? One *had* to come to an understanding about the Lord Jesus, however, because the fact that there was only *one* Lord had consequences for the church. Thus the Gentile mission, wherever it was affirmed as the common task of the church, became a unity-promoting force. At first it relied on the existence of the Jewish Diaspora; increasingly it became independent of it.

5. *Tradition.* Well before the post-apostolic age, the reference to the common Jesus tradition bound all the communities together. One can see that already in the earliest period. The earliest Christ confessions are crystallization points of the tradition. One can see that well in the confession of 1 Corinthians 15:3-5 that was shared by Paul and the Jerusalem apostles. It is like a short version of the passion and Easter narrative. Or, inversely, the passion and Easter story narrates and develops this confession. Thus Paul also knows about the night "in which Jesus was betrayed" (1 Cor. 11:23).

In the process of its development, the Sayings Source shows that the communities' body of tradition was continually expanded. There is also a long process of gathering traditions behind the Gospel of Mark. Local traditions became common property. The community in which the Gospel of Mark originated was not located in Palestine, yet it is clear that there must have been an exchange of traditions between it and the representatives of the Sayings Source. Otherwise we would not be able to explain the things that the beginnings of the Sayings Source and the Gospel of Mark have in common: the appearance and preaching of the Baptist, Jesus' baptism, the temptation, and a programmatic proclamation of Jesus (Mark 1:2-15; Q [= Luke] 3:1-4, 13; 6:20-49). We see such contacts elsewhere as well. One can compare, for example, the Sending Discourse of Q (= Luke) 10:2-16 and Mark 6:7-13. In my judgment the structure of the Gospel of John is not understandable without assuming that the Johannine community in some form knew about the Gospel of Mark or about all the Synoptic Gospels. In short, Jesus traditions are *common* traditions. They were not only collected; they were also exchanged and passed on. From the very beginning the church was constituted by a *common* tradition. One sees it also in the area of worship — for example, in the early and widespread use of the *abba* cry or the Lord's Prayer.

6. *The apostles.* An apostle is a person appointed and sent by the risen Lord (1 Cor. 15:7), who with his authority represents the Lord himself. In our context it is important to observe that an apostle exercises the Lord's authority in the entire church. We can see that clearly in the case of Paul but also with Peter and even with James, the Lord's brother, who was an authority in the entire church even though he scarcely left Jerusalem. The three "pillars" (Gal. 2:9), presumably the innermost circle of apostles, understood their ministry as a church-wide ministry. They were the decisive "bearers" of the church, God's temple or edifice. In any case, it is noteworthy that from the very beginning there was in Jesus' communities a whole-church ministry, although the functions, tasks, and charismatic gifts could be quite different in the individual communities. As "apostles of Jesus Christ," the apostles represent Christ, the basic gift of unity for the *whole* church.

7. *Jerusalem.* I speak with hesitation of Jerusalem's significance for the entire church, for here we enter a controversial area.[30] Indeed, there may not even have been agreement about it in primitive Christianity. That Jerusalem was important for the Jerusalem church and its representatives is clear. The Jewish Christians regarded Jerusalem as the center of the people of God, of whom they understood themselves to be the nucleus. Think of the testimony of people who were not particularly interested in Jerusalem: Two years after his conversion Paul went to Jerusalem to see Peter, and he expected to meet other apostles there as well (Gal. 1:18). Later, on at least two occasions, Paul went to Jerusalem at important points in his life (Gal. 2:1-10; Rom. 15:25, 31). He has "fulfilled the gospel of Christ *from Jerusalem* and around into Illyricum" (Rom. 15:19). The Gentile Christian Luke is of the opinion that the mission of the church extends from Jerusalem unto the ends of the world (Luke 24:47; Acts 1:8). Thus on this point he is a faithful Paulinist. In various

30. Since Karl Holl's article ("Der Kirchenbegriff des Paulus in seinem Verhältnis zu dem der Urgemeinde," in Holl, *Gesammelte Aufsätze zur Kirchengeschichte,* vol. 2: *Der Osten* [Darmstadt: Wissenschaftliche Buchgesellschaft, 1964], pp. 44-67), the thesis of Jerusalem as the "presiding capital" [*Vorort*] of primitive Christianity has been a constant part of the discussion. He claimed that Paul broke with the juridical claim of this center. I prefer the thesis that Jerusalem was a "spiritual presiding capital" with which Paul in no way could have broken, nor did he want to. Did the Jerusalem church understand itself to be the center of the entire church, which for it was the *ekklesia tou theou,* the "assembly of God"?

areas of early Christianity one finds the concept of the eschatological church as a heavenly Jerusalem (Paul, Hebrews, Revelation). Is it only in the memory of John the Seer that the heavenly Jerusalem bears the names of the twelve apostles on its gates (Rev. 21:14)? Or do we have here something of the knowledge that the earthly church and the earthly apostles were associated with the earthly Jerusalem? It seems to me that the entire early church knew of the significance of Jerusalem for the church, even if it was interpreted in quite different ways.

In most of these factors we discover the two fundamental points of the church's unity that we already noticed in the Twelve and in Jesus' circle of disciples: (1) the reference to Jesus, who made the community of disciples possible and who in the Easter experiences became the permanent basic gift of the church's fellowship — and the related point, (2) the reference to the people of Israel for whom Jesus proclaimed the kingdom of God and whose God according to the Easter confession had permanently and definitively allied himself with Jesus.

We summarize: since the early beginnings of Christianity one can see on quite different levels that the church at large is something real. It is by no means simply an idea that bound together local churches and Jesus groups. From the very beginning the common basis, Jesus, and the common horizon, Israel, determined that the earliest Christianity would become something different from other religions. From the very beginning the sense of belonging together and the lived ecumenical fellowship were constitutive. The centrifugal tendencies that exist in every religious movement were opposed from the very beginning by such strong centripetal forces that the church was never able to develop merely as a group of local churches existing side by side. It always struggled for solidarity and community. From the very beginning there was *the* whole church as a lived fellowship in a multiplicity of expressions.

The picture we have sketched here needs clarification. When we look at the centrifugal and centripetal forces at work in the earliest church, it might appear that it was primarily cultural, social, or socio-psychological factors that led to tensions in the church, while it was primarily the basic gift bestowed on the church — that is, Jesus Christ himself as he was experienced in preaching, in baptism and the Lord's Supper, by means of the figure of the apostles, etc. — that created community. Yet the view that "here are people, who cause division, there is God who brings them together" is too simple to be true.

Jesus Christ is at work as the basic gift in the centrifugal as well as in the centripetal impulses in early Christianity. One can see that, for example, in the conflicts in Galatia and in Corinth. There it was the conviction that the opponents proclaimed "another Jesus" that led to Paul's separation from them, and presumably the opposite was also true. A differing interpretation of Christ, the basic gift, was combined here with differing cultural and religious presuppositions and led to division. The role of the apostles is also ambivalent. On the one hand, they are people commissioned by the risen Christ for the entire church, and as such they are one of the strongest cohesive factors of the earliest period. On the other hand, they too interpreted Christ in differing ways and had at their disposal differing charismatic abilities. In addition, there were varying degrees of intensity in their relationship with the members of the community. First Corinthians 1:10-14 shows that they, too, could become the reason for divisions. In all these cases the unifying and at the same time dividing basic gift, Christ, and differing cultural, socio-psychological, and social factors work together. Thus it cannot be the case that "human" dissonance factors are played off against theological coherence factors. It is more the case that we are to think of the effectiveness of the basic gift Jesus Christ *in* human reality.

3. The Beginnings of Ecclesiology

There was also quite early a whole-church consciousness, something like a *rudimentary whole-church ecclesiology.* Of course, we learn very little from this early period.

The likely earliest self-designations of the followers of Jesus provide little information about a whole-church ecclesiology. One thinks here first of the self-designation *disciples of Jesus* that was important in various areas of earliest Christianity (Synoptic Gospels, John, Acts). One can at most indirectly derive a whole-church self-understanding from the term. The situation is similar with the expression *the chosen,* which is usually used in an attributive or predicate sense but can also be a name the Christians used for themselves (Mark 13:22, 27; Rom. 8:33; Rev. 17:14). Its roots lie in Israel's self-designation as the people of God. Much more widespread is the self-designation of the earliest Christians as *holy ones* (saints), which is found especially in Paul but may also have had earlier roots (cf. Acts 9:13, 32; 2 Cor. 8:4; 9:1; Revelation). The term expresses that one belongs to God. It does not explicitly call attention to Israel.

It is different, however, with the word *ekklesia,* the most important self-designation in the ancient church. It appears in almost the entire New Testament, especially in Acts, in the Pauline and deutero-Pauline letters, and in Revelation. In most of the places — especially in Paul, in Acts, and in Revelation — the word refers to a local church. In profane Greek *ekklesia* means the popular assembly that could be found in most free cities. One can still see something of the concrete meaning "assembly" in several, primarily Pauline, texts (e.g., 1 Cor. 11:18; 14:23, 34-35; Matt. 18:18). At the same time there are a number of texts in the New Testament where *ekklesia* clearly refers to the entire church and not a local assembly (Matt. 16:18; Acts 20:28; cf. 9:31; Col. 1:18, 24; nine times in Ephesians; 1 Tim. 3:15; Heb. 12:23). This use of the word cannot be related to the popular city assemblies. In addition one finds, especially in Paul, the expression *ekklesia tou theou,* occasionally when he speaks of the churches in Judea or Jerusalem (e.g., 1 Cor. 15:9; Gal. 1:13; 1 Thess. 2:14), but also other places where the apostle wants to emphasize that the local church belongs *to God* (e.g., 1 Cor. 1:2; 11:16, 22). In these texts, too, the idea of the popular assembly does not adequately explain the term. Instead, we should remember that in the Greek Bible *ekklesia* is one of the words used to translate the Hebrew *qahal* (= assembly), which is usually used for the assembly of the people of Israel. One also finds in the Greek Bible "assembly of the Lord" and "assembly of the Highest" but not "assembly of God," a term with which several texts from Qumran are familiar.

When we survey all the evidence, it becomes clear that in its meaning the word *ekklesia* resembles an ellipse with two focal points. On the one hand, it evokes biblical associations. The assembly of the nation Israel, the assembly of God, is behind the word. From the perspective of this focal point it is understandable that the word can be used for the entire church. On the other hand, it evokes associations with the popular assemblies of ancient cities. From the perspective of this focal point it is understandable why a local church is so often referred to as *ekklesia.* The meaning of *ekklesia* appears to oscillate back and forth between the two focal points. First one, then the other is more strongly emphasized. Often there is at least the connotation of both meanings.

It is therefore difficult to decide how to translate the word *ekklesia.* It is no accident that thus far I have simply used the Greek word. The Reformers translated it consistently as *gmeynd* (Zwingli) or *Gemeine* (Luther) (= Congregation). That was an innovation over the Vulgate, which had rendered it as *ecclesia,* but it does not do justice to the whole-church "focal point" in the word's ellipse. The Revised Standard Version of 1961 translates it sometimes as "congregation," sometimes as "church." However, that obscures the fact that it is always the same word. The New Revised Standard Version of 1989 translates it consistently as "church," but then one loses the sense that in many places the individual community, and often the concrete congregational assembly, is meant.[31]

What is probably decisive, however, is that both nuances of meaning belong together quite early. The *ekklesia* is a concrete fellowship gathered in one place that is also *God's* assembly and as such part of the whole church. Or, conversely, the church is the people of God but always manifest in a concrete local community.

This semantic discussion is important for the question of the unity of the church. Based on the linguistic evidence of the entire New Testament, one can say first of all that in every individual church the entire church is, so to speak, included. Every individual church, wherever it meets, is part of *God's ekklesia,* the "assembly of God" called by God that is gathered not only in a particular place but "with all who in every place call on the name of our Lord Jesus Christ" (1 Cor. 1:2). In its essence the church is concrete-local *and* ecumenical-universal. Second, one can say that the unity of the local assemblies consists in the reality that each one gathers up and carries on Israel's heritage. The local churches belong to the assembly of God that has found its historical form in the people of Israel. Stated concisely: the unity of the local churches lies first of all in the reality that they are Israel, or at least a part of Israel.[32]

Related to the designation *ekklesia* is the understanding of the church as *God's Temple.* In contrast to the designation *ekklesia,* we are dealing here with a metaphor that never became a direct designation of the church. The metaphor of the church as an "edifice" or "temple" is common in the New Testament (Matt. 16:18; 1 Cor. 3:10-17; 2 Cor. 5:16; Eph. 2:20-22; 1 Tim. 3:15; Heb. 3:1-6; 1 Pet. 2:4-9; Rev. 3:12). It is probably quite old. I think it is related to the designation of the three principal apostles, Peter, John, and James, as "pillars." They are "pillars" of the "temple" that is the church (Gal. 2:9). If that is correct, this metaphor comes from the earliest period. It probably also signifies the whole church and, as corresponding parallels from the Qumran texts show, also has its roots in the concept of the people of God.

31. For this reason our working group has settled on *Kirche* ("church") or *Ortskirche* ("local church") or *Gesamtkirche* ("whole/entire church"), whereby *Kirche* expresses the semantic (and substantive!) unity of both ideas and *Orts-* or *Gesamt-* expresses the sphere or extent that is meant. Cf. Kurt Stalder, "Die Einheit der Kirche in den Lokalkirchen," in Stalder, *Die Wirklichkeit Christi erfahren* (Zurich: Benziger, 1984), p. 111. [The careful reader will be aware that the problem is no less severe for the English translator. For *Gemeinde* one can use "church," "local church," "congregation," or "community." — Trans.]

32. This systematic arrangement of the systemic usage of *ekklesia* in the New Testament is not in the strict sense historical. Most New Testament authors will not have been aware of it.

Finally, it is probable that the metaphorical designation of the church as the "body of Christ," a concept Paul presupposes in his letters to the Corinthian church, originated in the Hellenistic sphere.[33] Properly speaking, this metaphor applies only to the whole church. It is not conceivable that Christ would have had separate bodies in the various churches such as in Corinth or in Rome. That is all the more probable if behind this metaphor is the concept of a cosmic body — for example, of the body of Zeus or of the body of the universe — an idea with which Philo also appears to be familiar. That the church is Christ's body emphasizes above all the close connection between the church and the risen and exalted Lord. It also underscores its own solidarity in one body. Paul will use this metaphor for the individual local churches when he develops it further (1 Cor. 12:12-31; Rom. 12:3-8).[34]

In summary: there were probably numerous designations for the church in the early period that were theologically important. They emphasized that the Christ fellowship belongs to Christ ("body of Christ," "disciples"), or they allied the Christ fellowship with the people of God/Israel ("temple," "assembly," perhaps "chosen"). Those are precisely the two dimensions we discovered in the "centripetal" forces of the Christ movement.[35] If that is correct, then with his own usage of "body" and "assembly" Paul applies what one might call congregational accents. The reality of the body of Christ must be shown in the individual local church. The individual local church — as it meets, for example, in Corinth — is "God's assembly" in the full sense of the word. But in no sense did Paul deny the reality of the whole church with these accents. His entire life's work will make that clear. But with that observation we have anticipated later discussions.

4. The First Basic Conflict: The Church's Unity with Israel

A Christian Gentile mission arose quite early that did not require circumcision. Dispensing with circumcision in this way was unusual, but it was still conceivable in Judaism of that day. In those days one could at least debate the question whether one should actually require Gentile converts to be circum-

33. One sees that in 1 Cor. 1:13; 6:15; 10:17.

34. Cf. below, pp. 79-80. On my view of the "body of Christ," cf. the brief excursus in Ulrich Luz, "Der Brief an die Epheser," in Jürgen Becker and Ulrich Luz, *Die Briefe an die Galater, Epheser und Kolosser,* NTD 8, no. 1 (Göttingen: Vandenhoeck & Ruprecht, 1998), pp. 126-30.

35. Cf. above, pp. 53-54.

cised.[36] The "god-fearing" Gentiles who participated in the synagogue service as uncircumcised persons were not yet unanimously rejected as part of the people of God as they were by the later rabbis. Jesus' critical attitude toward the ritual law and his openness toward individual Gentiles (cf. Matt. 8:5-10, 13; Mark 7:24-30) may have eased this move to the Gentiles. Still, it was felt to be an innovation, and it was expressly legitimated by a special word of Jesus (e.g., Matt. 28:16-20) or by an intervention by the Holy Spirit (Acts 8:26-39; 10:1-11, 18; 15:8). For his legitimacy Paul appealed to the commission he had received from God in his revelation near Damascus (Gal. 1:16).

This development forced the church to ask whether it could still maintain its understanding of itself as the core of the eschatological people of God/Israel. What position did the Gentiles hold in this people of God? Further, the addition of uncircumcised Gentiles to this core tarnished the Jesus communities in the eyes of that part of Israel which did not believe in him. In Jerusalem, Stephen's lynching because of his criticism of the Torah further complicated this relationship. The success of the Gentile mission must have had negative consequences for the mission to Israel.

The Gentile mission led to the first fundamental conflict that shook the Christian church and threatened its unity. This conflict came to a head primarily in the person and work of Paul.

4.1. The Apostolic Council

In Galatians 1:11-12 Paul understood his law-free gospel as something mediated to him not from humans but through a revelation from God. What did he do after receiving this revelation? According to the Lukan report of Acts 9:10-25, he joined himself to the community of Christians in Damascus. Galatians 1 says this only indirectly (v. 17), but it makes clear that he was conscious of belonging to the church of God he had previously persecuted. Thus the revelation of the Son to him made Paul not the founder of a religion but a member of the church. After two years he went to Jerusalem and made contact with Peter and James. In 1 Corinthians 15:1-11 he says the same thing with a different emphasis. Paul's concern here is to show that the gospel he had re-

36. One can see that, for example, in Josephus's report (*Antiquities* 20.38-48) of the discussion about the circumcision of Prince Izates, but the discussion between Rabbi Joshua and other rabbis, transmitted in *b. Yebamoth* 49a, shows that circumcision was always regarded as the normal ritual of entrance for male proselytes. Louis H. Feldmann (*Jew and Gentile in the Ancient World* [Princeton: Princeton University Press, 1933], pp. 348-56) offers many positive Jewish opinions about god-fearers from Hellenistic and Palestinian early Judaism.

ceived as tradition was identical with that of the original apostles. The revelation to Paul appears here also (1 Cor. 15:8), but it does not have the fundamental importance Galatians 1 has. It is obviously important for Paul that the gospel revealed to him is the same as that of the Jerusalem apostles. Jesus, who revealed himself to Paul from heaven, is none other than the earthly Jesus about whom the disciples in Jerusalem spoke. It is thus the revelation of the Son that brought Paul to the church and its tradition.

Fourteen years later the "council" in Jerusalem took place, about which Paul reports in Galatians 2:1-10 and Luke in Acts 15:1-11.[37] There was an open conflict between the representatives of the law-free Gentile mission and parts of Jewish Christianity. The unity of the church was threatening to come unraveled. The main issue in Jerusalem was whether one could dispense with circumcision for the Gentiles who believed in Christ. The question was vital for Paul, for on it was determined whether Christ alone saved people. He was opposed by Jewish Christians whom he disparages as "false brothers brought in secretly" (Gal. 2:4) and whom Luke makes marginal by referring to them as "some believers from the party of the Pharisees" (Acts 15:5). In today's scholarship they are often called, again in a disparaging sense, "Judaizers." Since we do not want to join history's winners in this negative labeling, we will use the neutral term "radical Jewish Christians." The circumcision question was just as vital for them, for it determined whether the church really was the eschatological people of God/Israel in the way that Jesus understood it. For Paul's Jewish Christian opponents, the Pauline gospel of the Gentile mission's freedom from the law made it impossible to understand the church as a church *in* and therefore *for* Israel. For Paul, however, that understanding of the church and the understanding of Israel lying behind it destroyed his gospel of God's unconditional grace in Christ. The Gentiles were still free to join the people of God/Israel by means of circumcision; for that Christ was not necessary.

Between Paul and the radical Jewish Christians there were the "pillars" (Gal. 2:9). These leaders of the Jerusalem church were also Torah faithful, but they were more liberal. They were James, the brother of the Lord; Peter; and John, the son of Zebedee. We will describe their theological positions later.

The upshot of the deliberations was that Paul and Barnabas came to an agreement with the Jerusalem "pillars," and that the Jewish Christian brothers, who demanded that Gentiles be circumcised, were not able to prevail. We can no longer know for sure why the decision went against them. For Paul, it

37. I proceed from the "normal hypothesis" that both texts refer to the same event, although that view is not uncontested in recent scholarship.

was obviously because they required for salvation a condition alongside Christ, and that made Christ superfluous. It would be interesting to know whether the "pillars" shared this view. Subsequent history does show that the conflict continued. Obviously many problems remained unsolved, and it is difficult to say whether both parties understood the unity they had achieved in the same way.

Paul's account in Galatians 2:1-10 leaves a number of questions open. He emphasizes his independence: he went to Jerusalem because of a revelation; he was, therefore, not summoned to give an account of himself to higher authorities. For him the meeting was a conversation between equal partners. But is that really what it was? It is noteworthy that the negotiations took place not in Antioch, where the problem was acute, but in Jerusalem. Paul feared that he was "running or had run in vain" (Gal. 2:2). In what sense did the truth of his gospel depend for him on the approval of the people in Jerusalem? He submitted his gospel to the opinion of the Jerusalem authorities (verse 2), not vice versa. "Even Titus was not compelled to be circumcised" (verse 3). Could the "pillars" have compelled him? Verse 6 is quite unclear, since Paul does not finish the sentence he had begun. Did he originally want to say that nothing had been imposed on him by "those who were reputed to be something"? It is then clear again in verse 9 that the "pillars" gave Paul and Barnabas the right hand of fellowship — thus that the two partners did not shake hands with one another. It is further noteworthy that verse 8 mentions Peter's apostleship but not that of Paul. And, finally, in verse 10, the collection for the poor is indeed an imposition of sorts. It moves in only one direction, from the Gentile churches to Jerusalem. It is, of course, questionable whether one can really make use of all these observations, but a certain asymmetry of the two conversation partners does show through the Pauline account against his best intention. Do we see here on the two sides different understandings of the church and church unity?[38]

We will try to ask both conversation partners how they understood church, church unity, and the church's relationship to Israel. Admittedly, that will be much more difficult with James, since we can approach him only indirectly.

38. All of these observations show that Karl Holl's thesis of Jerusalem as the church's presiding capital (above, n. 30) is not a mere fabrication. Martin Hengel ("Jakobus der Herrenbruder — der erste Papst?" in Hengel, *Paulus und Jakobus: Kleine Schriften* 3, WUNT 141 [Tübingen: Mohr/Siebeck, 2002], p. 567) accepts it.

4.2. *James and the Church's Unity with Israel (by Christoph Knoch)*

Unfortunately we do not have a letter written by James the brother of the Lord; the Epistle of James was not written until late in the first century A.D. Thus we must depend on the scarce information in the letters of Paul, in Acts, in the Jewish historian Flavius Josephus (A.D. 37 to circa A.D. 100) and in the church fathers. In spite of this precarious situation with the sources, we can still try to describe him and his idea of church unity.

In the western Christianity influenced by Paul, James quickly lost his initial important and influential position in favor of Peter, who, like Paul, was martyred in Rome. Yet the leader of the church in Jerusalem was long remembered in the Jewish Christianity of the East. One sees that in the canonical Epistle of James as well as in further apocryphal writings written under his name.[39] The oldest extant liturgy of the Orthodox Church, which remained active especially in Jerusalem, was named after him: "the Liturgy of James." The fact that in many Eastern biblical manuscripts the Epistle of James appears before Paul's letters also shows the esteem in which he was held in the East.

All of the sources agree that James was faithful to the Torah and to the traditions of the fathers. It was self-evident for him, who lived in Jerusalem, the center of Judaism, that one was to obey the food commandments and to keep the festivals. We can see that, for one thing, in his attitude in the conflict in Antioch: Peter and the Jewish Christian part of the church break off the table fellowship with the Gentile Christians when "people from James" come (Gal. 2:12). For another, it is confirmed by the role Luke gives him in Acts: the regulation that Gentile Christians should eat only meat that has been ritually slaughtered (Acts 15:19) comes from him. The Syrian Hegesippus (circa A.D. 115-185) also gives a detailed and fanciful description of his faithfulness to the Torah.[40] Finally, his surname, "the Just/Righteous," which appears in all the texts, is an important indication of the way he lived. It is given him already in the *Gospel of Thomas:* "Jesus said to them, 'Wherever you are, you are to go to James the Righteous, for whose sake heaven and earth came into being'" (logion 12). In much the same way that the surname Cephas (= the Rock, cf. Matt. 16:18) was to invest Simon with special authority, the Jesus saying from the *Gospel of Thomas* legitimates the authority of James, which continued to be influential in Jewish Christianity for many years. He was able to stay in Jerusalem for such a long time only because he was faithful to the Torah. Still,

39. Cf. the so-called *Protoevangelium of James,* the two apocalypses of James, and the so-called *Epistle of James* from Nag Hammadi.

40. Eusebius, *Historia ecclesiastica* 2.23.

that Paul's companion Titus did not have to be circumcised (Gal. 2:3) indicates that the Jerusalem "pillars" did not require Gentile Christians to be circumcised. That shows that James also had a more open understanding of the people of God than did Paul's opponents in Galatia who required circumcision (Gal. 4:10; 5:2-3).

James was able to stay in Jerusalem for more than twenty years, although the people associated with Stephen had to flee from the city much earlier because of their critical attitude toward the Torah (cf. Acts 6:14). Several years later Peter suffered the same fate (Acts 12:17). In the decade of the 60s of the first century A.D., the situation in Jerusalem became polarized. The latitude allowed to the messianic believers associated with James was increasingly limited. Eventually the Sanhedrin, the majority of whose members were Sadducees, sentenced the Lord's brother to death for violating the law, and, as Flavius Josephus reports,[41] he was executed in A.D. 62. James, however, was not the only person who suffered this fate. Since the "most zealous observers of the Law," that is, Pharisees, complained to the new governor about the executions, they cannot have regarded James as an opponent. Probably soon after his death, the Jerusalem church fled from Jerusalem, thus destroying a bridge to Judaism's majority that James had built with his faithful observance of the Torah.

How did James understand the unity of the church? One can still hear his voice indirectly through Paul's letters. We must try to open a way to his understanding of the church from his behavior. We can try to confirm from later witnesses what we surmise from the Pauline letters. It is clear that for James Jerusalem was the center not only of the people of God/Israel but also of the disciples of Jesus. We never hear that he left the holy city. From that we may probably conclude that for him the Jesus community was not a group alongside Israel but a group *in* Israel. In all probability, for him — just as presumably for Jesus himself — the disciples of Jesus were the nucleus of the eschatological, reconstituted twelve tribes of Israel. It was obvious for him that the Torah, as interpreted by Jesus, continued to be valid for the disciples of Jesus. That is why James demanded that the Jewish Christians in Antioch avoid eating with Gentile Christians. That probably meant for him that they were thus to observe the food commandments.[42] Peter, Barnabas, and the Jewish Christians of Antioch were "carried away" by his argument (Gal. 2:12-14). That makes sense

41. *Antiquities* 20.200.

42. In that day, table fellowship with Gentiles was possible for Jews only when they could eat their own kosher food (cf. *Epistle of Aristeas* 182; *Judith* 12.19; *Joseph and Asenath* 7.1). According to the stricter opinion advocated in *Jubilees* 22.16; Acts 10:28; 11:3; and later by most rabbis, table fellowship with Gentiles was to be completely avoided (cf. Str-B vol. 4, pp. 375-78).

only if the "men from James" of Galatians 2:12 actually spoke with the authority of the brother of the Lord. Yet Paul does not criticize James, the brother of the Lord. He accepts his decision and accuses only Peter and Barnabas who to that point had engaged in table fellowship without any difficulties.

Later witnesses confirm this picture, although they mirror only partially and indirectly the "historical James." The most important thing for us from the canonical Epistle of James is the opening line: "James, a servant of God and of the Lord Jesus Christ, to the twelve tribes of the Dispersion: Greeting" (Jas. 1:1). Thus there must have been a group within early Christianity that started from the idea of the gathering of the twelve scattered tribes into a reconstituted Israel and claimed for this the authority of the Lord's brother. One also sees this conception clearly in Luke, who attributed it to James. In Acts 15:16-17 he lets James quote the word from Amos about rebuilding the fallen tent of David, and in so doing he certainly does not misrepresent James's attitude.

A final important area with regard to James's concept of the church is the question of circumcision. Doubtless for Jewish Christians he continued to practice circumcision as the Jewish sign of the covenant. About the circumcision of Gentile Christians, however, the opinions are divided. There were three possible answers.

1. Israel is open to Gentiles, but all Gentiles who want to join the Jesus group and thus Israel must be circumcised and then also keep the commandments of the Torah. According to Galatians 5:2-3, this was the position of Paul's opponents in Galatians, the "radical Jewish Christians." Thus their understanding of the church is tantamount to identifying the church with the people of God/Israel. The church is nothing more than the true Israel called by God through Jesus in the end-time. This answer probably comes the closest to representing the view of Jesus himself.

2. Paul has the most open attitude. Not only does he never require circumcision of the Gentiles; he actually forbids it (Gal. 5:2). At the same time, all of the Torah's regulations are invalid for the Galatians with the exception of fundamental moral laws such as those of the Decalogue. According to Galatians, the entire Torah is fulfilled "in one word" — the commandment to love one's neighbor (Gal. 5:14). That is "the law of Christ" (Gal. 6:2). Although this answer accepts a concern of Jesus, it changes it and makes it more fundamental. Israel's openness becomes the fundamental universalism of the Christian church.

3. James and the people of Jerusalem probably take a middle position. Gentile Christians do not have to be circumcised, but they must observe part of the Torah (at least the food commandments in the common meals). That

follows from the demand of James's people in the conflict in Antioch (Gal. 2:12). Gentile Christians belong to the people of God even without circumcision. We see that when we read Galatians 2:3 and 2:12 together: Titus does not have to be circumcised, but he is still accepted into the Jerusalem church.

How are we to understand this liberal position? Wherever there were synagogues there were god-fearing Gentiles *(sebomenoi),* who observed the entire Torah of Moses but who nevertheless were not circumcised. In the view of most people in later rabbinic Judaism, they did not belong to the people of God. As we have seen, the situation was somewhat more open in the earlier period.[43] James and the "pillars" probably regarded the uncircumcised Gentile Christians as full members of God's people that had been gathered from the Dispersion. Otherwise they could not have received Paul with the right hand of fellowship (Gal. 2:9). James was "a man with a balanced position who attempted to maintain the unity of the messianic community of Jesus."[44] His answer is a middle solution that, although it remains relatively close to Jesus', takes into account the changed circumstances, namely, the unforeseeable and successful Gentile mission.

In summary: James understands "church" as the people of God newly gathered in the end-time by the message of Jesus. For him it consists of two concentric circles. First of all, there is Israel proper, the winning of whom is the task of the "apostleship to the circumcised" (Gal. 2:8), given especially to Peter. The second circle is made up of the god-fearing Gentiles whom Paul is to win for the people of God. James may be thinking here in terms of prophecies (Isaiah 2), and he sees the place of these Gentiles within the eschatological people of God/Israel. For this reason they are to keep parts of the Torah of Moses. Thus the unity of the church is possible only as a unity *within* Israel.

4.3. *Paul and the Church's Unity with Israel*

It is easier to understand Paul's concern than it is to understand James's, since we can trace it through all his letters. Even here, however, there are great difficulties. For one thing, it appears that his attitude toward Israel was not always the same. In 1 Thessalonians 2:14-16, the Israel that does not believe in Jesus is declared to be the enemy of Jesus, of the prophets, of God, and of people in general. It is an Israel that stands under God's final judgment. This statement

43. See above, n. 36.
44. Hengel, "Herrenbruder," p. 570.

even makes use of ancient anti-Semitic motifs. According to Galatians 4:21-31, only the church corresponds to the heavenly Israel and the promise of Abraham. Israel, by contrast, is identified not only with the earthly Jerusalem but also with Hagar's descendents in a way that turns the biblical texts upside down. In Galatians 6:16, the church — and only the church — is regarded as "God's Israel."[45] According to Romans 11:25-32, for the sake of the gospel all Israel will finally be saved when Christ comes from Zion at his parousia. One cannot harmonize these differing statements of Paul. The only way to understand them is to assume that on this point Paul's theology has evolved. From a harsh rejection of Israel — a rejection that reflects his own conversion near Damascus and his negative experiences as a missionary of Christ with many representatives of Judaism — he made an about-face and developed in Romans a new, positive view of Israel. He came a long way in his thinking, and from the gospel of God's faithfulness and God's righteousness he gained a new understanding of Israel.

His relationship to the Jerusalem church also remained full of tension. From his letters one gets the impression that Paul almost always strove for fellowship with precisely those Jerusalem apostles who may have been very skeptical about his apostleship[46] and who as a result may not have accepted without reservation his gospel served by this apostleship. Since Paul's relationship to the people in Jerusalem remained unstable and full of tension,[47] one might ask why he wanted fellowship with them.

We have already gained insight into what for Paul was the defining basis: Jesus, the Son of God, is a historical figure, not simply an imaginary mythological construct. Thus one can believe in him only together with those who also believe in him and only when that belief is nourished by the common traditions that are related to Jesus.[48] That is why, after Christ was revealed to him near Damascus, he became not the founder of a religion but an apostle of the church.

That means that the Pauline gospel had two fundamental dimensions.

45. In Gal. 6:16, "Israel of God" cannot refer to the part of Israel that does not believe in Jesus; it can refer only to the church. Otherwise we would have a completely unexplained break in Paul's thought.

46. Cf. above, p. 60. In Paul's report about the Apostolic Council there is explicitly no reference to his *apostleship.*

47. Walter Rebell, *Gehorsam und Unabhängigkeit: Eine sozialpsychologische Studie zu Paulus* (Munich: Kaiser, 1986), esp. pp. 30-43.

48. This presupposes that one understands the well-known text 2 Cor. 5:16 not as a rejection of the earthly Jesus but as an expression of the reality that as a "new creation" one cannot understand Jesus apart from faith — that is, not "according to the flesh."

One is the experience of God's unconditional and universal love: the gospel of Christ means that, through Jesus, God gives to all people his redeeming love. Through Christ, the God of Israel calls all people, Jews and Gentiles, to himself. Every attempt to declare that along with this love other things are necessary for having access to God is for Paul contempt of God, one's "own righteousness" (Rom. 10:3), and thus sin against God's being God — that is, against the first command of the Decalogue.

The other dimension is that of fellowship. It, too, corresponds to Jesus' proclamation of love and to the community that had emerged in Israel through his activity. Thus it is part of the Pauline gospel that in the name of Christ it brings people into the new fellowship of the one church. Accepting the gospel means for him that people are "new creatures" (2 Cor. 5:17) and that the differences between Jews and Greeks as well as between men and women or between slaves and masters become irrelevant. It is a part of the gospel that baptized persons "are one in Christ Jesus" (Gal. 3:28). Thus for Paul a rupture of the fellowship of the church would also have destroyed the gospel, for the Lord Jesus Christ who embodies God's unconditional and universal love is at the same time the basic gift for the community of the church. Sharing in Jesus Christ leads to fellowship in the church (cf. 1 Cor. 1:9).

Nevertheless, for Paul there were also situations in which it was the gospel itself that made the fellowship of the church impossible. It is not always easy to trace the decisions Paul had to make in these situations. We will try to describe them here to the degree that they deal with the relationship to Jewish Christianity and thus to Israel.

4.3.1. The Antioch Conflict (by Peter Lampe)

At issue in the Antioch conflict between Paul and Peter (Gal. 2:11-21) was the table fellowship of Gentile and Jewish Christians. In Antioch the two groups met in their homes to eat together. That was possible because the Jewish Christians, including Peter and Barnabas, had decided to eat without worrying about the Torah (Gal. 2:14, 12). For a long time nothing stood in the way of this table fellowship, which presumably included the eucharist, until the arrival of James's people from Jerusalem.

For a number of reasons, in Antioch the Torah-faithful people from James ate separately from the Gentile Christians. One reason was that in Jerusalem the situation was different from that in the Gentile metropolis of Antioch. In Judea the Jewish Christians struggled to convince their Jewish neighbors that in spite of their faith in Christ they were still proper Jews. They were even persecuted by the synagogues (1 Thess. 2:14; cf. Luke 6:22; 11:49-51).

Thus it was important for them to keep the Law as strenuously as possible so that they would not give even greater offense to their Jewish neighbors.

A further and more principled reason was that under "people of God" they obviously understood something different than did the people of Antioch. In following Jesus, James's people were of the firm opinion that Israel was the people of God to be renewed and that the Jesus community constituted the already renewed nucleus. The Jewish Christian Peter had to confront the question whether he had renounced the fellowship of the Jesus community *with* Israel and thus had placed himself outside the people of God. In addition, James's people will have remonstrated with him: "How can you abandon the Torah when at the Apostolic Council you were appointed missionary to the Jews? How does someone hope to convince Jews when he knowingly violates the commandments of the Torah? It may be permissible for Gentile Christians not to keep the Torah, but how can Jewish Christians stop being obedient to the Torah?"

Peter gave in to James's people, either from conviction or under pressure. He no longer went to the common meals with the Gentile Christians, and the other Jewish Christians, including Barnabas, followed his example. Thus Jewish and Gentile Christians were separated. In Antioch the one church consisting of Jews and Gentiles was fractured.

For Paul, who continued to participate in the law-free table fellowship with the Gentile Christians in Antioch, Peter's step meant two things:

1. By acting as he did, Peter was forcing the Gentile Christians to join James's people in their Torah obedience if they wanted to continue to eat with the Jewish Christians (Gal. 2:14). Peter may not have directly demanded that of the Gentile Christians, but that was the practical consequence of his behavior. Whether he wanted to do so or not, Peter was forcing the Gentile Christians to be obedient to the Torah. Paul understood Peter's behavior as an attack that had to be resisted (Gal. 2:11).

2. It did not bother Paul that Jews such as James's people, who had obeyed the Torah from their youth, continued to do so after their baptism. Nowhere does he engage in polemics against James's people. Furthermore, he had shared in the Jerusalem agreement that permitted a Torah-faithful mission to Jews. What aroused his anger was something else. People who, like Peter, had already given up the Law and who then "built [it] up again" (2:18) — or especially those who, like the Gentile Christian Galatians, introduced it after their conversion — demonstrated that for them the gospel of Christ's death on the cross did not have sufficient saving power. When he took this step, Peter revealed, whether he wanted to or not, that he attributed justifying power only to the works of the Torah and not to faith in Christ alone (2:16). In

so doing, Peter contradicted himself, since he knew (2:16a) that this was not the truth. Otherwise he would not have previously lived a law-free life. For Paul, the consequence of Peter's behavior was that it represented Christ as having died in vain (2:21).

Paul reacted sharply: Peter has departed from the "truth of the gospel" (2:14); he is a hypocrite who acts contrary to his better knowledge (2:13, 16); he is "condemned" by his behavior (2:11). Paul openly opposed him (2:11, 14), and there was an open break between Peter and Paul. Or, more precisely, Paul himself placed his seal on Peter's abandonment of the table fellowship by separating himself from Peter. "The truth of the gospel" (2:14) was more important to him than fellowship between the two apostles.

For Paul, fellowship was not an end in itself — not a goal to be reached at any cost. In Antioch he subordinated it to the truth of the gospel. It had to correspond to the gospel of the unconditional love of God, not betray it. Thus the gospel justified both things: the table fellowship between Gentile and Jewish Christians *and* breaking off the fellowship between Peter and Paul. It united and separated at the same time. By contrast, what was important for James's people was the fellowship between the Jewish Christians and the as yet "unbelieving" part of Israel. *Here* is where they placed the emphasis. In so doing, were they, too, wanting to express the "truth of the gospel"? Was their understanding of the gospel different from that of Paul (cf. Gal. 1:6)? Probably so. Ultimately, for them the community of Israel was more important than the new, universal community of Jews and Gentiles established by Christ. Paul, however, did not let it come to a break with James. The break with Peter in Antioch — a temporary break as it turned out — was enough for him. It was for Paul a sign of the truth of his gospel.

4.3.2. The Conflict between Strong and Weak in Rome (by Peter Lampe)

Some years later in Rome Paul dealt with what was probably another conflict between Jewish and Gentile Christians. The Jewish Christians observed holy days and food regulations (Rom. 14:2-3, 5), and Paul called them "weak in the faith" (14:1). By contrast, for the Gentile Christians and for Paul nothing was in and of itself unclean "in the Lord" (14:14). What is noteworthy is that at first glance Paul's decision in this conflict is completely different from his decision in Antioch. For the Romans, Paul recommended that out of love to the Jewish Christians the strong believers should forgo their freedom from the Law and at the common meals eat only kosher food (14:21).

Paul was able to do that because in its symptoms the situation was different. In Antioch the behavior of the Judaizing Peter constituted an assault.

For all practical purposes it forced the Gentile Christians to act like Jews. In Rome — and this was the first difference — it was probably the law-free members of the community who aggressively (cf. 14:1) went after the Jewish Christians. They had no patience (cf. 15:4-5) with them and their weak faith that still clung to the Torah. It was not the "weak" who posed conditions; the "strong" obviously wanted to get the weak to practice their own freedom from the Law, and thus were demanding something the weak were not yet able to give (cf. 14:14, 20). Therein lay the second difference from Antioch. In Antioch the Jewish Christians had already shown that their faith was strong enough to live without the Torah. Previously they had eaten food that was not kosher and had lived free of the Law. In Antioch the "strong" and "aggressive" members were Jewish Christians. In Rome they were Gentile Christians.

What do Rome and Antioch have in common? Paul says that the strong people in Rome do not accept the weak ones as they are (Rom. 14:1), even though Christ has accepted them (14:15; 15:7). With their uncharitable attitude they are in danger of defaming the saving work of Christ, who also loves the weak and died for them (14:20, 16, 15). As a result they must receive the same reproach Paul leveled against Peter in Antioch (Gal. 2:21). Both of them act contrary to the gospel of Christ's saving death, except that each one represents it differently. Either way, one disgraces Christ's saving death. The gospel of this death on the cross is the sole criterion for determining where and how one is to have fellowship in Christ, be it without or with kosher meat.

If Paul has not himself changed since the incident in Antioch — that is, if we must understand the two conflicts together — then it is clear that Paul's gospel in Antioch did not mean that one or the other attitude toward the Torah is right in every circumstance. It is not important whether one is free from the Law or obedient to the Law. Such things are *adiaphora* (cf. 1 Cor. 7:19). In Paul's eyes they contradict the gospel only when they become obligations, as did the Torah observance by the Jewish Christians in Galatia or practically by Peter in Antioch, or as did the freedom from the Law on the part of the strong in Rome.

4.3.3. *Paul and His Opponents*

Paul was continually forced to deal with opponents in his churches. It seemed that they were always following him. Wherever Paul did his missionary work, sooner or later they showed up. It happened in Galatia, in Corinth, and in Philippi. Scholars are not in agreement about who these opponents were. They were certainly Jewish Christians, not only in Galatia but also in Corinth and Philippi (Phil. 3:3-6; 2 Cor. 11:22). In my judgment they were part of the great Jewish Christian opposition with which Paul had to deal his entire life.[49] In Galatia and Philippi (Phil. 3:2-3, 8) the issue was circumcision; in Corinth it was Paul's apostleship. At the very least the opponents in Galatians and in Philippians are from the "radical Jewish Christians" we have already met at the Apostolic Council. Their concern was that the Gentile Christians who had been converted to Jesus should be completely integrated into the people of Israel through circumcision.

In a portrayal of the early Christian struggle for unity, there must also be a place for these radical Jewish Christians, for in their own way they impressively indicate how fundamentally important was the idea of the unity of the church. Wherever there were people who believed in Christ, these Jewish Christians obviously could not leave them as they were — half, or even completely, "pagan." No matter the cost, they had to integrate these followers of Jesus into what for them was the "true church" — namely, into the people of Israel, the center of whom were the Jesus communities. That is why their circumcision was so important. "Church unity" meant something quite different for Paul and for his radical Jewish Christian opponents; nevertheless it was, paradoxically, a concern they shared.

Paul's reaction here was sharp and abrupt. He said that such people had a "different Jesus," a "different Spirit" (2 Cor. 11:4), or a "different gospel" (Gal. 1:6). It is important that not every theological difference of Paul was evaluated this way. It is clear from 1 Corinthians that Paul had completely different opinions about Peter and Apollos. That is especially interesting in Peter's case, since 1 Corinthians shows that Paul obviously had not maintained his harsh judgment and the repudiation of fellowship he had made in Antioch. The false brothers in Galatia and the false apostles in Corinth, however, were not part of the fellowship Christ had made possible through the gospel. The reason for their exclusion was that they took something that was for Paul an *adiaphoron* and made of it a condition. Where the gospel was negated as the gospel of God's grace solely through Jesus Christ, it could not work for Paul as a fellowship-promoting force. Where there is no "fellowship of Jesus Christ" (1 Cor. 1:9), the fellowship of the church is also not possible. This is Paul's basic conviction, but it does not completely exclude the possibility of having church fellowship with Jewish Christianity. In spite of his puzzling intimations in 2 Corinthians 11:5, Paul knew that the Jerusalem apostles did not side with his opponents. Otherwise neither his enthusiasm for the collection nor his final trip to Jerusalem would be understandable.

49. I am essentially agreeing with the view of Gerd Luedemann, *Opposition to Paul in Jewish Christianity*, trans. M. Eugene Boring (Minneapolis: Fortress, 1989), pp. 35-111.

4.3.4. The Collection (by Andreas Karrer)

Part of the church fellowship between Paul and the Jerusalem church that had been worked out in Jerusalem was a collection to be taken up by the Gentile Christian churches for the Jerusalem church (Gal. 2:10). Even before we have clear news about the beginning of this collection, the fellowship had been damaged by the incident in Antioch.[50] The practice of Gentile and Jewish Christians of eating together as a visible sign of their unity was broken off. Paul broke with Barnabas and Peter and in so doing apparently also broke with the church in Antioch. Yet it was clearly important for Paul that this disagreement not lead to a break with Jerusalem, and for that reason he adhered to the agreement to gather an offering for the Jerusalem church. The money was gathered in all the churches with no problems. Paul was even able to emphasize the zeal of the Macedonians (2 Cor. 8:3), and he used it to encourage other churches. When there were questions from Corinth about how the money was to be gathered, Paul recommended that each one lay something aside on the first day of the week. In this way a considerable amount would gradually accumulate, and no one would have to scrape together extra money when Paul came again (1 Cor. 16:1-4).

Later there were difficulties in Corinth when opponents caused an uproar in the church and raised doubts about Paul's apostleship. Thus, after he had been reconciled with the Corinthian church, he needed to advise them again in detail about the collection (2 Corinthians 8–9). To get the Corinthians to complete the collection they had already begun, he had to emphasize his own sincerity (8:20-21). There were also other co-workers active in the collection (8:6, 18-19). Paul mentions Titus by name and emphasizes his commitment (8:6, 16-17). The latter traveled from church to church, perhaps as a kind of "collection specialist." He had also been present at the meeting in Jerusalem when the decision was made about the collection, and he was accepted there as an uncircumcised Gentile Christian. He thus personified a continuity in the checkered history that had taken place since the Jerusalem meeting.

Originally Paul may have assumed that the churches would bring their offering to Jerusalem independent of one another. In that case he would have given letters to the delegates of each church and would have gone to Jerusalem only "if it had been worth the effort" (1 Cor. 16:3-4). Obviously the effort then became necessary. The situation between him and Jerusalem had become so sharp that he decided that he could not avoid going to Jerusalem himself. Since he knew he would be in personal danger, before his departure he even asked

50. Cf. above, pp. 66-68.

the church in Rome, which he had not founded, to support him in prayer (Rom. 15:30-31). In addition, all the churches were to turn over to him the money they had collected. In Acts 20:4 delegates from Beroea, Thessalonica, Derbe (the province of Galatia), and Asia (Ephesus) are named as his traveling companions. In spite of tensions within and among the churches, Paul had succeeded in getting almost all the churches he had founded to participate in this collection for Jerusalem.[51] Moreover, according to 2 Corinthians 8:20, he expected to have a large amount to turn over to the church in Jerusalem.

We can discover the purpose of the Jerusalem agreement about the collection only from Paul's notes. He first mentions it in Galatians 2:10. In other letters (1 Cor. 16:1-4; 2 Corinthians 8–9; Rom. 15:25-28) he offers abundant reflections about it and emphasizes aspects that may not have played such a major role in Jerusalem. Unfortunately we have no sources from the Jerusalem side that could inform us whether they understood this agreement in the same way Paul did. According to Galatians 2:10, the purpose of the collection was to support "the poor." It was a one-sided assistance from the Gentile Christians for the Jerusalem church. The wording does not preclude thinking of a continuing arrangement rather than a one-time offering, even if in reality it came to only one major operation. The text gives no indication that either Paul or the people of Antioch were in any fundamental sense legally subject to Jerusalem. It is no longer clear whether behind the "poor" of Galatians 2:10 there is a term the members of the Jerusalem church used for themselves. It is clear, however, that when Paul uses the term he is thinking of those people in the Jerusalem church who are actually poor (Rom. 15:26). This social aspect is very important for him. In addition, with the collection for the Jerusalem church the Gentile Christian churches show that, even without the sign of circumcision, they are aware of being united with the Jerusalem people. It is a sign of thanks in the "physical" sphere to the mother church in Jerusalem for letting the Gentiles share in the "spiritual" sphere (Rom. 15:27). For both — the physical and the spiritual — Paul uses the term *koinonia* (= share, fellowship). The collection is to make visible in the fellowship of the church made up of Jews and Gentiles the "sharing of Christ" God has already made available. From this perspective it became for Paul the model and test case of his Christology and his ecclesiology.

Especially in 2 Corinthians 8–9, Paul uses the collection as the occasion for further theological reflection. He designates it as *charis* (= act of grace; 8:4-7) and thereby associates the human offering with God's prevenient demon-

51. Wolf-Henning Ollrog, *Paulus und seine Mitarbeiter,* WMANT 50 (Neukirchen: Neukirchener Verlag, 1979), esp. pp. 52-58.

stration of grace that is also designated as *charis*. God's free turning to human beings, the saving act of the Lord Jesus Christ for people (8:9), is what makes the collection possible as *charis*. From God's demonstration of grace, the abundant stream flows in the spiritual area from Jerusalem to the Gentiles and in the material area from the Gentile Christians back to Jerusalem (8:14-15). Overwhelmed with acts of grace by God himself, the Corinthians can by no means keep them for themselves. They can only pass on to others what they themselves have received. Paul's will is that the local churches should always deal with one another this way.[52] In this manner the collection becomes a "gift of grace" alongside the other charismata such as faith, word, and knowledge (8:7). When the collection is given this kind of theological justification, the idea that it was originally an arrangement with the Jerusalem church that the Gentile churches had to comply with almost disappears, yet even the material settlement is not the sole reason or final goal of the collection. And this interpretation also means that its reason and goal can no longer be simply to support the poor. As a *charis* it involves received grace, passing on material possessions, and devotion to God (cf. 8:5). Properly understood, it finally leads all who participate in it to praise, thank, and glorify God (cf. 8:16; 9:12-15).[53] One can regulate charity but not devotion to God. For this reason Paul emphasizes free will and the givers' own initiative. He also refuses to command the people to complete the offering. Instead, he calls attention to the zeal of other people as a way of encouraging the churches to gather the money. It is in the collection that love shows that it is genuine (8:8).

4.3.5. *Paul's Last Journey to Jerusalem (by Andreas Karrer)*

Paul personally took the collection to Jerusalem, even though in doing so he risked not only his life but also his missionary work. Clarifying his relationship to the Jerusalem church was that important to him. Unfortunately, we have no direct news from Paul himself about what happened with the collection after he arrived in Jerusalem. Even the author of Acts lets us down in this matter. From his portrayal in Acts 21:17-30 one can infer that, given the already existing tensions in the Jerusalem church, Paul's visit had to lead to a stress test. Once Paul appeared in the headquarters of the Jewish Christians, a clearing of the air was unavoidable. James, who was still the leader of the church, had a difficult time as mediator. In this situation James and Paul

52. Cf. the general statements in 2 Cor. 9:13, and already in 8:4.

53. As far as the structure is concerned, Paul argues the same way in his comments about the Philippians' financial contribution to him (Phil. 4:10-20).

worked out a balancing act they could both live with. Paul, himself a Jewish Christian, would publicly show his obedience to the Torah by fulfilling a Nazarite vow and performing acts of purification. In this way James could take the wind out of the sails of the conservative Jewish Christian group and free the way for accepting the collection and thus demonstrating the fellowship with Paul and his Gentile Christian companions. Yet the agitation of extreme Jewish Christians led to Paul's arrest, and he probably was not able to deliver the collection. That explains why the author of Acts, a man so concerned about harmony, persistently says nothing about the delivery of the collection. As Acts 24:17 shows, he obviously knew about the collection. When it failed, he preferred to say nothing about it rather than display such inner-church conflicts before his readers. Paul was never released from custody and was probably executed.

What did the journey to Jerusalem and the meeting there mean for Paul? Would it not have been easier for him to avoid the obvious dangers, which after all were largely connected with his person, by carrying out his original plan of simply sending the delegates from the churches? Did he perhaps make the problem worse by going to Jerusalem himself? Paul saw the situation quite differently. The journey to Jerusalem came at a new turning point in his mission. He was wanting now to turn his attention to the area west of Rome, reaching as far as Spain. Delivering the collection thus coincided with the end of his missionary activity in the East. He had interpreted the collection of money as an "act of grace" in such a way that it became what one might call the confirmation of his gospel of God's love for Jews and Gentiles. He had to be and wanted to be responsible for it himself. He could not leave it to the delegates from the churches. Precisely because of the strong Jewish Christian hostility, to which he was continually subjected in his churches, he wanted to use the symbolic act of handing over the collection to exhibit and confirm the fellowship of Gentile and Jewish Christians. To this point he had not been able to leave his old mission areas and turn to new ones. He first had to be certain that his Gentile Christian churches would continue to be united with the Jerusalem mother church. He came to Jerusalem for the unity of the church, even at the risk of his life; and he gave his life for it.

4.3.6. Church vis-à-vis Israel and for Israel

It is fundamental for Paul that Christ establishes fellowship between Jews and Gentiles in the church. This fellowship comes from the gospel that unconditionally justifies both of them, Jews and Gentiles, as sinners before God. Paul hoped that James, the brother of the Lord, would agree with him on this point. Where he differed from James was in his understanding of the church over against the part of Israel that did not believe in Christ.

Although for James there could be church only *within Israel,* in Romans 11:11-32 Paul understands the Gentile mission as distinct from Israel: God has indeed broken off some branches from his tree and grafted in others (Rom. 11:19-20). That does not simply mean, however, that Israel has been replaced by the church; it means that the church remains vis-à-vis Israel. Its existence will make "some" in Israel jealous and lead them to salvation (11:14). In the end, however, God will in Christ, despite Israel's unbelief, save all Israel (11:25-26), true to his own word. At the beginning of the three chapters on Israel, Paul asks rhetorically if the Word of God has failed (cf. 9:6). At its conclusion he can answer this question: "The free gifts and the call of God are irrevocable" (11:29).

Thus the original concept of the church as something *within* Israel, always advocated by James, was replaced for Paul only temporarily by the idea of a church *without* Israel. Nevertheless, it would be better to characterize the Pauline concept as one of a *church vis-à-vis Israel* that, however, is also a *church for Israel.* For Paul the church is an ecumenical fellowship between Jewish and Gentile Christians created by the gospel. It is temporarily divorced from Israel but remains disposed toward Israel, and in the eschaton it will be with Israel again. Thus even for Paul church unity without Israel is not conceivable, even though it is no longer a unity within Israel.

To be sure, with this understanding Paul is no longer in full agreement with the original understanding of the Jesus community of disciples and of the church in early Christianity. He has incorporated into his thinking the experience that large parts of Israel rejected the gospel of Jesus. Although in his understanding of God's righteousness as God's unconditional love he was close to Jesus' understanding of the reign of God and simply expanded God's unconditional love to include the Gentiles, his missionary experiences led him to an understanding of the church's relationship to Israel that differed from that of mainstream Jewish Christianity. Because, however, Paul thought through the experience of Israel's rejection in the light of the gospel of God's gracious righteousness, he was able to preserve essential concerns of Jesus and of Jewish Christianity in his own new view.

One can no longer say that of many of the later descriptions of the relationship between the church and Israel — descriptions found in the New Testament and in church history. The experience of Israel's temporary rejection of Jesus became the experience of a definitive rejection, and it was cemented when the synagogues and the Jesus communities went their separate ways.

The theological concepts that incorporated this experience — such as the Gospel of Matthew, the Gospel of John, and Hebrews — come close to a model that one can best describe as *church instead of Israel.* When later the church understood itself as a new people of God or even as the only people of God and thus forgot that its Lord spoke initially not to it but to the people of God/Israel, there opened up, in our judgment, an enormous gulf between the church and its Lord. When the church's relationship to Israel is broken off in this way, an essential part of the heritage of Jesus and his early disciples is lost, even when Israel's theological heritage and Bible are highly valued in this church.

By contrast, our question is: *Can the church define itself without defining its relationship to Israel?* Can one talk about church unity and be enthusiastic about it without at the same time being enthusiastic about the church's unity with and for Israel? Our conviction is that from the perspective of the deeds and words of Jesus one cannot.

Yet that is what largely happened in the later history of the church. Unity is defined by a way of thinking whose beginnings are expressed especially clearly in the Gospel of Matthew or in the Gospel of John: Israel's election has passed over to the church. The kingdom of God is taken from Israel's leaders and given to another nation that will produce its fruits (Matt. 21:43). The church later became the church without Israel — indeed, often enough it has been a church against Israel. Because this is what largely happened in the later church, historical developments have moved beyond the radical Jewish Christians as well as James and his understanding of the church and have made both of them obsolete. It would be more accurate to say that Paul as well, who on the whole has remained victorious in the church, was able to do so only because a not inconsiderable part of his thinking about the church has been repressed.

5. The Church as the Reality of Christ in Paul's Thought

5.1. *The Basic Gift of Unity: Christ*

In Corinth there were divisions among the followers of Peter, of Apollos, and of Paul, and the so-called Christ party. Paul asked the Corinthians: "Is Christ divided?" (1 Cor. 1:13). The question was not merely rhetorical. For Paul, dividing the church is dividing Christ himself. As constituted by the exalted Lord, his church is that real. The concept of the church as the body of Christ probably lies behind this imagery. In another place Paul says: no one can lay another foundation of the church other than the one that is laid, Jesus Christ (1 Cor. 3:11). Christ is the foundation of the church. The metaphor of the church as a building or edifice lies behind this language.

For Paul, Christ is the church's real, basic gift and the real foundation of its unity. For Paul, Christ is more than merely a word. In various ways his reality can be concretely experienced in unity's "forces."[54]

a. Paul understands *baptism*[55] as being incorporated into the body of Christ — a body that exists before and is given to the individual. Greeks and Jews, slaves and free have experienced one and the same Spirit and are baptized into one and the same body (1 Cor. 12:13). Paul may also be thinking of the universal body of Christ when he says that the contrasts between women and men, slaves and free, Jews and Greeks are overcome. All have "put on" the same Christ, and "in Christ" all are "one man" (Gal. 3:28). They are "one body" — the body of Christ (Rom. 12:5).

b. Something similar is true of the *Lord's Supper.*[56] In 1 Corinthians 10:16 Paul speaks of the "fellowship" of the blood and the fellowship of the body of Christ in the Lord's Supper or, more precisely, of the "sharing" in Jesus' blood and Jesus' body — that is, in his death. This sharing establishes the fellowship of the church: "Because there is one bread, we the many are one body, for we all partake of the one bread" (1 Cor. 10:17). Thus the "vertical" sharing in Christ's death is the basis for the "horizontal" fellowship of Christians with one another. This is what one can experience intensely in the Lord's Supper. In the Corinthian church the Lord's Supper is a fellowship-creating power. Nowhere do we hear that the individual Corinthian groups — the Peter people, the Paul people, or the Apollos people (cf. 1 Cor. 1:12) — had celebrated separate eucharists. The Lord's Supper is the meal of the *entire* church, yet that is also true beyond the individual church. "We, the many, are one body" is as fundamental a statement as it is possible to make.

c. Third, Paul refers to the experience of the *Spirit.* It is here especially clear that the "basic gift" of unity is ambivalent. What unifies can also divide. In Corinth it was probably the experience of the Spirit itself that made many of the Spirit-filled people "rich in all things" and thus led them to act arrogantly as a spiritual elite. By contrast, Paul understands the Spirit as a power that creates unity. Before he applies the idea of the body of Christ to the individual congregation in 1 Corinthians 12, he speaks of the differences of the gifts of the Spirit and of the *one* Spirit: "There are varieties of gifts, but the

54. Cf. above, pp. 47-54.

55. Cf. above, pp. 48-49.

56. Cf. above, p. 49.

same Spirit; there are varieties of ministries, but the same Lord; there are varieties of workings, but the same God who is working in all" (1 Cor. 12:4-6; cf. verse 11). In 1 Corinthians 12:13 he says again emphatically that in baptism we are "all given to drink of *one* Spirit." And in Philippians 1:27 it is "standing in *one* Spirit" that makes possible the harmonious striving in faith.

Why is Paul able to associate the Spirit with the idea of unity? For Paul, experiences of the Spirit are not simply any special religious experiences by individual persons. It is rather the case that *in* these experiences the person experiences the *one* God and the *one* Christ, in and for the church. For this reason one cannot separate the Spirit from Christ and neutralize it as if it were simply a religious experience, for the Spirit is the Lord (cf. 2 Cor. 3:17) and is united with the Lord (cf. 1 Cor. 6:17). It was only for this reason that Paul was able to remind the Galatians that they had received the Spirit not by works of the Law but by the hearing of faith (Gal. 3:2). Not only does the Spirit bring together all Spirit-filled persons; it binds them to the Lord Jesus and his gospel.

d. Finally, we need to speak here of the *confessions.*[57] Paul refers to traditional *Christ confessions* and uses them as the basis for creating community and overcoming divisions. He appropriates quite different confessional formulations and makes use of them in quite different ways.

In 1 Corinthians 1:18-25 it is the crucified Christ who exposes as foolishness every human wisdom that causes division. Because Christ is the basic gift of unity and because all members of the church and apostles belong to Christ, it is foolishness to make human authority absolute.

In Romans 14:9 it is the confession of the lordship of the Risen One that makes human points of view on such things as eating or not eating unclean meat penultimate. Practices of eating or not eating and opinions about clean and unclean do not constitute the church's fellowship; it is the Lord who forbids judging one's brother.

First Corinthians 12:3 is interesting. Here the basis for the apostle's argument is the acclamation of the Lord Jesus: "No one can say, 'Jesus is Lord!' except by the Holy Spirit." Of course, *all* Christians in Corinth confessed that Jesus is the Lord. The supposition one sometimes hears that some Corinthian Christians may have cursed Jesus is absurd. Nevertheless, by reminding people of this acclamation Paul formulated a criterion that enabled him to "discern the spirits." The effect of the criterion is inclusive, not exclusive, however; it works to create community, not to divide. Paul uses it against the Corinthian Spirit-Christians for whom their spiritual wisdom and their char-

57. Cf. above, p. 49.

ismatic gifts were so important that they felt superior to "normal" Christians. At the beginning of his three chapters on the gifts of the Spirit Paul says: *all* Christians who call on the Lord Jesus have the Spirit. Then on this basis in 1 Corinthians 12–14 he brings to the foreground the charismata that create fellowship, especially love.

In Romans 1:3-4 Paul begins his letter to the unknown church in Rome with a confession that serves as the common basis on which the church and he, the controversial Paul, both stand. That is not a trick Paul uses because he wants to be accepted in Rome and because he needs support for his mission to Spain. He is interested, rather, in the common ground that supports him and the church in Rome — Christ, to whom Paul owes his apostleship. Thus the confession calls attention to the basic gift of unity — to Christ.

All of this is not to say that words alone constitute the unity of the church. The living Christ, of whom the confessions bear witness, is actually present in the church. Indeed, the church is his "body." The presence of Christ in the church — that is, the "basic gift" of unity — is something that can be experienced! That is why Paul speaks in this context of baptism, the Lord's Supper, and the Spirit. They are unity-creating "forces."[58]

5.2. *The Whole Church and the Local Church*

As one can see in Galatians 3:28, 1 Corinthians 1:13, and 1 Corinthians 12:13, the body of Christ is for Paul *one* body, the *one* church. Our thesis was that in his genuine letters Paul also presupposes a whole-church understanding of the "body of Christ."[59] To be sure, in the letters he wrote himself he emphasizes that this church is *lived* locally by its members. Therefore in Romans 12:3-8, 1 Corinthians 1:13, and 1 Corinthians 12:14-31 he applies the body-of-Christ idea to the local church. Paul's basic idea here is not that the whole church is broken up into individual churches but that the whole church is experienced and lived in the local churches. One sees that in the double Pauline use of "body of Christ" for the whole church and for the local church.

It is much the same with the metaphor of the church as a "building" or as a "temple," which also originally referred to the whole church. Paul combines the two images and applies them to the individual congregation. For him, "building up" (edification) is the most important criterion for how the Spirit is to work in the churches. Here "building up" does not have the mean-

58. See above, n. 27.

59. Cf. above, p. 57. On Colossians and Ephesians cf. below, pp. 127-29.

ing common in modern pious speech of the personal edification of the individual. Instead, "building up" means the "upbuilding" of the community (1 Cor. 14:4-5, 12, 26). That is why love is for Paul the highest charism: it "builds up" (1 Cor. 8:1).

One can also see the close relationship of whole church and local church in another basic Pauline word for church, namely, in the word *ekklesia.* We have noted that the term *ekklesia,* formed by the Old Testament, was an old Jewish Christian designation of the entire church.[60] Paul uses the word almost exclusively, however, for the local church, for it is a visible, concrete "assembled" community. For this reason Paul speaks often and probably intentionally of the "the assembly," or "the assembly of God that is [assembled at a particular location]" — for example, in Corinth (1 Cor. 1:2; 2 Cor. 1:1), in Cenchreae (Rom. 16:1), in Galatia (Gal. 1:2), or in a particular house (Phlm. 2; cf. Rom. 1:5). Thus he says, "as I teach in *every ekklesia*" (1 Cor. 4:17) rather than some such thing as "as I teach everywhere in the church." Or he uses the plural and speaks of "the churches of God in Judea" (1 Thess. 2:14). Thus Paul can also make a verb from the word "assembly" *(ekklesia)* in a fluid way. He uses the verb "to come together" (1 Cor. 14:23; cf. 11:17-20). "Coming together" is his word for what we would call today the worship service. It is important for Paul that the *ekklesia* comes together concretely and visibly. In the process the word *ekklesia* does not lose its biblical and salvation-history reference. It is God's assembly that is gathered in a particular place. When Paul speaks of *ekklesia,* he does not mean that somewhere a number of people just happen to meet; he means that these people who come together are the assembly of God's people he has called together in a particular place. In his letters Paul makes concrete for the local church what the church is.

Thus it is not true that "Paul . . . knows nothing of a whole church."[61] It is right that he does not have different terms for the whole church and the local church, because for him the whole church is present in the local churches, and the local church lives as a part of the whole church. All local churches are cells in which the whole lives, yet the life of the whole is more than simply a group of individual cells living for themselves. It also belongs to the essence of the whole church that the individual cells live together (cf., e.g., the collection).

To summarize: in Paul's thought the church lives from its fellowship with Jesus Christ; it is his body. As the body of the one Christ it is more than the sum

60. See above, pp. 55-56.

61. Thus Josef Hainz, *Ekklesia: Strukturen paulinischer Gemeinde-Theologie und Gemeinde-Ordnung,* BU 9 (Regensburg: Pustet, 1972), p. 251.

of individual assemblies in particular places. The fellowship with Christ has an ecumenical dimension, and at the same time it determines the life of the local churches.

We turn now to an attempt to make both of them concrete, beginning with the whole church (section 5.3) and moving then to the local churches (section 5.4).

5.3. *Christ's Effectiveness in the Whole Church (with Corinna Diestelkamp)*

We have already spoken of Paul's unceasing struggle for fellowship with the church in Jerusalem and of the collection.[62] Here we will speak of some of the other aspects of Paul's ecumenical practice and theology.

(a) Above all, we must call attention to the Pauline *missionary activity.*[63] Paul consciously thought of his mission ecumenically. He "fulfilled [the gospel] from Jerusalem and around as far as Illyricum" (Rom. 15:19). His mission was part of the Lord's universal rule. It was grounded in salvation history, for the gospel went out from Jerusalem, the sacred city of the people of God. As an apostle it was his task to proclaim the gospel in the entire Gentile world. That is why the horizon of his plans reached as far as Spain and why he set up bases of Christ in the metropolitan centers of the provinces. Corinth, Philippi, and Thessalonica represented their provinces, Achaia and Macedonia (Rom. 15:26; 1 Thess. 1:7-8; 2 Cor. 1:1), just as the Christian Epaenetus was the first convert in Asia (Rom. 16:5). Although Paul established "assemblies" in various places, he did so to "fulfill" the gospel in the whole world — that is, to plant the universal church. Paul understood and organized his mission as the task not of an individual but of the church. It is not the mission of an individual and his co-workers; it is the mission of the apostle and his churches. Ollrog's study[64] in particular has demonstrated that Paul systematically involved his churches in his missionary work. They were responsible for providing and supporting co-workers in the mission. Second Corinthians 8:23 makes a distinction between Titus, obviously Paul's personal companion, and the "representatives" *(apostoloi)* of the churches who are Paul's brothers. Among them were, for example, Epaphroditus from Philippi (Phil. 4:18), perhaps Stephanas, Fortunatus, and Achaicus from Corinth (1 Cor. 16:17),

62. Cf. above, pp. 64-65, 71-73.

63. Cf. above, pp. 50-51.

64. Cf. above, n. 51, esp. pp. 119-61.

Aristarchus (from Thessalonica?; cf. Acts 19:29), Tychicus and Trophimus (from Ephesus; cf. Acts 20:4; 21:29), and others.[65] Paul intentionally involved the churches in his missionary work and in so doing made clear that the task of proclaiming the gospel is a task of the whole church, of all congregations, and indirectly of all their members. The note in Acts that in his journey with the collection Paul was accompanied by delegates of the churches (Acts 20:4) also fits in with this picture of the Pauline mission.

(b) There was also a great deal of *contact among the churches.* Christians traveled frequently to other churches. An indication of this contact is the large number of members of the church whom Paul knew in Rome even though he had never been there (cf. Romans 16): Phoebe, the deaconess from Cenchreae; Prisca and Aquila; Epaenetus, the first convert in Asia; Andronicus and Junia; and Urbanus, one of Paul's co-workers, were all in Rome. In some six cases Paul's acquaintances in Rome were active church co-workers. Are we to assume that all of them had come to Rome privately and by coincidence? In many cases a church-related mission may have been combined with personal motives. Paul knew at least four different house churches in Rome. First Corinthians 16:3 shows that church-related journeys — in this case by Corinthians to Jerusalem — obviously were taken for granted, and 1 Corinthians 16:6 and 11 show that the Christians traveled not alone but with brothers and sisters. Obviously, there were always people who were able to interrupt their work and to travel on behalf of the church. It may be that the churches bore the expenses of the journeys. Hospitality and personal friendships were part of the travel. In most ancient religions only the upper classes of the Roman Empire were generally mobile. Christians, by contrast, including the poorer members of the church, traveled more frequently in the service of the church. One sees here an example of the lived fellowship of the body of Christ.

(c) At the Apostolic Convention in Jerusalem there was an *agreement about mission.* The practice of working in "another's field" (2 Cor. 10:16) did not sit well with Paul. Nevertheless, it is significant that as a rule he assumed that other people would work in his churches. He opposed such work only when it involved a counter-mission that challenged his mission. He himself was not going to Rome as an apostolic founder but simply to comfort and be comforted by the church (Rom. 1:11-12). Apollos was in Corinth, and Paul encouraged him to go back there (1 Cor. 16:12), not alone but in the company of others. And he did so in spite of the earlier difficulties in Corinth with the Apollos party. One can trace something similar in later times as well. Peter,

65. See above, pp. 71-72.

the missionary to Jews, later found a field of activity among the Roman Christians. After the Jewish War, John, the Jewish Christian prophet and author of Revelation, and his people settled quite naturally among the Pauline churches of Asia Minor. Obviously they knew brothers and sisters there, even though these brothers and sisters were Gentile Christians, some of whom even ate meat sacrificed to idols (Rev. 2:14, 20). Similarly, in the earliest period the itinerant radicals in Palestine and Syria accepted the support and hospitality of churches where they were not known. For their part, the churches recognized that they had a responsibility for such itinerant preachers.

(d) One can see an important dimension of Paul's lived ecumenicity in the *introductions and conclusions of his letters.* In Romans 1:9-10 he says that the faith of the Romans is known throughout the entire world, and he thanks God for it without ceasing. First Corinthians has an ecumenical character and is directed to all who call on the name of the Lord "in every place" (1 Cor. 1:2). Had Paul always thought that his letters would be exchanged among the churches (cf. Col. 4:16)? Or does this simply mean that the Corinthian church is part of the Oecumene? Prayers of intercession and requests for such prayers (1 Thess. 5:25) are important.

Also informative are the closing greetings. They show that the Pauline letters always include the entire local church and also want to connect the local churches to one another. Of course, the letters, even Philemon (2), were read when the church was assembled (1 Thess. 5:27). The closing greetings are nothing short of stereotypical, consisting of three elements that are especially clear in 2 Corinthians: (1) the blessing of God, thus the vertical dimension of the fellowship (2 Cor. 13:13; 1 Cor. 16:23-24; Phil. 4:23; 1 Thess. 5:28); (2) the greetings of "all the saints" (2 Cor. 13:12; cf. Phil. 4:22), not only of the sending church to the receiving church; in 1 Corinthians 16:19-20 the ones sending the greetings are "the local churches of Asia" and "all the brothers," and in Romans 16:16 they are "all the local churches of Christ"; (3) the fellowship within the local church that is encouraged by the reading of the letter: "Greet one another with the holy kiss" (2 Cor. 13:12; Rom. 16:16; 1 Cor. 16:20; 1 Thess. 5:26). Together one has here in almost stereotypical form the three basic elements of the Pauline understanding of community: the sharing of God — or Christ — and the Spirit, the universal fellowship of the church, and the local fellowship in each "assembly." It is characteristic of Pauline letters that the apostle's understanding of community is condensed in such practical actions as the closing greetings.

(e) *Galatians,* an epistle we have not yet mentioned in this context, shows us an interesting variation of this schema. Corinna Diestelkamp makes the following contribution to our discussion:

In Galatians Paul does not wait until the closing greetings to mention the relationship of the churches to one another; he does it already in the heading. He does not want to be seen as the only sender, the person responsible for the contents of the letter. In this special case it is also not enough for him to mention other missionaries as co-senders (as in 1 Cor. 1:1; 2 Cor. 1:1; Phil. 1:1; 1 Thess. 1:1). All the brothers who are with him (Gal. 1:2) "sign" this letter.

But do the churches in Galatia really know who is with Paul? Obviously names are not a factor this time. What is important here is that it is not an individual but a community of brothers that speaks to the Galatian Christians, for something decisive is at stake: the truth of the gospel itself (2:5). It is betrayed when the Galatians let themselves be circumcised (2:21; 5:2) as the Jewish Christian missionaries demand (5:13). In this situation Paul has to muster every conceivable effort — his own as an apostle of Christ (1:1) but also that of all the brothers who are with him (1:2). Whether that means his co-workers, the entire church where he is at the moment, or even all the Christians of a province is, perhaps intentionally, unclear. The readers have the impression that all the Christians around Paul share his opinion, and Galatians is an epistle of the entire church.

When the gospel is in danger, the fraternal community brings its authority to the controversy. An understanding of the church that overcomes geographical and cultural distances comes to bear here: churches are responsible for one another and influence one another. This is not an authoritarian responsibility; a letter should be enough to move the recipients to change their behavior. The decision remains with the Galatian Christians themselves. Thus in a sense the Galatian epistle constitutes a first step toward the Roman church's "ecumenical" intervention in Corinth in *1 Clement.*

In summary: in the Pauline mission, in the life of the churches, and in the Pauline letters the fellowship of the whole church is strongly emphasized. Worldwide community is not merely an idea for Paul; it is something lived. It is founded on Christ as its basic gift; one feels that repeatedly. To be sure, in his extant letters Paul did not develop his understanding of the fellowship of the entire church into a systematically reflected ecclesiology. He simply assumes an ecclesiology that interprets the whole church.

5.4. Christ's Effectiveness in the Local Church

In the local church one can see even more clearly how the reality of Christ is embraced and experienced as fellowship. We will choose four examples from 1 Corinthians.

5.4.1. The Parties in Corinth (1 Corinthians 1–4) (by Peter Lampe)

Fissures were tearing apart the church at Corinth. Christians who were converted by the missionaries Paul, Apollos, or Cephas called themselves by the names of their spiritual fathers and thus formed three different parties that were "puffed up" toward each other. They announced with pride, "I belong to Paul," "I to Apollos," "I to Cephas."

The Corinthians saw nothing wrong with this behavior. From their pagan surroundings they knew that anyone who was inducted into a mystery religion developed a close relationship with the priest who had initiated him.[66] Thus it is understandable that they felt a special relationship to "their" apostle. They will have been astonished when one of the honored apostles himself rose up against that kind of personality cult. Paul proclaimed that the church's division into apostle-parties was keeping Christ from being realized in the Corinthian church. If the Corinthians do not change, Christ himself will be divided (1 Cor. 1:13).

Why was their behavior wrong? In honoring Paul, Cephas, and Apollos they had forgotten that the same person works through all three of these men. With his spirit Christ created everything that happened through these apostles. For this reason the Corinthians could boast only of Christ the Lord, not of these three men — men who did not work by their own power and on the basis of their own qualities. Indeed, the apostles had not come to the Corinthians with exalted human wisdom that would have distinguished them as human teachers worthy of honor. Instead, they — or at least Paul — preached "in weakness and in fear with much trembling," "not in eloquently persuasive words of wisdom" (1 Cor. 2:3-4, 13). Paul came to them as "the world's rubbish" (4:9-13). The spirit of Christ could work full of power only in the weak apostle in whom the cross of Christ was portrayed. The honor belongs to Christ alone, not to the apostles.

Paul has "planted, Apollos watered, but God has given the growth" (1 Cor. 3:5-6). This "but God . . ." is the key to solving the conflict among the parties. To the degree that people lose sight of God and his activity in the church and thus make absolute what humans do, the church is in danger of splintering into partisan groups following "great men." Instead of boasting of allegedly distinguished human beings (3:21), the Corinthians should learn to boast in the Lord (1:31). They are encouraged to think more of what Christ does in the church. The Corinthians belong not "to Paul," not "to Apollos,"

66. For the Isis and Osiris initiations, cf., e.g., Apuleius, *Metamorphoses* xi.21.3; 22.3; 25.7–26.1; 27.3-8; 30.1; 20.1.

not "to Cephas," but to Christ (1:21; 3:23). If they do not take this to heart, they will divide the one body of Christ, the church, with their apostle-parties.

5.4.2. *Meat Sacrificed to Idols (1 Corinthians 8–10)*

In Corinth there were "strong" members who unhesitatingly exercised their freedom to participate in cultic banquets in the pagan temple, for they knew that the pagan gods are nonentities about whom Christians, who stand under the lordship of Christ, no longer need to worry. Other Corinthian Christians, however, did not have this strength. They were afraid that if they ate meat sacrificed to idols they would once again be under the power of the heathen gods. They are the "weak." Unlike the dispute in Rome,[67] the issue in Corinth was not the validity of the Jewish ritual law. Unlike the controversy in Antioch (and also unlike Rome?), the issue in Corinth also does not seem to have been the problem of the meals in the church. It was, rather, a question of the personal life of the "strong" Christians — their participation in the city's temple feasts. The strong did not demand anything of the weak, nor the weak of the strong. Doubtless the issue was that the publicly flaunted freedom of the strong created a problem for the conscience of the weak (1 Cor. 8:10).

Paul says in Corinth what he probably also said in Rome and Antioch.[68] He does not say that eating meat sacrificed to idols is right in all circumstances. Eating or not eating "will not commend us to God" (1 Cor. 8:8). The issue in Corinth was not that one or the other group declared its own position to be the absolutely right position or tried to force it on the other group. That would have given the lie to the truth that Christ alone "commends us to God." The issue, rather, was that Christ creates community and that therefore all behavior by a Christian that wrongs a brother and violates his conscience is a sin against Christ (8:12). When it is Christ who creates a community, all behavior that damages this community becomes a sin against Christ, even when it has to do with *adiaphora* — that is, with things that in themselves do not matter. Thus 1 Corinthians 8 supplements Galatians 2. Just as negating the gospel of Christ destroys the fellowship of the church that the gospel creates (as in Gal. 2:11-20), breaking fellowship with the brother destroys fellowship with Christ — the fellowship that wants to lead us to the brother for whom Christ died (1 Cor. 8:7-13). When you sin against your fellow brother, even if it is in the name of an opinion you regard as Christian, you sin against Christ, and you fall away from the gospel.

67. Cf. above, pp. 68-69.
68. Cf. above, p. 69.

5.4.3. *Divided Lord's Supper? (1 Corinthians 11:17-34)*

Tensions broke out in Corinth around the Lord's Supper. They revolved not around today's controversial questions about the understanding of the Lord's presence in the supper but around much more "worldly" questions. In Corinth the celebration of the Lord's Supper was connected with a common evening meal the church held. It took place in the private house (of Gaius? Rom. 16:23) in which the church met. Many members, especially the rich, came early and, without waiting, began to eat. Others, especially slaves and poor people who had to work, came late and, in any case, had little to bring to contribute to the common meal. They found that their wealthier sister and brother Christians were already full and that nothing was left for them. "When you come together it is not possible to eat the supper of the *Lord*. For in eating each one eats *his* own supper before the others, and one is hungry, another is drunk" (1 Cor. 11:20-21). To celebrate the Lord's Supper this way is to be guilty of the body and blood of the Lord.

The text is interesting in a number of ways. First of all, because it shows how closely the "vertical" fellowship with the Lord and the "horizontal" fellowship with the brother or sister belong together. Destroying the fellowship of the church means destroying the Lord's Supper itself. Second, because it shows how Paul thought of church fellowship holistically. It takes place not only in the spiritual area but also in the physical area — in eating and drinking and becoming filled together. Earlier we saw something similar with the collection that Paul understood as a physical repayment of the Jerusalem church's spiritual gift.[69] Third, because it shows that church fellowship is not a precondition of the celebration of the Lord's Supper; it is response and analogue. Paul excludes no one from the Lord's Supper, but whoever in celebrating the Lord's Supper does not become part of the fellowship that goes along with it eats judgment on himself.

Looking at our own situation of the "divided" Lord's Supper, the Pauline insights are so striking that we might be permitted a small observation in passing. As 1 Corinthians 10:1-13 shows, Paul is little concerned about the precise understanding of the presence of Jesus in the Lord's Supper. In this text he is merely concerned to prevent a magical understanding of the real presence that would negate the fundamental significance of the way Christians act. Yet the destruction of the Lord's Supper by the social disruption of fellowship troubles him. It is possible that if Paul were alive today he would only shake his head over the absence of eucharistic fellowship among the classical

69. Cf. above, p. 72.

Christian denominations, but he would probably call attention to the problem posed by the existing eucharistic fellowship between starving Christians in the South of our planet and well-fed Christians in the North. But after this digression let us return to the past and to the Corinthian church.

5.4.4. *Tensions in Worship (1 Corinthians 12–14)*

In the Corinthian church, a church "enriched in him in everything, in all speech and in all knowledge" (1 Cor. 1:5), spirit-filled people were feeling self-important. People who spoke in tongues and "gnostics"[70] ran the risk of making absolute their possession of the Spirit. In this situation Paul accentuates anew the body-of-Christ idea. For him the body of Christ — that is, the church as the reality of Christ — begins in the local congregation. In 1 Corinthians 12:12-31, to be the body of Christ does not primarily mean to draw spiritually from the fullness. To be the body of Christ means, rather, something as simple and humdrum as what in those days was expressed with the idea of an organism. One part of the body is dependent on the other part; none can live without the other; each must give to the other the honor due it so that the body is really a body. The idea of an organism is here a way of talking about the love of which Paul speaks in 1 Corinthians 13. Thus Paul says that the reality of Christ that has been given us is only real when those who have been embraced by it live it in the practical everyday life of the local church. Possessing the Spirit without love is not the reality of Christ; it is a "clanging cymbal" (1 Cor. 13:1). Thus in Paul's view the reality of Christ becomes a process; it becomes human action. Of course, that does not mean that it is only human action; it is, rather, the already-given reality of Christ out of which one lives. On the basis of 1 Corinthians 12:13 one could say that to live in the body of Christ is to grasp the potential for action in baptism. Or on the basis of 1 Corinthians 1:9 one could say that "sharing" in Christ leads to embarking on the way of "fellowship" with one's brother and discovering Christ there. Or in the language of 1 Corinthians 14 one could say that the church as God's "building" (edifice) becomes real when the "building" becomes a process of "building up" (edification). Christ's work as the basic gift is dynamic. When no dynamic results, one has lost Christ.

70. The reference here is not to "Gnostics" in the sense of the pagan gnosis that appeared in Syria toward the end of the first century or in the sense of the Christian gnosis of the second century. It is likely, however, that "gnosis" in a pre-Gnostic sense was an important word of the religious vocabulary of the Corinthian pneumatics (cf. 1 Cor. 8:1, 10; 12:8; 13:2).

5.4.5. *Conclusion*

In Paul, the fellowship of the church is not a fellowship whose boundaries and conditions one can *first* define and then *later* realize. It is, rather, a living gift that can and must be embraced. It brings those who receive it into a process and leads them to sisters and brothers, into the local churches and into the whole church. The process of community that results is a continuous struggle and an unceasing series of ever new efforts. For their part they are a flaring up of that already-given unity, a fragment of the reality of Christ himself. In Paul, Christ's fellowship is first celebrated and confessed and then practiced. And when it is not practiced, it has not been correctly confessed and celebrated. One sees an example of that in the celebration of the Lord's Supper in Corinth.

Two questions remain to be clarified and require more thorough consideration.

(a) *The problem of "heresy."* Where are the limits of the dynamic of Christ? In several of his letters Paul spoke quite sharply. There are the false teachers in Philippi whom he calls "enemies of the cross" (3:18). There are the "false apostles" who proclaim "another Jesus" (2 Cor. 11:4, 13). There are above all the radical Jewish Christians in Galatia who advocate a "different gospel" (Gal. 1:6). Here Christ, who elsewhere is the basic gift and power of unity, becomes the dividing line that prohibits fellowship. Admittedly Paul would not say it that way. Presumably he would say: since Christ is denied here, he is not able to exercise his own unique power of love. For Paul, it is never Christ who nullifies unity; it is always the people who deny Christ. Of course, we should not forget that Paul presupposes his interpretation of Christ. According to Paul, his opponents in Corinth proclaim "another Jesus," but according to their own self-understanding they also preach the *one* Jesus. They, too, regarded *their* interpretation as the right one. Here one can see clearly the basic problem: we always have Christ, the basic gift of unity, only in particular interpretations. Obviously that must be the case, otherwise Christ would have no content. It is the interpreted Christ, however, who becomes the wall of separation.

For Paul, this interpretation lies in his gospel of justification. Its main point is that Christ alone is the way to God. Only those persons who acknowledge Christ alone as the form of God's love stand with him in the energy grid of fellowship. Thus every attempt to place something else alongside Christ, be it works of the Torah or apostolic authorities, becomes a denial of Christ. Now we must admit that Paul was more than ready to speak on behalf of his gospel of justification in the church. He was also ready to move beyond his own dark side and to reconsider his theological decisions, as he did, for example, about Israel. He was ready to return to a previously disrupted church fellowship, as he did, for example, with Peter. His "anathema" against specific people was not always definitive. In a given conflict, however, there were limits to his willingness to communicate. According to his own words, he would break off church fellowship even with angels if they proclaimed a different gospel (Gal. 1:8).

In my judgment, there are open questions here. Who has the final word about the *right* interpretation of Christ and thus about the boundary between one's "own" Jesus and the "other Jesus"? Above all, however, is there a timeless "right" interpretation of Christ that is always valid beyond a concrete situation? The Risen One is the living Lord who speaks in the Spirit. Could that mean that the divisive distinction between him and the "other Jesus" must be sought and determined anew in every historical situation? If so, then we would have to draw a distinction between exclusions and ruptures that Christ would require in concrete situations, and passing on and making permanent those ruptures which in new situations may miss the gospel.

(b) *The "ethical heresy."* Along with the betrayal of Christ that could lead Paul to break fellowship, there is another form of betrayal that is just as severe. It is the breach of fellowship that ultimately is a form of destroying Christ. That is the issue with which Paul deals in Romans 14–15. There he declares that loving the weak brothers is more important than clearly documenting that in the Lord there is no longer purity or impurity (Rom. 14:14-15). The argument is similar to that in 1 Corinthians, where destroying the fellowship is destroying the Lord's Supper itself (1 Cor. 11:27). Here the sin against the weak brothers is a sin against Christ himself (8:12; cf. 1:13). One could say that, although in the conflict in Galatia and in Paul's controversies with his opponents in 2 Corinthians and in Philippians we have the basic form of what later was called dogmatic heresy, the content of these texts deals with the later so-called "ethical heresy." Its essence in Paul is the destruction of love, the essence of the "law of Christ" (Gal. 6:2). Thus with Paul there is not only the case that fellowship must sometimes be terminated for the sake of the truth of faith; there is also the case that the destruction of fellowship destroys Christ himself. It is not only the maintenance but also the breaking of fellowship that can destroy the church. The church can also betray her Lord by refusing fellowship.

The most difficult problem lies in deciding when fellowship can no longer be continued for the sake of the truth of faith, and when, on the other hand, refusing fellowship *destroys* the truth of faith. Paul was able to decide one way, as he did in Galatia with Peter and the Jewish Christians, or the other way, as he did in Romans with the weak brothers. Is there a criterion for this decision? We have suggested that whenever "brothers" make their own position a *condition* and thus declare it to be necessary, Paul resisted them.[71] That was the case where "false brothers" tried to win the church over to their side. Wherever people (such as those who thought differently from Paul in matters of the Torah) did not try to do this, Paul continued to regard them as brothers. That is to say, where Christ is no longer the *sole* creator of fellowship, but it is based on other principles and truths along with him (for example, the *principle* of freedom from the ritual law or the *principle* of obligation to it), the fellowship is destroyed with him. That is true even when this "other" is a particular interpretation of Jesus Christ himself.[72]

THE POST-APOSTOLIC AGE

6. Developments in the Church after the Death of the Apostles

6.1. Tensions and Divergences

Even after Paul's death, his conflict with Jewish Christianity had by no means come to an end. It is true, of course, that historical developments worked to the advantage of law-free Gentile Christianity. It increased numerically and geographically. Especially wherever Jews did live as minorities, it had a considerable absorbing power. Adult second-generation Christians of Jewish Christian families, who in primarily Gentile Christian churches no longer actively participated in Jewish community life, most likely were simply assimilated into the Gentile Christian church. They brought into the churches many of the traditions of the Diaspora synagogues, but the problem of Torah observance and circumcision just naturally disappeared. One sees this, for example, in *1 Clement,* which throughout shows the influence of Hellenistic Jewish traditions. In many ways the same is true of James and Hebrews. Even the Deutero-Pauline epistles and the Lukan writings show, each in its own way, how the problem of Law observance and circumcision disappears.

On the other hand, where Torah-faithful Jewish Christianity was able to maintain itself — that is, in areas in the East with a large Jewish population — Paul often remained controversial and fiercely opposed. As examples one can cite the Ebionites, the Elkesaites, and the Jewish Christians of the Pseudo-

71. Cf. above, pp. 68-69.

72. As a critical question to myself I acknowledge that one might ask: Is that the interpretation of Paul of a liberal Protestant who has no place for absolute (e.g., dogmatic) principles?

Clementines.[73] They all rejected him. Luke, who in Acts writes a story of Paul with an extensive introduction, has to defend him. He anchors Paul firmly in the primitive apostolic church, has the twelve Jerusalem apostles approve of his move to the Gentiles, and introduces James, the brother of the Lord, as his greatest defender (Acts 15:13-21; cf. 21:22-26).

The Apocalypse of John bears witness to a sharp religious-cultural conflict. Behind this work stands a group of Jewish Christian prophets who, presumably after the destruction of Jerusalem, found a new home in the Pauline churches of the province of Asia. Admittedly, the conflict is primarily between church and state in the time of the Domitian persecutions of the Christians, but the way these persecutions are considered in the Apocalypse is characteristically different from the somewhat contemporary authors of 1 Peter or the Lukan writings. Why? It is because one also sees in the Apocalypse a social and cultural conflict between Hellenistic-Roman urban life and poor Jews from an outlying area of the Roman Empire who had suffered through the gruesome times of the bloody rebellion against Rome. The visions of the Apocalypse give us a glimpse into the hearts of people who were not at home in the Hellenistic-Roman, urban-capitalistic world. The religious traditions they brought with them made them strangers in this world. They represented an apocalyptic dualism and a rigorous ethos and rejected every compromise with the Gentile-urban world. The prophet John rose up against the crushing luxury of the "whore," Rome, and against the Roman state, the beast from the abyss (Revelation 13 and 17). He saw no way out of the situation, and his only hope was that Christ would soon return.

From the letters of Revelation 2–3 one can get an impression of how much — or how little — the prophet John and his Jewish Christian fellow prophets were able to attract a following in the Gentile Christian churches of Asia Minor. It happened in various degrees, depending on the church. According to the letters, in some of the churches there are serious tensions with the Gentile Christian majority. John has only words of condemnation for people who find nothing objectionable about meat sacrificed to idols or who share in the prosperity of the age (Rev. 2:14, 20; 3:17-18). He says nothing at all about the apostle Paul, who directly or indirectly influenced many of the

73. *Ebionites:* an imprecise term usually used as a collective designation of the Torah-faithful Jewish Christians of the post-apostolic period about whom the church fathers report; cf. Irenaeus, *Adversus haereses* 1.26.2. *Elkesaites:* followers of a Jewish Christian prophet (name unknown) active in eastern Syria at the time of Trajan. His followers called him "hidden power" (Aramaic: *hjl ksj,* bowdlerized as Elxai or Elkesai). *Pseudoclementines:* a voluminous Jewish Christian work of fiction from the third/fourth century, parts of which were older. On the anti-Paulinism of Jewish Christianity, cf. Lüdemann, *Opposition to Paul* (above, n. 49), pp. 119-99.

churches to which he writes. There is no place for Paul's name on the gates of the heavenly Jerusalem (cf. 21:14). On the other hand, it is important that John and his like-minded supporters regarded the Gentile Christian churches of Asia Minor without reservations as "their" churches. That is by no means self-evident in view of the difference between their understanding of faith and that of the Pastoral Epistles that came from the same area. Thus the existence of this Jewish Christian circle of prophets in the Gentile Christian churches of Asia Minor itself calls attention to the integrating power of the common confession of Jesus, and at the same time it is an indication of the breadth and tolerance that was possible in those churches. In any case, that the Johannine Apocalypse was accepted into the canon shows that the Gentile Christian church was able and ready to integrate these prophets with their uncompromising dualism and their severe Jewish Christian ethos.

Other tensions from the early period continue to exist. It is likely that *tensions between rich and poor* lie behind the Epistle of James. Such tensions also lie behind the Lukan writings. The fundamental renunciation of possessions on the part of Jesus and his disciples is designed to summon the well-to-do members of the churches to solidarity with the poor. The detailed slave paranesis of some of the household codes may reflect *controversies about the position of slaves* in the church (Col. 3:22-25; 1 Pet. 1:18-25).

We find a *generational conflict* in the Corinthian church at the time of *1 Clement,* but now the signs are reversed from those in Matthew 10:34-37. Now the young are admonished to be obedient to the (Christian) elders. We hear little of possible *controversies over the position of women in the churches.* Only 1 Corinthians 14:34-36 (in my judgment a post-Pauline addition) and the parallel instructions of 1 Timothy 2:11-15, which deprive women of the right to speak in worship, might serve as evidence of such controversies.

In the post-apostolic period, however, there are new tensions and problems we have not yet seen. An important problem is hidden in the designation "post-apostolic period." The *death of the apostles* confronted the Christian communities with problems of a special nature. The death of Peter or of Paul or of other apostles left an authority vacuum in the churches. For the first Christian generation, the apostles, and only the apostles, were authorized representatives of the exalted Lord Jesus. Yet the apostles had not only a unique authority but also an authority in the whole church. Except for the itinerant prophets and teachers in the region of Syria, after the death of the apostles there were no living persons who were recognized as authorities in the whole church. The apostles had not arranged for successors. We do not know whether the reports that they appointed elders in the churches (Acts 14:23; cf. *1 Clement* 42.4) are historically reliable, but it is certain that in their churches the elders were able neither to replace the authority of the apostles in the whole church nor to carry on their unique authority rooted in the authorization granted by an appearance of Jesus. Characteristic here is the evidence of the Pastoral Epistles. They are aware of an ordination, presumably of the presbyters by a council of presbyters, but they give no indication that the apostolic disciples Timothy and Titus had been appointed by Paul to a function in the whole church. Even in *1 Clement* we read only that in the districts and cities in which the apostles preached they had appointed "their first converts . . . to be episkopoi and deacons" (42.4). Thus there is a "succession" of the apostles only in the local churches, not in the whole church. It is possible that after his death disciples of Paul to an extent may have carried on his work (cf. 2 Tim. 4:9-13; Col. 4:7-17), but they did this not as apostles and not with an authority in any way comparable to that of the apostles.[74] Thus the death of the apostles meant the loss of something irreplaceable and was a major problem precisely for the oecumene.

Moreover, we see in the post-apostolic period that the churches were increasingly disturbed by *false teachers.* I am not yet speaking here of Gnostics, whom (in my judgment) we do not meet until the latest New Testament writings, produced around the year 100 (Pastoral Epistles, 2 Peter, perhaps the Johannine letters, and Acts). Even before the threat from Gnosticism, however, we meet an amazingly large number of false teachers. Several factors play a role here. As the temporal and geographical distance from the origin of Christianity increased, unruly and damaging elements were introduced into the tradition. The number of churches increased and thus also the possibility of diverse developments. In Gentile areas early Christianity ran into a milieu in which syncretism and religious borrowing were simply taken for granted. Prophecy posed a special problem. Early Christianity was a movement strongly influenced by prophecy. The more prophets and prophetic traditions there were, the greater became the problem of constraining and controlling them. One can scarcely find any writings from this period in which prophetic false teachers do not appear (cf. Mark 13:6, 21-22; Matt. 7:15-23; 24:11-12; Rev. 2:20; 2 Pet. 2:1; 1 John 4:1-6; *Didache* 11–13; *Hermas Mandate* 11). And this was precisely in the difficult time of transition after the death of the apostles, when the corrective function of apostolic authority was missing. Naturally, in this time of transition after the death of the founding fathers, such experiences caused great uncertainty in the churches.

74. The pseudonymous Pauline letters make that quite clear. They presuppose the continuing authority of the apostle and not an authority of his disciples that would compare with his authority.

6.2. Unity-promoting Forces: Overview

For the following period we must now repeat much of what is true of the church of the first generation.

Baptism and the *Lord's Supper* continue to be a fundamental bond of unity. One sees that in texts such as Ephesians 4:5 or *Didache* 9.4. Many texts also make clear how important the *Christ confession* is as a verbal expression of the basic gift of unity. First Timothy 2:1-6 understands the confession of the *one* God and *one* mediator Jesus Christ as the basis of the church's prayer for all people. This in turn goes hand-in-hand with the missionary task that Paul, the teacher of the Gentiles, and the churches have received from God. In his letter to the Smyrnaeans Ignatius of Antioch describes the death and resurrection of Jesus as the "insignia" of the *one* church (1:1-2). First John 4:15 says: "Whoever confesses that Jesus is the Son of God, God remains in him and he in God." Since God is love, this remaining with the confession also means remaining in love, and that means remaining in the lived unity of the church. The Pauline idea that the truth of the gospel and the fellowship of love are inseparable is expressed in 1 John with special clarity.

In this period the *contacts among the churches* continued to be important as an experience of belonging to one another. It is true that, apart from the timely light the journey to Rome of the martyr-bishop Ignatius gives us, there are almost no direct sources, but it is possible to draw conclusions from the evidence. The circle of prophets around the apocalyptic-thinking John in Asia Minor or the circle around the Elder of the Johannine letters shows how interregional contacts among the churches functioned. Ephesians,[75] 1 Peter, and the Apocalypse of John with its letters are directed to several churches in Asia Minor. The Pastoral Epistles speak to all the churches in Paul's area, and they presuppose intensive communication among the churches. For the area of Syria, Palestine, and, in part, Asia Minor, contacts among the churches continued to be maintained by itinerant prophets or disciples of the Lord such as the ones who were important for Papias. From the *Didache* one can see how numerous they were and how much, under certain conditions, they could cause problems.[76]

The rapid *spread of traditions and writings* also suggests that there were many contacts among the churches. The Sayings Source is known not only in its native Palestine but also in neighboring Syria and in that area of the church (perhaps Rome) where Luke expanded it with his special material and

75. Ephesians is a circular writing directed to several churches in Asia Minor.
76. *Didache* 11–13.

used it as an important source of his Gospel. Quite soon after the Gospel of Mark was written (possibly in Rome), it was used by Matthew (in Syria) and by Luke. It must have also directly or indirectly influenced the Johannine circle. The historian Luke was a great collector of traditions; his Gospel and his book of Acts give the impression that he was well traveled. Ignatius is already familiar at least with the Gospels of Matthew and John and with several letters of Paul. We must ask ourselves whether the Gospels, much like certain pseudonymous letters, had not been written from the very beginning for larger areas of the church or even for the whole church.[77]

That brings us to the unifying forces that in our age have received special, new importance. They are the following:

- The young Christian movement was increasingly regarded by its contemporaries as a separate religion. That was not without consequences for its own inner cohesion (section 6.3).
- The common tradition gained increasing importance — both the tradition of Jesus and the apostolic traditions (section 6.4).
- The figures of the deceased apostles became founding figures of the entire church (section 6.5).
- A homogenous structure of ministries gradually developed in the entire church (section 6.6).
- And, finally, there now arose ecclesiological concepts that regarded the whole church as a given and that reflected on the unity of the church (section 7).

6.3. Christianity as an Independent Religion

Our first unity-promoting force has nothing to do with Christ as the basic gift of unity; it is an external factor. With the beginning of the post-apostolic pe-

77. This is the thesis of Martin Hengel, *Der unterschätzte Petrus* (Tübingen: Mohr/Siebeck, 2006), pp. 51-52. In Matthew's case, 28:16-20 could be cited in support of the thesis. In the case of John, the Johannine circle was made up of itinerant teachers who maintained contacts with the churches and could circulate the writings (2 John; 3 John). In the case of Mark and Luke-Acts, both of which may have been written in Rome, the network of churches in the capital city helped spread their material quickly. We can assume that almost all early Christian writings were read in church gatherings — something that naturally helped make them known. Unlike other ancient authors, the earliest Christians did not need to organize special "readings" to promote their books. In the case of Luke-Acts, it is also possible that Theophilus, as the person to whom the book was dedicated, was expected to disseminate the work.

riod, early Christianity was increasingly recognized as an independent religion separate from Judaism. In quite different ways this was the case from both Jewish and non-Jewish perspectives. This change in the way outsiders perceived Christianity had internal consequences.

I will begin with the Jewish perspective. In the period of time we are discussing, the church experienced an increasing separation from Israel. Naturally it happened in quite different ways. Generally one can say that it was hardly noticeable in Gentile Christian churches. The former pagans who became Christians without first having been proselytes or "god-fearers" did not need to separate from Israel. They had never worshiped in synagogues. As time passed, they became more and more numerous.

On the other hand, for many Jewish followers of Jesus the separation from Israel was quite painful. The Gospel of Matthew speaks, for example, of persecutions (23:34-36), and the Gospel of John of expulsions from the synagogue (9:22; 12:42; 16:2). Such experiences and the identity crises associated with them make it understandable that we find sharp demarcations from Judaism precisely in New Testament texts with a Jewish Christian background. Matthew's wholesale and largely historically unjustified polemic against the "hypocritical scribes and Pharisees" (Matthew 23) is well known. It ends with Jesus and his disciples leaving the Temple — for good, never to return (Matt. 24:1-2). After this harsh polemic, followed by Jesus' pronouncement of judgment (Matt. 23:34-39), readers who were at least inwardly undecided had no choice but to follow Jesus. They, too, left the Temple with Jesus. One of the purposes of this chapter was to underscore the inner break with the Temple and its leaders. Yet severing the connection to the Jewish leaders and to the Temple automatically strengthened the fellowship of the followers of Jesus among themselves. Now they had to depend on themselves.

Things are similar in the Gospel of John. In its first part (chapters 2–12) it portrays Jesus' increasingly harsh conflict with the Jewish leaders, who with growing frequency are simply called "the Jews." The central point on which they take offense is that Jesus, who of course is a human being, "made himself equal with God" (5:18; similarly 10:33). For this reason the Jews wanted to stone him. The official decision of the high priests and the Pharisees that Jesus must be killed (11:47-53) serves as the transition to the passion. Jesus himself says conclusively that the majority of the nation is hardened (12:38-41). After the foot washing and before his death, Jesus gives his disciples alone his farewell discourses, introduced with the new commandment of brotherly love that corresponds to Jesus' love for them (13:34-35). In the large trial scene before Pilate, however, the hostile "Jews" demonstrate that they are definitively incapable of meeting and understanding Jesus. Along with rejecting Jesus, they betray their own faith. They say, "We have no king but Caesar" (19:15). In the Gospel of John "the Jews" are blackened in studied and literarily skillful ways. The kinds of negative "antitypes" we find in the Gospels of John and Matthew strengthen the reader's own identity and the consciousness of belonging to a new religious community different from Israel. People who must burn their bridges know the significance of the new community that supports them.

The parting of the ways of Israel and the Jesus communities is mirrored in other New Testament writings as well. It is almost always accompanied by a people-of-God ecclesiology. The church is understood in them as the people of God that has replaced Israel as the people of God or that has tacitly inherited the position. People-of-God ecclesiologies are always oriented toward the whole church, and thus at least indirectly they strengthen the unity of the church. The opposition to Israel that is part of such a people-of-God ecclesiology is not necessarily explicit. Sometimes the church can also assume people-of-God titles as if Israel had never existed, but usually the antithesis is explicit. It does not always lead to a "hard" substitution theology according to the model, "Israel rejected Jesus; the church has replaced Israel as God's people." There are also various kinds of models of "transition" theologies. This model says: "Israel has become the church, because parts of Israel have accepted Jesus." One can also connect the "hard" substitution model and the "transition" model and call the result a "soft" substitution model.

The canonical Epistle of James is an example of a work with an implicit people-of-God ecclesiology. In literary style it follows the pattern of a Jewish Diaspora letter, and it is directed to the "twelve tribes in the Dispersion" (Jas. 1:1). The reference is to the church, and that means the whole church — not Israel, which is not even mentioned. Another example is 1 Peter. The members of the church are "the chosen race, the royal priesthood, a holy people, the people of the possession." Earlier they were "no people, but now [they are] God's people" (1 Pet. 2:9-10). Israel is mentioned only indirectly: the "chosen and precious cornerstone" that had been laid in Zion has become the stone of offence (cf. 1 Pet. 2:6-8).

More numerous are the works that mention Israel explicitly. Ephesians 2:11-22 is an example of a "soft" substitution model.[78] Christ, "our peace," has reconciled with one another and with God those who at one time were near — namely, Israel — and those who at one time were far — namely, the Gentiles — and he did so by bringing them together into *one* body, the church (Eph. 2:14-18). Acts is an example of what one might call a "half soft" substitution model. Jesus, and after him the twelve apostles, and finally James, the brother

78. Cf. below, p. 127.

of the Lord, gather the people of Israel to Jesus with great success. It is Paul's missionary activity that increasingly shows another picture. Now the Gentiles flow to Jesus, and with increasing clarity the Jews become nay-sayers and disturbers of the peace. At the end of Acts, Paul calls out to the Jews of Rome that now God's salvation has been sent to the Gentiles who will listen to him (Acts 28:28).[79] Hebrews offers an example of a "hard" substitution model. It speaks of the pilgrimage of the true people of God who have a heavenly high priest, and it sets the old and the new covenants in opposition to one another. The "disinheritance" of the old people of God/Israel is especially drastic here: the Temple cult in the old covenant is obsolete and ineffective. The Apocalypse of John is also one of the writings with a "hard" substitution model. The titles and the hope of the people of God/Israel are transferred to the church; harsh words are spoken on Israel itself.[80] The Gospel of Matthew evidences tendencies toward a "hard" theology of substitution: the kingdom of God will be taken from Israel's leaders and given to a people who produce its fruits (Matt. 21:43). Admittedly, this new people is not directly identified with the church; it will have to prove itself in the final judgment as the true church.

All of these works use Israel's self-understanding to lay out a whole-church, people-of-God ecclesiology. In all of these cases, this ecclesiology serves to strengthen the church's own identity, and in so doing it also strengthens its solidarity and unity. The connections between a people-of-God ecclesiology and the unity of the church are not explicitly clear in all cases. Later we will discuss in more detail several places where this happens (sections 7.1-3). In all the cases it will be true, however, that this people-of-God ecclesiology has little to do anymore with the people-of-God ecclesiology of James, the brother of the Lord ("church in Israel"), and the people-of-God ecclesiology of Paul ("church vis-à-vis Israel and for Israel"). It is true that in the later history of its influence this people-of-God ecclesiology often strengthened the unity of the church, but it sometimes did so in problematic or even horrible ways.

Not only from the Jewish side but also from the Gentile side, in the post-apostolic period Christianity was increasingly seen to be an independent religion distinct from Judaism. According to what is likely a historical note in Acts, the disciples of Jesus were called "Christians" from the early days of the church in Antioch (Acts 11:26). The name was not a Christian self-designation; it was given by outsiders, and it presupposes that in those days the followers of Jesus were already recognized as an independent entity. That

79. On Luke's ecclesiology and his view of church unity, cf. below, pp. 111-12 and 132-36.
80. Cf. below, pp. 129-32.

was not true everywhere. It was not the case in Rome at the end of the 40s, if the note in Suetonius that Emperor Claudius expelled the Roman Jews who "were constantly causing disturbances at the instigation of Chrestus" (Suetonius, *Claudius* 26.4) actually refers to Jesus Christ and the inner Jewish controversies between Jesus Jews and Jews hostile to Jesus. A decisive turning point, however, was the persecution of Christians in Rome under Nero, who made scapegoats of the Christians for the fire in A.D. 64 that he himself may have started. That was possible only because, first of all, in the Rome of that day the populace saw the Christians as a special religious group — as Christians — and in the second place because the Christians did not have the best reputation. Their religion was widely regarded as a "pernicious superstition" (Tacitus, *Annals* 15.44.3). Naturally, these events in the capital city quickly became widely known and influential. They introduced the epoch of Christian persecutions that flared up from time to time. Internally they became a powerful force promoting cohesion. Suffering creates bonds among people! Since the suffering came from the Roman state and thus was "ecumenical," it strengthened not only the local churches but also the ecumenical fellowship. The Apocalypse of John is the best example here (section 7.2).

6.4. Tradition as a Unity-promoting Factor (with Joachim Diestelkamp)

The post-apostolic period was a time of increased orientation to tradition. It was characterized by the need to receive the traditions of other churches as well — that is, of openness to the church's entire tradition.

The most important tradition was the *Jesus tradition.* Especially in the communities far removed from the land of Israel, one had to explain who this Jesus was whose teachings, atoning death, and resurrection the church confessed; and with the passage of time it became increasingly important to secure the traditions about him. Far from Israel, probably in Rome after the persecutions and martyrdoms under the emperor Nero, there arose the need to tell the entire story of the earthly Jesus and in the process to focus attention on his path of suffering to Jerusalem. That was the permanent basis of tradition, the authoritative "beginning of the proclamation" (Mark 1:1), and it was the concern of the Gospel of Mark.

In Syria there lived the Jewish Christian evangelist Matthew, whose communities looked back on the break with the synagogues and in addition were troubled by prophets who performed miracles and exorcised demons in the name of Jesus (Matt. 7:22-23). In this situation Matthew retold Mark's story of Jesus. In so doing he wanted to say that this Jesus is the one who "is

with us always until the end of the world" (28:20); he is God's Immanuel (1:24). An important part of his story of Jesus was Jesus' preaching — Jesus' gospel of the kingdom (4:23), the message the Jesus missionaries proclaimed in the whole world (28:20).

Luke, who was probably a companion of Paul in his earlier years, may also have lived in Rome. He collected the traditions about Jesus more thoroughly and more reliably (Luke 1:3) than any of his predecessors. It was he who first made many of the Jesus traditions known in the churches of the Diaspora. His purpose was to provide the Christian catechumens with a complete and reliable basis in tradition for everything they had been taught (1:3-4). We have already seen that the Gospels were understood as a priceless possession of the whole church.[81] They were sent immediately to other local churches and quickly became known in the entire church.

In the post-apostolic period it was also clear that Jesus Christ is the basic gift for church unity. More than earlier, however, one found this basic gift in the common, authoritative tradition. In the second century the appeal to the Jesus tradition became increasingly important. One understood Jesus' words as the words of the living "Lord." As a rule they were mediated through the texts of the Gospels, but then they were again made part of the oral tradition and were applied anew in new contexts. The *Didache*, *2 Clement*, and Justin show this with special clarity.

Along with the words of the Lord, there was the tradition of the *apostles*. Here, too, traditions of the entire church were collected and exchanged. In the case of Paul, his letters were already an expression of his ecumenical authority. When he composed his letter to the Roman church as a comprehensive account of his beliefs, it was more than a tactical move to introduce himself in Rome. He also directed 1 Corinthians to the believers "in every place" (1 Cor. 1:2), Galatians to the churches in Galatia (Gal. 1:1), 2 Corinthians to the church in Corinth and to "the saints in all Achaia" (2 Cor. 1:1). Colossians — perhaps written by a companion of Paul while he was still living — was to be read in Laodicea and, conversely, the (lost) letter from Laodicea was also to be read in Colossae (Col. 4:16). Kurt Aland has conjectured with good reasons that the Pauline letters were passed on by the churches to which they were addressed "to the neighboring churches as soon as possible to strengthen the sense of solidarity."[82] That would explain why Galatians was preserved even though the Galatian churches did not survive and why differing small collec-

81. Cf. above, p. 96.

82. Kurt Aland, "Die Entstehung des Corpus Paulinum," in Aland, *Neutestamentliche Entwürfe*, TB 63 (Munich: Kaiser, 1979), p. 350.

tions preceded our present Pauline corpus. Thus the churches did not regard the apostolic letters they received as a private possession that spoke only to them. When the Pauline churches collected and exchanged apostolic letters, they demonstrated that the authority of the apostle was something permanent, unique, and unrepeatable for the whole church. Given what it was, it could not be taken over by some other officeholder in the church.[83]

This is the very thing the pseudo-apostolic letters also express. It would be wrong to try to understand them simply in terms of the (multiform and complex) general phenomenon of ancient pseudepigraphy, for it is evident that there was a special outpouring of pseudonymous writings precisely during the post-apostolic period.

Taking a closer look at the subject of *pseudonymity:* with certainty, or probability, almost all[84] of the New Testament witnesses from the post-apostolic period are or became pseudonymous. The literary character of their pseudonymity varies. In some cases they are letters written by pupils, of which there were many in antiquity. They are to be regarded as forgeries only when they use literary devices to try to make their authenticity plausible.[85] In other cases — especially when other documents appear as letters — we have originally anonymous works that later were attributed to apostles.[86]

Usually the pseudonymous documents of the post-apostolic age are *letters.* That is noteworthy. It shows that later generations regarded the letter as a specifically early Christian form. As far as we know, however, the apostle Paul was the only one who wrote letters. When there are in addition pseudonymous letters under the name of Peter, of James, or of Barnabas, it shows that the apostle Paul had a wide-ranging influence far beyond his direct sphere of activity. This, too, is an expression of whole-church thinking.[87]

All pseudonymous texts are attributed to *apostles.*[88] In early Christian-

83. Cf. Kurt Stalder, "Die Nachfolger der Apostel," *IKZ* 59 (1969): 192-211.

84. Exceptions are, in my judgment, 2 and 3 John, Revelation (which comes from a prophet, John), and the Lukan two-volume work (which, in my judgment, was written by Luke, the companion of Paul).

85. That is the case with 2 Thessalonians, the Pastorals, and 2 Peter, but not with Ephesians, James, and 1 Peter.

86. I am thinking here of the Gospels according to Matthew, Mark, and John as well as the tracts Hebrews and 1 John.

87. In addition to James, works that show influences of or connections with Pauline ideas are the letters of 1 Peter (which also presupposes the Gospel of Matthew), 2 Peter, *1 Clement, Barnabas,* and the letters of Polycarp.

88. According to 1 Cor. 15:7 and Gal. 1:19, James, the brother of the Lord, was regarded as an apostle. He is probably also regarded as an apostle in Acts 15:2, 13, 22. Apostleship is uncertain only for the Lord's brother, Jude. Cf., however, 1 Cor. 9:4-5.

ity there are no pseudonymous letters attributed to figures from a distant past, such as the letter of Baruch to the nine-and-a-half tribes (*Syriac Baruch* 78–86), which originated in Judaism at about the same time. That shows how strongly the post-apostolic period was focused on the authority of the apostles. It was a post-apostolic time not only in a temporal but also in a material sense. That is to say, it understood that it had a relationship to the authority of the apostles and that it was itself of a lesser order. In many pseudo-apostolic letters, the authors are not hiding behind the authority of the apostles simply to give weight to their own minimal authority. They are, rather, directly advocating in their own time the apostles' concern, and they are reminding the church of the apostolic authority that alone was the basis of the church's life. It may well be that after the apostles died and before there existed a clear official authority, there was a certain feeling of helplessness in the church. More important than this, however, is the conviction of the writers of letters that the church continued to be grounded on apostolic authority.

Finally, we need to remember the *ecumenical character* of most pseudo-apostolic letters. Ephesians is presumably a circular writing sent to several Pauline churches in the province of Asia. First Peter is directed to the churches in the northern, western, and central parts of Asia Minor. The Pastorals speak to the entire area of Paul's churches; their geographical horizon reaches from Nicopolis in Epirus to the border of Syria, and they were written possibly from Rome or Ephesus. James is directed to the twelve tribes of Israel in the Diaspora — that is, to the entire church, not merely to the Jewish Christianity scattered throughout the world. Second Peter, Jude, and the *Epistle of Barnabas* are also ecumenical letters. In the case of Hebrews, one can entertain the possibility that a concrete address — which, along with the name of the apostle, originally may have stood at the head of the letter — was omitted in order to emphasize its ecumenical character. Only 2 Thessalonians, which really was addressed to the church of Thessalonica, is an exception here.

In short, it is amazing to what extent the pseudo-apostolic letters are ecumenical letters. It is an indication that people were aware that apostolic authority embraced the entire church. The pseudo-apostolic letters make it clear that people regarded the whole church as a reality and that a church life in which each community was completely autonomous and lived only for itself would contradict the essence of the apostolic heritage. Thus people were aware that there was such a thing as the whole church centuries before it had a visible representative in the form of the papacy and quite some time before all local churches had secured an official structure in the form of the office of bishop — a structure that made communication and coordination possible among the churches in a relatively simple way.

All of that is captured in an especially meaningful way by the *Pastoral Epistles*. Here the apostolic tradition becomes the basic gift of church unity, and remaining in it becomes its condition. Joachim Diestelkamp explains (in the next six paragraphs):

At first glance the Pastoral Epistles appear to be private letters of Paul to two of his closest co-workers that quite by accident were passed on to the church. The ecumenical perspective seems to be completely absent from them. Yet this impression changes completely as soon as one looks at how these letters functioned in the churches for which in reality they were conceived.

Certain (probably Gnostic-oriented) false teachers are undermining large parts of Paul's former missionary territory (2 Tim. 1:15; Tit. 1:10-16). For the author of the Pastorals that threatens the Pauline-apostolic tradition. To counter the threat, he attributes to Paul the instructions, ordinances, and admonitions so characteristic of the letters. And he does so because he knows that he has an obligation to Paul's work and because he wants to protect the apostolic tradition.

The loss of the personal (or epistolary) apostolic presence must have been drastic. Paul's co-workers could not even come close to replacing it, and after they died the threat was even greater that the church would lose a coherent theological tradition that united churches and provinces and that previously had been embodied in living persons. Now a fictitious Paul, as he is presented in an exemplary way in the fourth chapter of 2 Timothy, must fill this vacuum.

Also, as presented in 2 Timothy, Paul is not a solitary missionary. Shortly before his martyrdom he holds all the threads of his mission work in his hand. The apostle's pupils are the bridge to the local churches. Beginning with Timothy and Titus, Paul orders his co-workers to and fro in the entire area of the church that is under his influence (1 Tim. 1:4; 2 Tim. 4:12; Tit. 3:12). He is informed about each of them, and he knows who is faithful and who is unfaithful (2 Tim. 1:15; 4:10; etc.). Through the apostle's pupils the author relates the various towns and provinces to Paul, and he combines a number of former mission areas. Through them Paul's instructions once again reach his church. Both temporally and geographically the co-workers bridge the distance to Paul. Paul himself is the "vanishing point" on which attention is focused. Thus what is at stake in the letters is the unity of the Pauline church.

The activity of the false teachers has raised the truth question. The Pastoral Epistles show pointedly how the issue was dealt with in the post-apostolic period. In them one no longer argues theologically; now one engages in polemics — indeed, one resorts to insult and slander (cf. 2 Tim. 3:1-

9). The bulwark the letters direct against the false teachers is in part a shallow and rigid Pauline "doctrine." Its purpose is to protect the gospel and keep it pure. As a consequence, the ongoing task is to preserve and pass on this tradition (1 Tim. 6:14; 2 Tim. 1:13-14; 2:1-2). Without the Pauline-apostolic tradition one can no longer truly have the gospel. Thus the tradition becomes a basic gift of faith. For those who do not believe in accordance with this Pauline-apostolic tradition, Christ is distorted, and they place themselves outside the unity of the church, together with the false teachers. Here the "healthy doctrine" has become a connecting link, but it is also a precondition of unity. In my judgment the process is justified by the situation. It was a time in which the church could preserve its identity only by preserving the apostolic tradition. And yet, when tradition becomes the highest principle, the gospel itself is shackled, because the tradition destroys the gospel's own freedom to find new expressions in changing situations.

Such an established apostolic tradition places limits on the separate development of local churches. A congregational principle is hardly compatible with it. Timothy is charged to bring certain congregations back "in line" (1 Tim. 1:3). That doubtless means that for all practical purposes a certain mutual supervision of the Pauline local churches is intended, but the Pastorals do not yet think in terms of an official supra-congregational structure that could provide this supervision institutionally. Even their author does not believe that he is empowered to speak by his own authority or, like Ignatius, to claim authority over congregations as a bishop. And yet he believes it is necessary to exercise authority over congregations, since various churches are going their separate ways. His letters are designed to spring into this breach. They require and urge their readers to remain steadfastly in the Pauline-apostolic tradition, to remain united under Paul's authority, and to struggle against the deviates who endanger that unity.

The attention given to tradition in its double form, to the "Lord" and to the apostolic writings, began the process that led to the creation and canonization of the New Testament. Thus the post-apostolic period prepared the groundwork for what today, because it is recognized as such by all churches, is probably the most important basic gift of unity — the Bible. Soon after 100, written texts — the Gospels — were already the most important container for the transmission of the authority of the Lord. For its part, the apostolic tradition had a written form from the beginning. The need for a catholic basis in tradition that was as comprehensive as possible, such as one sees, for example, in the preface of the Gospel of Luke, is analogous in the second century to the reality that four Gospels rather than a single Gospel transmit the words and deeds of the Lord and that not only the Pauline letters but — in contrast to the Pastorals and to Marcion — the entire apostolic tradition becomes the foundation of the church. Thus initially the tradition given the church as its basis was by no means uniform.

We should not think that collecting the books of the New Testament was a defensive act on the part of the church. From the very beginning the New Testament canon was not suited for combating Gnostic heresies, since the canon of the Christian Gnostics never looked different from that of the orthodox Christians. Unlike Marcion, who in his exclusive attachment to Paul is much like the Pastorals, the churchly Christians emphasized how much more open they were. Only later did the developing canon *also* take on a defensive character — namely, in the church's defense against the claims of the increasing number of Gnostic and non-Gnostic pseudo-apostolic works. Collecting the canon, however, was initially an acknowledgment of the basic gift of unity that is authoritative for all Christians, Christ, and the apostles who represent him and who now, in the second and third generations, become the tradition.

Something similar is true of the rule of apostolic faith, the creed. Here, too, the development proceeds slowly. In the second and third early Christian generations we still find a multiplicity of different and sometimes newly accentuated confessions. The concept of the "apostolic" confession of faith emerges gradually.[89] Only in the anti-Gnostic struggle of the second century are certain formulations of the confessions used against the heretics,[90] and not until the anti-Gnostic struggle of the third century is the thesis widely accepted that the solid and unchanging wording of the creed in the whole church is something fundamentally important.[91]

6.5. *The Apostles as Primary Figures of Unity*

Not only the apostles' tradition but above all the apostles themselves became in the post-apostolic period a unifying bond for the church. *Peter and Paul — Poles of Unity:* under this title Franz Mussner has written a small, widely respected book on the unity of the church, and in view of the division between Catholicism and Protestantism he has spoken of Peter and Paul as the "ecu-

89. Irenaeus, *Adversus haereses* 1.10.1: the universal church has "received from the apostles and their disciples this faith."

90. Cf. the "truly" in Ignatius, *To the Trallians* 9–10; *To the Smyrnaeans* 2.

91. Tertullian, *De virginibus velandis* 1: "The rule of faith is altogether one *(una),* alone immovable, and irreformable *(sola immobilis et irreformabilis)*."

menical yokefellows."[92] We would like to add a third person to these yokefellows — James, the brother of the Lord. In the post-apostolic period he also became a primary figure of unity — admittedly, in his way and limited in part to Jewish Christian circles. By adding him to the "ecumenical yokefellows," we want to remind ourselves of Jewish Christianity, which in the post-apostolic period was repressed and largely forgotten, and of its concerns, which were rendered marginal. An essential part of the unity of the church is its unity with Israel.

6.5.1. *James*

In later times James, the brother of the Lord, became a primary figure of unity. In the Lukan Acts of the Apostles it is he, of all people, who becomes the great defender of the Pauline mission to the Gentiles (15:13-21).[93] There Luke develops a line that is already intimated in the Pauline letters. In Galatians 1 and 2, Paul takes it for granted that James is part of the one church. Thus he mentions him only when he knows that the two of them are in agreement (Gal. 2:9-10). When that is not the case, he mentions him only indirectly (cf. Gal. 2:12; perhaps 2 Cor. 11:5).

In the Epistle of James, written to the "twelve tribes in the Diaspora" (Jas. 1:1), the brother of the Lord is a primary figure of unity for the entire church. To be sure, this letter is far removed from James's basic concern — the church's tie to Israel and to the principle of faithfulness to the Law. Only in the work's deep skepticism about some (vulgar distortion of) Pauline ideas (2:14-26) is there an echo of one of James's concerns. On the other hand, when the work understands the church as the twelve tribes (1:1), thus divorcing the idea from the actual nation of Israel, it turns what James wanted on its head.

A number of Jewish Christian texts speak of something resembling a "primacy of James." According to the Gnostic *Gospel of Thomas* (logion 12), James the Just is "great" among the disciples after Jesus' death. The disciples are to go to him, because heaven and earth were created on his behalf. For the Jewish Christian (in part, Torah-faithful) Pseudo-Clementine writings, a Jewish Christian romance written in the third century, as the bishop of Jerusalem James is the "bishop of the bishops" and "lord" of the entire church.[94] Our

92. Mussner, *Petrus und Paulus*, p. 5.

93. Jacob Jervell, "James: The Defender of Paul," in Jervell, *Luke and the People of God* (Minneapolis: Augsburg, 1972), pp. 185-207.

94. *Epistle of Clement to James* 1.1.

meager sources are in agreement that James was *the* (sole) leader of the Jerusalem church. If the Jerusalem church in any way understood itself as the "presiding capital" of all Christianity, historically the first monarchical episcopate and something resembling a claim of primacy may well have been in Jerusalem and not in Rome.

The Pseudo-Clementines include many other important figures of early Christianity (for example, Peter) in their view of the church, and in this sense they have in their own way a strong ecumenical and whole-church orientation. Admittedly, Paul is not part of this oecumene.

On the whole, as a primary figure of unity James reflects the diminished significance of Jewish Christianity in the entire church. James is primarily a "unity figure" of a marginal group. Only in the church's beginnings was this marginal group an integral part of the movement. That is why it was relatively easy to alienate the figure of James from those things for which it originally stood and to make him the advocate of other concerns. Since the Jewish Christian church in Jerusalem, of which he had been the leader, no longer existed, it could no longer come to his defense. With the author of the canonical epistle James has little in common and almost nothing at all with the (Jewish Christian) Gnostic authors of later James texts.

6.5.2. Peter

We are speaking here of the image of Peter in the post-apostolic period — that is, of Peter as a primary figure of unity in the retrospective of a later time. We have not yet spoken of the significance of the historical Peter for the unity of the church, because much here is hidden in obscurity. Nevertheless, a few brief observations should help reveal how and for whom Peter was able to become a primary figure of unity.[95]

It is probable that Peter already had a prominent position among the disciples of the earthly Jesus. That may have been because he had been called to discipleship especially early. It is conceivable that his surname, *kepha* (Aramaic = stone, lump of stones, seed-stone, infrequently = boulder),[96] comes from the time of Jesus. Therefore, its interpretation as the "rock of the church

95. Following especially Raymond E. Brown, Karl P. Donfried, and John Reumann, *Peter in the New Testament* (Minneapolis: Augsburg, 1973); Rudolf Pesch, *Simon-Petrus: Geschichte und geschichtliche Bedeutung des ersten Jüngers Jesu Christi,* PuP 15 (Stuttgart: Hiersemann, 1980); Christfried Böttrich, *Petrus: Fischer, Fels und Funktionär,* BG 2 (Leipzig: Evangelische Verlagsanstalt, 2001); Joachim Gnilka, *Petrus und Rom: Das Petrusbild in den ersten zwei Jarhhunderten* (Freiburg: Herder, 2002); Hengel, *Der unterschätzte Petrus.*

96. Peter Lampe, "Das Spiel mit dem Petrusnamen," *NTS* 25 (1978/79): 227-45.

of Jesus" in Matthew 16:18 is probably secondary. In all probability, after Easter he received special attention because Jesus first appeared to him (1 Cor. 15:5; Luke 24:34).[97]

In the earliest period he most certainly played a leading role in the Jerusalem church. Not only Acts but also Paul, who soon after his Christ vision went to Jerusalem to meet Peter (Gal. 1:18), testify to this. In contrast to James the brother of the Lord, he traveled early, visited Christians in other places (Acts 8:14-24; 9:32-43), and engaged in missionary work, so that it is no accident that at the Apostolic Council it was he and not James who was entrusted with the mission among the circumcised. Similarly, according to Galatians 2:12 he was personally in Antioch, unlike James. In the Antiochene conflict he assumed a mediating (according to Paul, a vacillating) attitude between Paul and James. Obviously he affirmed table-fellowship with the Gentile Christians and was personally willing to act contrary to the Torah's purity regulations, yet he let the people from James persuade him that table-fellowship did not mean freedom from the Law for all Jewish Christians.[98] Thus the table-fellowship with the Jerusalem people and with it the fellowship of the entire church was very important for him. The old note in Acts 9:43 also testifies to Peter's openness in ritual questions. There Peter was living in Joppa with Simon, a tanner — in other words, with a tradesman for whom ritual purity most certainly was not characteristic.

We know little about the later missionary activity of Peter. The division of the mission into Jewish and Gentile spheres undertaken at the Apostolic Council could not be maintained in the Diaspora, especially since everyone agreed that there should be no separated churches. Thus Peter also became a missionary to the Gentiles. That is reflected in the Cornelius tradition of Acts 10. Although there is a Cephas party in Corinth (1 Cor. 1:12), it is not certain that Peter was ever there. The relationship between Paul and Peter in the years after the Apostolic Council is also a matter of debate. Some assume that in 1 Corinthians 3:10-17 Paul is indirectly speaking against Peter. Martin Hengel even thinks that Peter is the actual authority and a "superlative apostle" (2 Cor. 11:5) behind Paul's opponents, who, according to 2 Corinthians 11–13, attack Paul's apostleship.[99] I do not believe that is the case. If it were, then in

97. Assuming that the first appearance of Jesus was not to Mary Magdalene, which is historically quite possible.

98. Thus, when confronted with the emissaries from Jerusalem, Peter returned to the purity laws of the Torah for the sake of fellowship with them. Did he "become as a Jew to the Jews" (1 Cor. 9:20) for the sake of the fellowship of the church? Paul could well have interpreted his behavior this way. In this case his judgment would have been less harsh.

99. Hengel, *Der unterschätzte Petrus*, pp. 124-25, 149.

1 Corinthians 3:5-15 Paul most likely would have based his argument on the example of Peter rather than on the example of Apollos. Thus, relatively soon after they clashed in Antioch, Peter and Paul had a rapprochement. Another argument in support of this view is that the Cephas people, like the Apollos people and Paul, in principle stood for freedom from the Law. It is clear then that later (after Paul!) Peter worked in Rome and suffered martyrdom there.

Finally, let us consider the controversial question of the origin of the two primacy texts, Matthew 16:18 and John 21:15-17. The Johannine version is part of an Easter appearance, the Matthean version not. A remaining question is whether it is historically appropriate that John 21:15-17 connects the primacy of Peter with an Easter appearance. On the whole, however, John 21 is a much later text,[100] and, just like Matthew 16:18, it does not speak of a *first* appearance of Christ to Peter. It is conceivable, and in my judgment more probable, that both texts have been formulated looking back on the apostolic period. That is to say, they came from a time when it became clear that the apostles really were the "foundation" on which the edifice of the church is built (cf. Eph. 2:20). Naturally, one could write this way only if Peter actually did have a "supporting" significance for the emerging church in the first generation — a significance that exceeded that of the other apostles.

Peter becomes a key figure in the post-apostolic period. What is more, he does so in writings that bear a Jewish Christian imprint (in the Gospel of Matthew and the Gospel of John) as well as in writings with a Gentile Christian stamp (in the Lukan writings, in the Petrine epistles, in the Gospel of Mark according to the church's early tradition[101]). In the Gospel of Mark he is by far the most frequently mentioned disciple of Jesus. Furthermore, he appears in key passages in the composition of the Gospel: at the beginning (Mark 1:16-18), in the middle (8:27-33), and at the end (16:7). In the Gospel of Matthew he is the first disciple called by Jesus (4:16-18; 10:2) as well as the most frequently mentioned spokesman for the disciples; in addition, he is the one who in his "little faith" is the typical disciple (for example, 14:28-31; 16:13-23; 26:69-75). In the first part of Acts, Peter appears as the leader of the Jerusalem church, as *the* one who proclaims the message of Jesus to the Jews, and as the virtual initiator of the Gentile mission, before disappearing from view after the Apostolic Council. In the Gospel of John, Peter is not only the spokesman for the disciples (6:68; 13:6-9); he is also — especially in the postscript

100. The text presupposes Peter's death.

101. The Gospel of Mark has been associated with Peter since Papias and Justin, probably even since 1 Peter.

21:15-19 — the shepherd and representative of the whole church. From the many accents and colors of the New Testament portrait of Peter we will single out those that are especially important for the unity of the church.

First of all, Peter passes on the *Jesus tradition* that is fundamental for the church. This is related to Matthew's report that he was the "first" one called (Matt. 10:2). Luke emphasizes Peter's call even more clearly (Luke 5:1-11). Since for Luke the twelve apostles are witnesses of everything that happened between Jesus' baptism and his ascension (cf. Acts 1:22), one does expect that Peter, as the first one called, would play a special role in the early church. He is also the one who gives the Gentile Cornelius the basic report "from Galilee after the baptism John preached" down to Jesus' resurrection and missionary command (cf. Acts 10:37-42). Second Peter also regards Peter as an eyewitness and guarantor of the tradition. He heard the heavenly voice on the mount of transfiguration (1:16-18), and along with the other apostles he conveyed to the descendants the "commandments of the Lord and Savior" (3:2). The author sets this tradition against the seductions of the false prophets and false teachers. Thus the author of this, the latest New Testament letter, argues not by appealing to a ministry or to the power of the keys given Peter according to Matthew 16:19, but solely on the basis of the tradition of which Peter is the guarantor. In the same way and at about the same time in Asia Minor, Papias appealed to Peter as the guarantor of the tradition contained in the Gospel of Mark.[102] Later, the ancient church interpreted the primacy text of Matthew 16:18: "For the true faith and because his teaching was an exceedingly secure foundation, [Simon was] appointed . . . to be a foundation-stone of the church."[103]

A second important dimension of the New Testament portrait of Peter most likely builds on the mediating position of the historical Peter. In a special way Peter becomes the figure who represents the unity of the *whole church.* One sees that initially in Acts. Luke portrays the primitive church in Jerusalem as being in complete harmony, praising God with *one* heart and *one* soul. It is under the leadership of "Peter and the apostles" (for example, Acts 5:29). Peter is then also the one who, in the name of the church, proclaims the word that increases the church (Acts 2:14-36; 3:12-26; 5:29-32; 10:34-43). Peter's function as a unity figure is especially important with reference to Paul. According to Luke, Peter programmatically takes the lead in the law-free Gentile mission that Paul will later follow in agreement with the Jerusalem apostles. Peter presents to the Jerusalem assembly the Pauline

102. Eusebius, *Historia ecclesiastica* 3.39.15.
103. *Epistle of Clement to James* 1.2.

kerygma of justification by faith alone apart from works of the Law (Acts 15:8-11). Conversely, Luke can have Paul deliver a sermon to the "Israelite men" of Antioch in Pisidia that has the same schema as Peter's previous sermons to Jews and in many of its expressions is reminiscent of them (Acts 13:16-43). In Acts Peter's preaching is Pauline and Paul's is Petrine! It would be difficult to image a more skillfully created testimony to the unity of the church. It may be that we can see something similar in 1 Peter, which a number of exegetes regard as the most Pauline of all pseudepigraphic apostolic letters. Be that as it may, it is clear that its author is not at all interested in advocating a specifically Petrine theology under the pseudonym Peter.[104] In the Gospel of John, Peter represents the mainstream church over against the sectarian Johannine circle.[105]

In summary: especially after his death Peter becomes important as a unity figure of the church. Nowhere does he represent a particular group in competition with other groups. Instead, in the words of 2 Peter, he belongs with his "beloved brother Paul" (2 Pet. 3:15), and together with him he represents the *one* apostolic church.

In the New Testament we are still far removed from a primacy or office of Peter for the whole church. Still, what we know about Peter and the postapostolic New Testament portrait of Peter, makes it understandable why the Pontifical Ministry of Peter was later able to appeal for legitimacy to the New Testament traditions about Peter. (A "ministry of Paul" or a "ministry of James" for the whole church would be less conceivable in terms of the New Testament.) Both as a disciple of Jesus and as a post-Easter apostle and missionary, Peter was a commanding figure. Like no other unity figure, he built bridges among various parts of the church. As with no other early Christian figure, his work encompassed the whole church geographically. Like no other unity figure, he was able to authenticate and embody both parts of the New Testament tradition — the tradition of the "Lord" and the apostolic tradition.

Nevertheless, there is no basis in the New Testament for a consistent and linear development to the later primacy of Peter, for the fact that Peter suffered martyrdom in the imperial city of Rome and thus became an especially important figure for the capital city is as much a historical accident as is the fact that Christianity's expansion took place in an "ecumenical" impe-

104. Which, of course, does not mean that Peter did not have a theology of his own. We simply do not know what it is.

105. Cf. below, pp. 137-39.

rium headed by a monarch whose political structure then called for a corresponding ecclesiastical structure.

6.5.3. Paul (with Joachim Diestelkamp)

Paul is the third major unity figure. Here the picture the texts give is somewhat different, because during his lifetime Paul was by no means a unifying person; he was a controversial figure over whom the spirits divided. In addition, Paul so openly and unchangeably advocated a theology of his own and publicized it with his letters that it was impossible to strip his preaching and his activity of its special profile, as was done with Peter and James, and to draw it back into apostolic unity. The most important texts for us are the Deutero-Paulines, especially Ephesians and the Pastorals, as well as Acts. First, however, I would like to make a few general observations about how Paul was received.

1. Paul became not only an apostle of a particular area of the church or a particular ecclesiastical school of thought. He also became, except for Jewish Christianity, an apostle of the whole church. Among the people to know and use the collection of Paul's letters are not only the "Paulinist" Polycarp but also the theologically un-Pauline Ignatius and the author of 2 Peter. Paul is consistently seen as world missionary, as "herald in the East and in the West" (*1 Clement* 5.6), and as an apostle of the Gentiles (Col. 1:27; Eph. 3:8). His "mission field" is the cosmos. Thus Paul is accepted in the whole church.

2. Paul is almost always included in the oecumene of the apostles. He is not the only apostle. He stands together with Peter (*1 Clement* 5.4-5; 2 Pet. 3:15) or is organically part of the circle of the other apostles (Acts). That confirms what Colossians already states: Paul is a "servant of the church" (Col. 1:25). Admittedly, there are two exceptions to this generally valid observation. In the writings of the church, the Pastoral Epistles give the impression that Paul is not an apostle but *the* apostle, herald, and teacher. For Marcion, then, Paul becomes simply *the* apostle.

3. In keeping with this point is a third observation. The fact that a later period was interested in Paul does not mean that it was interested in his theology. People have often observed (and then drawn conclusions from their observation) that in the post-Pauline mainstream church Pauline theology played a reduced role. That may be because most members of the church did not understand it either during his lifetime or after his death. But it could also be because many of its basic themes, such as the controversy with the Torah, in a later period were no longer relevant or at least no longer appeared to be relevant. Of course, it may also be a matter of our modern perspective. Perhaps we take it too much for granted that Paul was primarily a theologian,

while the post-apostolic witnesses understood him primarily as a missionary, as apostle and planter of churches. Above all, however, here too we can see a clear tendency of the post-apostolic period. Pauline theology is accepted to the degree that it becomes the theology of the whole church. With Luke, for example, Jesus (Luke 18:9-14; cf. 10:29; 16:15) and Peter (Acts 15:8-11) proclaim the Pauline message of justification. Otherwise, Luke takes over little Pauline theology; he does not use Paul's letters as a source. One sees that precisely in his sermons of Paul in Acts. In another way Pauline theology appears in 1 Peter. Here it is taken over as Peter's theology — that is, to the degree that it has become a common Christian possession, apostolic theology. The Pastoral Epistles speak of the tradition that is to be preserved without change *(paratheke)* and of the "healthy doctrine" entrusted to the church without explaining what its content is. They combat false doctrine, but they do so without making use of Paul's theology. Only the two indirectly Pauline or deutero-Pauline letters, to the Colossians and the "Ephesians," constitute, relatively speaking, an exception, since their authors as immediate disciples of Paul were strongly influenced by him. But even they interpret Paul clearly as *the church's* teacher.

We can *summarize* as follows: the people who come after Paul understand him not as a thinker or as an individual but as *one* of the principal apostles and teachers of the church alongside others.

Here we can only sketch briefly some of the special features of the picture of Paul found in individual New Testament writings. For the post-Pauline *Epistle to the Ephesians,* Paul's apostolic activity is part of the divine stewardship *(oikonomia)* (Eph. 3:2). The revelation to Paul near Damascus becomes a milestone of God's comprehensive economy of salvation (Eph. 3:3). Since Colossians and Ephesians meditate on the church as a whole, they reflect on the significance of the Pauline apostleship for the whole church. Ephesians does this in a form that is especially relevant for the question of the church's unity. Ephesians 2:11-18 looks back to the proclamation of "our peace" through which the dividing wall between Israel and the Gentiles, the Torah and its regulations has been broken down. For the author, the miracle of reconciliation brought through Christ is that Jews and Gentiles have become *one* church. Through God's plan the apostle Paul has become the instrument through which the *one* church consisting of Jews and Gentiles came into being. For the author, that is Paul's apostolic work. When one considers how much Paul struggled his entire life for this unity, sacrificing his own life for that cause with his journey to Jerusalem, one sees that the author of Ephesians understood Paul well. He differs from his teacher in only one point. Now that Christ has broken down the dividing wall between Israel and the nations, Israel's special "citizenship" no longer has any significance. The church, the body of Christ that reconciles Jews and Gentiles, makes it superfluous. The author says nothing about the remaining promise for Israel, the *old* people of God. Nothing in Ephesians corresponds to Romans 9–11.

Luke also sees the apostle Paul in the service of the one apostolic church. We will probably find the readers of the Lukan writings where Paul's journey ends: in the law-free Gentile Christianity of Rome, detached from Israel. Luke describes the way from Israel to the Gentiles that God went first with Peter, then especially with Paul. It is a way led by the Spirit and approved by the whole church (Acts 15). Paul is the representative of this way to which Luke's readers owe their own existence in the church. In various ways Luke makes it clear that it is not Paul's own private special way: Paul is accepted by the local church in Damascus (Acts 9:10-22). Peter begins (Acts 10) and provides the theological basis (Acts 15:7-11) for Paul's Torah-free Gentile mission, and James demonstrates that this way is biblical (Acts 15:13-21). After his missionary journeys Paul returns to Jerusalem, where Luke once again emphasizes his agreement with James, the brother of the Lord (21:18-26). Finally, under the leading of the Spirit and according to God's plan (cf. Acts 20:22-24; 21:10-14), Paul goes to Rome, to his execution, just as once Jesus had gone to Jerusalem. Polemically, perhaps against a Jewish Christian opposing position, that means that Paul's way is not an arbitrary distortion of the original gospel. Nor is it the way of a God-contrary defection from the church's original unity in the midst of Israel. According to Luke, it was the unbelieving Jews, not Paul, who shattered this unity. James himself stands on Paul's side in this conflict. Again, what that means is that Paul is an apostle for the entire church.

A number of scholars are of the opinion that Luke wanted to portray Paul as a great proclaimer among the church's witnesses but not as an apostle. I think this widely held thesis is completely wrong. Acts 14:4 and 14, which refer to Barnabas and Paul as apostles, are by no means merely expressions Luke took over with his tradition or the result of literary carelessness. One would not expect such things from a careful stylist like Luke! For Luke, "apostle" is a collective term. He never uses it for an individual — neither for Peter, nor for another member of the Twelve, nor for Paul. Thus the title of "apostle" appears only where Paul appears with other apostles, such as in 14:4 and 14: "the apostles Barnabas and Paul." In my judgment it is obvious that Luke regarded Paul as an apostle and that he was not in the least inclined to place him on a lower level in the church as, for example, a "thirteenth witness."[106]

106. This is the title of a book by Christoph Burchard, *Der dreizehnte Zeuge,* FRLANT 103 (Göttingen: Vandenhoeck & Ruprecht, 1970).

In the *Pastoral Epistles*, Paul plays a distinctly central, almost exclusive role. Joachim Diestelkamp describes it as follows (in the following five paragraphs):

Based on the way he appears in the Pastoral Epistles, one would not automatically include Paul as a primary figure of the one church. The church's apostleship is here exclusively limited to Paul. Does the author of the Pastorals ignore all other apostles because he regards them as insignificant? Or is he writing for a Pauline part of the church? In any case, here there is quite a difference from Luke's portrayal of Paul. Paul alone is the normative teacher, preacher, guardian, organizer, colleague, master, model, and martyr.[107] Is this an appropriate description of Paul for Christianity at large?

The Pastoral Epistles are notable for their wide geographical scope, ranging from the border of Syria to Rome and from Epirus to Crete. It is therefore significant that they take no notice of the East. Syria and Palestine, areas that played an enormous role in Paul's life, are not mentioned, not to speak of the theologically important city of Jerusalem. The relationship to Jewish Christianity — even retrospectively, as with Luke — is completely missing in the Pastorals, thus omitting something that for Paul was a fundamental dimension of the one church. Yet, the geographical horizon is almost identical with the areas in which Paul or his co-workers did their missionary work. Thus if the Pauline local churches are the author's intended recipients, it is understandable why the person of Paul is so prominent, almost to the point of being the object of the proclamation (cf. 1 Tim. 1:16). The churches attribute their Christian identity to Paul (1 Tim. 2:7). He is honored as teacher of the Gentiles and as apostle (2 Tim. 1:11). This is where the author begins. When now the Pauline tradition appears to be in danger, he is not satisfied to let Paul simply speak authoritatively; he also presents him as the prototype of the true Christian (1 Tim. 1:16) and the model in the Christian way of life (2 Tim. 3:10-13; 4:8). Thus he is able to motivate the readers to form the necessary tie to the Pauline apostolic tradition by appealing to their personal obligation to the person of Paul.

With great psychological skill he makes this concrete by using the relationship between Paul and Timothy as a model. He dedicates all of 2 Timothy to this theme. Thus the image of the apostolic disciples Timothy and Titus has a twofold function. For one thing, it is, of course, part of the historical fiction. For another, however (and this is the more important point), Timothy and Titus perform tasks that at the time the letters were written were to be carried

107. Norbert Brox, "Historische und theologische Probleme der Pastoralbriefe des Neuen Testaments," *Kairos* 11 (1969): 86.

out by the typical local officeholder (e.g., 2 Tim. 4:2); the reader is able to identify with them. Thus the reader has his ideal role model before his very eyes, and at the same time, if he sees himself in the apostle's disciples, he forms such a close relationship to Paul that the distance between them disappears.

Thus the epistles secure the unity of the church not through the apostolic tradition — that is, abstractly — but emphatically through the pattern-copy *(Vorbild-Nachbild)* structure and thus by means of a personal dimension. In this way the author's concern becomes more concrete, livelier, clearer. This personal element is also part of the understanding of ordination (2 Tim. 1:6) and of transmitting the Pauline tradition (2 Tim. 2:1-2). Of course, one cannot find evidence in the Pastoral Epistles for what today we call apostolic succession, but one can see certain "trace elements" that have contributed to the later doctrine.

In summary: thus the exclusive Paulinism attributed to the Pastoral Epistles serves a basic concern of the letters. Every Christian, especially every officeholder, has a duty to Paul, to his work and his apostolic tradition. The suggestion that the Pastorals have no ecumenical consciousness, or even that they represent a provincial development of a strange kind of early Christian literature, overlooks the thrust of this exclusive focus on Paul. The relationship to the other apostles, to other circles in the church, and to Jewish Christianity is not the theme of the epistles. The oecumene and other traditions are automatically blocked out because the author is primarily anxious about Paul's work in his own churches.

Looking back: in the post-apostolic period, James, Peter, and Paul become primary figures of unity. They usually represent the one, apostolic church together. As eyewitnesses and heralds, as bearers of the Spirit and representatives of his life and suffering, they transmit Christ to the church. They become part of God's revelation in Jesus Christ and thus belong to the basic gift of unity. What James, Peter, and Paul have struggled for in their lives, the unity of the church, now in retrospect becomes part of the basic gift of unity that molded and supported the church. The apostles whom the Lord has appointed are singular figures with special authority at the beginning of the church. Thus they are permanently given to the later church as representatives of the Lord and his spokesmen. That would explain why nowhere in the New Testament do the apostles have successors.

One could say pointedly that in the first century and the first half of the second century what we call "apostolic succession" was above all that the *tradition* of the apostles — later the apostolic *canon* of the New Testament — represents the authority of the apostles, and that the *person* of the apostles and their activity is an exemplary model, especially for the officeholders. Nevertheless, according to the New Testament there is simply no such thing as a succession of the apostolic *ministry.*

6.6. Ministerial Offices as a Unity-promoting Force (with Jürg Liechti)

Already in the New Testament period, the ministries of the church became an important factor supporting the unity of the church. This was true for the various local churches but not yet true for the whole church. In the New Testament period there were only some initial beginnings of supra-congregational ministries. To say it pointedly, the nascent "early catholic" official church was "congregational."

First, an overview. We see in the post-apostolic period a development in the ministerial offices about which there was as yet no theological reflection. Paul's order of ministries in 1 Corinthians 12:28-30 could not be transmitted in later times without being changed. Paul says that God appointed apostles, prophets, and teachers in the church (1 Cor. 12:28). Beyond that he mentions only functions, no ministries: healings, leadership functions, serving, mighty deeds, speaking in tongues. In addition, in the Pauline churches there were deacons (Phil. 1:1; Rom. 16:1; cf. 12:7) and "overseers" *(episkopoi)* (Phil. 1:1). In neither case do we know exactly what their functions were.[108] The (male and female!) deacons may have served at the table for the Lord's Supper. The deaconess Phoebe in Cenchreae obviously owned a house and entertained guests of the church, including Paul. With the "overseers," who are first mentioned in Philippians 1:1, we are completely in the dark. Obviously the leadership in the Pauline churches was arranged in different ways. Sometimes the first converts played a role (cf. 1 Cor. 16:16). Paul can also speak in general terms of the "leaders" (1 Thess. 5:12). Thus the question of church leadership was not determined in a way that was binding on the future.

In the post-Pauline period, what had proved its worth was preserved. Among them was the office of deacon, which appeared in the entire church relatively early. The apostles, prophets, and teachers had been primarily responsible for the task of preaching, although in principle all members shared the responsibility. Here there was a natural evolution. When prophets, teach-

108. From the Greek word "overseer" (*episkopos* = a supervisor in government and in social organizations) evolved the later "bishop." *Episkopos* is a secular title taken over in the Philippian church that can designate completely different kinds of supervisors. In Philippi the term may refer to the supervision of the collection.

ers, or other members of the church performed their task well, they automatically acquired a certain prominence in the church, and when they were not effective the opposite was true. It was likely that the weight such proven people carried in the church was early connected with the designation "elder," which came from Jewish Christianity. It was a term that in contemporary Judaism designated not only members of the ruling body of the synagogue or the *gerousia* of a city; it was in general a title of honor without official character. "An elder is only a person who has wisdom" (*b. Qiddushin* 32b). The word "elder" first appears in Acts 11:20 (cf. 15:2-23) in connection with the Jerusalem church. We do not really know, however, whether "elder" had already become the designation of an office in early Jewish Christianity or what functions the elders had there.

The tendency was for the preaching in worship increasingly to become the task of such proven members of the church. What then was more natural than selecting from their number someone for the "oversight" *(episkope)* of the church, thus for church leadership? In the texts we must decide case by case whether "overseer" is merely the description of a function or whether it has already become the designation of a fixed ministry. The former appears to be the case in Acts 20:28, where the elders of Ephesus are addressed. Their "supervisory function" is described with the word "to shepherd." This verb and the noun "shepherd" appear in other New Testament texts as metaphors for church leadership (Eph. 4:11; 1 Pet. 5:2; cf. John 21:15-17). In the Pastoral Epistles "overseer" is already an officeholder, and "oversight" is a ministry a man[109] can seek (1 Tim. 3:1). Then, in the writings of Ignatius of Antioch, the bishop is indirectly referred to for the first time as "shepherd" (*Romans* 9.1; *Philadelphians* 2.1). Thus in time, tested and honored members of the church (with the designation "elder") became the holders of an office. The transition from function to the designation of a ministry is fluid. That is also clear in Acts, where elders — in itself an open title of honor — were "appointed" by Paul and Barnabas (Acts 14:23).

The development to a local church order with the ministries of deacons, elders, and episcopes progressed naturally and without a break. Yet it is by no means linear. As late as the Deutero-Pauline Ephesian epistle we can still only recognize that the task of preaching was essential for the church but not how it was made institutional.

109. But not a woman, in contrast to the office of deacon (cf. 1 Tim. 3:11, which does not refer to the wives of deacons). There absolutely were female officeholders in the ancient church, however — not only deacons, presbyters, and prophets but occasionally bishops as well. See Ute E. Eisen, *Women Officeholders in Early Christianity,* trans. Linda M. Maloney (Collegeville, MN: Liturgical Press, 2000).

Ephesians 4:11 says that Christ appointed some as apostles, others as prophets, others as evangelists, others as shepherds and teachers. The author uses 1 Corinthians 12:28 as a pattern, but he limits himself to the ministries of preaching and leadership. Healings, miracles, speaking in tongues, and serving are no longer mentioned. It is not possible, however, to connect the "evangelists" and "shepherds" mentioned before the "teachers" with concrete church ministries. Instead, the author is interested in expressing the tasks of preaching and leadership that are fundamental for the church. He is not interested in the persons in a church who assume the functions of evangelists or shepherds. Thus we do not learn whether in that day there were "overseers/episcopes" in the post-Pauline churches of Asia Minor.

Hebrews speaks simply of "men in a position of leadership" (13:7, 17, 24; cf. *1 Clement* 1.3). James (5:14) is familiar with church elders, obviously a fixed council. First Peter (5:1, 5) offers a similar picture. Here the age of an elder is clearly important (cf. 1 Tim. 4:12). At the time of the Pastorals one must assume that Pauline local churches in Asia Minor and elsewhere had an order of elders with the ministry of "overseer" and "deacon."[110] It is noteworthy, however, that for the Seer of Revelation these officeholders are so unimportant that in his letters to the seven local churches of Asia Minor he completely ignores them. He simply addresses the churches and is familiar only with the prophetic ministry.

The same is probably true for the churches of the Gospel of Matthew, which comes from Syria, perhaps Antioch. It mentions prophets and teachers, criticizes exalting them too highly (23:8-10), and presupposes a brotherly and sisterly church order. The responsibility for church discipline lies not with a church leader but with the assembled community (18:15-18). Even two or three people gathered in the name of Jesus constitute a congregation of Christ where he is "in their midst" (18:19; cf. 28:20). Matthew clearly uses Jesus' word about serving in the context of claims made in connection with church ministries (23:11). He never implies the existence of bishops and elders. Likewise, the Gospel of John nowhere alludes to leadership structures in the churches; Jesus alone is the "good shepherd." Of course, Ignatius of Antioch emphasizes the monarchical episcopacy, yet it is noteworthy that in his letter to the Roman church he mentions no bishop there. Obviously there was none.[111]

Thus in the first and second centuries the development to a uniform

110. For the details, see below, pp. 121-22.

111. Peter Lampe (*From Paul to Valentinus: Christians at Rome in the First Two Centuries* [Minneapolis: Fortress; London: Continuum, 2003], pp. 397-412) shows that a monarchical episcopacy in Rome first evolved slowly in the second half of the second century.

structure of bishops and elders progressed very slowly, and it happened differently in different parts of the church.

Admittedly, one can see a certain tendency toward unification of church structures. Sooner or later, what had proven to be successful was adopted generally. Because the church understood that its parts belonged to one another, the individual local churches also intentionally organized themselves in similar ways. This de facto unification had important consequences, for only an intentionally identical organizational structure in all churches could achieve theological merit and itself become a basic gift of unity.

"Proving itself" means primarily that the ministries of elders, and especially that of the bishop, have proven their value extraordinarily well in the struggle against false doctrines. The experiences of the churches showed that the common tradition and the Scriptures were not enough to secure union, for the Scriptures could always be interpreted differently. Even the quintessence of the tradition, the "rules of faith," the firmly formulated creeds, proved to be inadequate as a basis of unity in the struggle against Christian Gnostics, for the Gnostics also laid claim to the apostles. Thus, over and over, the early catholic, orthodox churches experienced their ministries as the instrument through which the church's Lord most visibly cared for its unity.

For the medium term, that could not be without consequences for ecclesiastical organization. The experiences of the apostolic period had made the apostles the indispensable ingredient of every ecclesiology. Now the same thing happened with the episcopal structure of the church. Through the experiences of the post-apostolic period and the second century it became an indispensable part of every ecclesiology. An important reorientation was introduced that has determined the nature of the quest for unity down to the present day.

In the post-apostolic period we are standing at the very beginnings of this new orientation. We will take a closer look at these beginnings in the light of three documents. Jürg Liechti writes of the *Pastoral Epistles:*

The author of the Pastorals discusses church ministries with a detail that is remarkable for the New Testament. Here it is simply taken for granted that the ministries of bishop and deacon and the elders are part of the structure of every local church. They even express the wish that elders be appointed "in every city" (Tit. 1:5). Nevertheless, the Pastorals are still far removed from the established order of ministries of later times. Much is still fluid or unclear.

Above all, the relationship of the bishop (of whom one still speaks only in the singular) to the elders is unclear. Are they identical? One gets that impression from Titus 1:5, 7. Or is there in every church only *one* bishop, much as there is only one master of every household? That bishops are mentioned only in the singular could support such a conclusion. In that case, the bishop would be the leader of the church, and the elders, for example, could aspire to that position. First Timothy 5:17, however, speaks of multiple presbyters who lead the church. Some of them also preach and teach, tasks for which they are paid.

The Pastorals appear to be familiar with an ordination of officeholders (1 Tim. 4:14; 2 Tim. 1:6) that took place with the laying on of hands, but in addition to elders and deacons hands could be laid on other members of the church as well (cf. 1 Tim. 5:22). Thus the laying on of hands is not exclusively a rite of ordination.

Nevertheless, most of the tendencies in the Pastoral Epistles are in the direction of a fixed order of ministries. They appear to presuppose, or at least to require, the same church order in all the churches in the Pauline area. Of special importance is the merging of the functions of teaching and leadership in the office of bishop and also in the office of presbyter.

And yet there is still no particular order of ministries that is a necessary prerequisite for the unity of the church. For the Pastorals the ministries have more of a serving character. An officeholder is to help the church remain in the "tradition" and the "healthy doctrine." He is to be a model for the church (Tit. 2:7; cf. 2 Tim. 3:10-11). The church is to hold him answerable for this task. In an extreme case this can even result in an accusation against him (1 Tim. 5:19).

From this perspective the Pastoral Epistles stand in the Pauline tradition. For Paul, except for the apostles, prophets, and teachers the churches were free to create their own organization. The further development in the Pastorals shows that the churches made use of the freedom Paul granted. The formation of the ministries in the Pastorals was a response to the changes in the situation of the churches since Paul's time. According to them, what is decisive for the unity of the church is not the ministry but the "healthy doctrine" and the things that have been "entrusted" — that is, the tradition.

Not far removed from the Pastoral Epistles is the non-canonical *1 Clement*. For Rudolph Sohm,[112] this work is an expression of the church's great fall from grace, since it is here that the church lost its own nature as a spiritual reality and took on a legal structure. For this reason the work is for him justifi-

112. Rudolph Sohm, *Kirchenrecht,* vol. 1: *Die geschichtlichen Grundlagen* (1892; repr. Munich-Leipzig: Duncker & Humblot, 1923): *1 Clement* "was destined to bring an end to the early Christian constitution in the church" (p. 157); "At the end of the first century the epistle of Clement signaled the birth of canon law. An event of incalculable consequence!" (p. 160).

ably not in the canon. On the other hand, many authors associate *1 Clement* with the late New Testament works, not in spite of but precisely because it draws a sharp distinction between ministry and laity. It is the "function of the office . . . to continue the mission of the apostles."[113] Jürg Liechti advocates the view that *1 Clement* differs little from the Pastorals regarding the concrete form of the ministries. However, in part, at least, the ministry is given a different rationale. He writes (in the following three paragraphs):

In this letter Clement speaks to a particular incident in the local church in Corinth. A rebellious faction in the Corinthian church has removed the long-standing leaders of the church (*1 Clement* 3.3; 44.3) and replaced them with younger leaders who are superior to the older people in spirit and speaking ability (cf. *1 Clement* 21.5; 57.2). Clement argues in great detail that the old leaders of long standing should be reinstated.

It is interesting how Clement argues for their legitimacy. Although he refers to their faithfulness in preaching the right gospel and in their service to the church (44.3-4, 6), he bases his argument primarily on another point — on the order that regulates the entire cosmos (*1 Clement* 20). For him the Christian community, like the Old Testament cult, is governed by a divine order (40.1–41.4). This order is the primary reality; it is beyond question. Thus the church's existence is guaranteed not only by doctrine but also by the order of its ministries. That makes the church's ministry of decisive significance for the question of unity.

Clement is less concerned to argue for a particular structure of ministries than he is to say *that* the church should be regulated. His theory speaks more of the "that" of church order than of the "how." For him it is important that everything takes place "in accordance with the appointed order of God's will" (42.2). Here he differs from Ignatius, whose theory argues for a particular order of ministries.

Thus one can indeed say that according to *1 Clement* the "order" in the church is important for church unity, but one should not overemphasize the new element in *1 Clement.* The author is more interested in the local church than in the ecumenical dimension. He is focused on practical problems. He is concerned about peace in the church and in its fellowship — things that require an order imposed by God. He is not trying to develop a theory of the church but, in a concrete instance, to gather as many convincing arguments as possible in order to convince the Corinthians to retract the removal of their elders.

113. Otto Knoch, *Die "Testamente" des Petrus und Paulus,* SBS 62 (Stuttgart: Katholisches Bibelwerk, 1973), p. 97.

It is with *Ignatius of Antioch* that we first encounter a fundamentally new view. Again, Jürg Liechti writes:

The letters of Ignatius of Antioch offer a new view of church ministries on two levels:

1. On the level of church organization we find for the first time the threefold ministry (bishop-elders-deacons). For the first time the elder is an independent officeholder under the bishop *(episkopos)* and over the deacon. What once was a lateral relationship has become hierarchical, above and below, "with the bishop presiding in the place of God and the presbyters in the place of the council of the apostles," and "the deacons, who are most dear to me, are entrusted with the service of Jesus Christ" (*Magnesians* 6.1). The elders are subordinate to the bishop, and the deacons are subordinate to them. Apart from these three ministries, Ignatius speaks of no other ministry.

2. What is really new with Ignatius, however, is that only this ecclesiastical structure corresponds to God's will. A church without this structure of ministries is inconceivable for him. "Without these (that is, bishop, elders, and deacons) one cannot speak of 'church'" (*Trallians* 3.1). Ignatius justifies this with analogies "between heavenly and earthly realities, between the ideal apostolic time and the present."[114] The *one* bishop corresponds to God the Father, the council of elders to the assembly of the apostles, the deacons to Christ (*Magnesians* 6.1; *Trallians* 3.1). The use of various prototype-copy *(Urbild-Abbild)* relationships may reflect the idea that the church is the mystical body of Christ of which the local church is the visible image.

Thus with Ignatius the unity of the church is not guaranteed by tradition or "healthy doctrine," as it is in the Pastorals. It is represented instead in a very specific structure of ministries that is beyond question. As the head of the hierarchy, the office of bishop has an authority that appears to be almost unlimited.

Nevertheless, it would be wrong without further examination to describe Ignatius as an advocate for a church of hierarchically structured ministries or too quickly to interpret his view in terms of the later Catholic understanding. One must be mindful of the way the spiritual and the official are combined in his thinking. Ignatius speaks to his churches as a spiritual figure and never justifies his authority legally. Thus for him the authority of the bishop is not the abstract authority of an office but the living and lived authority experienced in the church of one who has the Spirit and who stands in the church in place of God. It is also important that Ignatius's order of minis-

114. Peter Meinhold, "Die Anschauung des Ignatius von Antiochen von der Kirche," in Meinhold, *Studien zu Ignatius von Antiochen,* VIEG 97 (Wiesbaden: Steiner, 1979), p. 59.

tries applies not to the whole church but only to the local church. Ignatius himself never claims the authority of a bishop over the (foreign!) churches to which he is writing.

Unity is a central theme for Ignatius's ecclesiology, as for all of his theology. In *1 Clement,* words with the root "to order/order" play a major role. In the seven letters of Ignatius, words that express and allude to "unity" dominate. He uses two words here. With the term *henotes* he designates the already existing unity given to the church — the unity of God that is seen as God's unity in himself, as well as the unity of Jesus Christ with God the Father. There is no longer any place in this unity for division. In God all differences are abolished or brought together into a unity. For Ignatius this divine unity is why the church's primary characteristic is that its members belong together. "As then the Lord was united to the Father and did nothing without him . . . so do you do nothing without the bishop and presbyters. . . . Let there be in common *one* prayer, *one* supplication, *one* mind, *one* hope. . . . Hasten all to come together as to *one* temple of God, as to *one* altar, to *one* Jesus Christ, who came forth from the *one* Father, and is with the *one* and returned to him" (*Magnesians* 7.1-2). Ignatius is thinking not of an inflexible, identically governed order but of a condition of abundance and harmony. He repeatedly describes it with musical images. "Now do each of you join in this choir, that being harmoniously in concord you may receive God's melody in unison and sing with *one* voice through Jesus Christ to the Father" (*Ephesians* 4.2).

With the word *henoosis,* on the other hand, he designates the task of "uniting" or "unification" that has been given to the church. The church must enter into God's unity through the gate opened by Jesus Christ; it must lay hold of the unity already given it. Thus Ignatius places the static, special concept of "unity" *(henotes)* over against the dynamic concept of "unification" *(henoosis),* which describes a process aiming at practical conduct in the church. Caring for unification is the bishop's task. Ignatius can even say that the bishop "is created for unification" (*Philadelphians* 8.1). Thus with the bishop and his council the two terms "unity" and "unification" come together. The bishop can "produce unification" because he is himself God's likeness and thus also shares in his unity.

Ignatius was ahead of his time. It took almost a century for the Antiochene structure of ministries to be accepted in the whole church. His heritage extends far beyond the ancient church even to the present day. The difficulty of his heritage for the present ecumenical dialogue is that it has been accepted on widely different levels. In the Roman Catholic Church it is predominantly centralized on the level of the whole church, with the focus on a papal office of unity. In the Orthodox and Anglican churches it is predominantly regional and episcopal, focused on the "choir" of all the bishops. In many Protestant churches it is predominantly local, congregational, and focused on the "unity" within a hierarchically structured local church. We should not, however, understand Ignatius primarily as the precursor of a later time; we must interpret him as a theologian with his own imprint.

We *look back* at the development that came to a provisional conclusion with Ignatius. The freedom to determine the form of church ministries in a given situation that was present with Paul has disappeared. For Ignatius, God has provided the church with a particular structure. With him the threefold ministry clearly expresses the basic gift of unity. Therefore the bishop is for him not only the center of the event of unification; agreement with him is also a precondition for the unity of the church. With Ignatius the office of bishop has an authority similar to that of apostleship in early Christianity. The gap left by the death of the apostles in the post-apostolic church is filled here for the local church — *nota bene,* not by the idea of apostolic succession, an idea not yet known to Ignatius.

Finally, we should note that no modern Christian denomination may regard itself as the heir of Ignatius in a direct sense. The Catholic and Orthodox churches may not, because for them the *local* office of the bishop has become a *regional* office. The Protestant churches may not either, for even though locally the ministries of pastor, elder, and deacon often de facto correspond to Ignatius's structure of ministries, they understand their ministries in a way completely different from that of Ignatius.

7. The First Ecclesiological Concepts of Church Unity

It was unavoidable that the first theological concepts of unity also appeared in the post-apostolic period. It is axiomatic that the reality of Christ that gathers the church preceded the theological concepts of the post-apostolic period. Preceding them also, however, was the struggle in the apostolic period on behalf of the church's fellowship — the experience of reconciliation between Jews and Gentiles and the experience that, through Christ, the Christians became a new fellowship that was different from the world. Theological reflection began with such experiences, took up already existing conceptual approaches, and developed them into theological concepts. Then, in later times, these concepts gave the impulse for new attempts to achieve church fellowship.

Five of these concepts are especially important for the theme of church unity: Ephesians, Revelation, Acts, John, and the letters of Ignatius of Antioch.[115]

7.1. *The Epistle to the Ephesians*

Paul reflected little, or perhaps not at all, about the unity of the universal church, but he practiced ecumenical fellowship and fought for church unity. When Ephesians thinks of the church, it is of the whole church. Ephesians is the only text of the New Testament that uses the word *ekklesia* exclusively for the whole church. Christ is the redeemer less of the individual than of the church (5:23). In its understanding of the church, however, it is influenced not by the biblical-Jewish idea of the people of God but by the body-of-Christ idea. The church is, much like the body of the world, a cosmic reality. Christ is the head (1:22; 5:23),[116] the church his cosmic body. In the body the power of the head that "fills all in all" (Eph. 1:23) is at work. Thus the church is understood in a dynamic way. It is Christ's power grid in the cosmos, and as such it grows (Eph. 2:21). As a church filled by the power of Christ, it is characterized by movement. The reconciliation of the Jews and Gentiles, previously separated by the dividing wall of the Torah, also takes place in this body. The once "far off" Gentiles and the always "near" Jews, now reconciled by Christ in his body, become *one* new person (2:14-18).[117]

Along with the concept of the body of Christ, the author of Ephesians also makes use of another idea found in Paul, the concept of the temple of God. The apostles and prophets are its foundation, Christ its cornerstone, and the members of the church the building blocks of the holy temple in which God himself dwells (Eph. 2:20-22). Again the author speaks of the whole church. Again he thinks of it in dynamic terms — God's temple is "under construction."

The most important text for our theme appears at the beginning of the great hortatory section of the letter in Ephesians 4–6. The first and most important point of the exhortation deals with unity in the church (Eph. 4:1-6). Already that is important. Obviously there is no more central concern for the author. That is understandable, if the church is the power grid of Christ or if

115. On Ignatius, see above, pp. 124-26.

116. In a similar way, for Philo the Logos is the head of the world-body (*Quaestiones in exodum* 2.117).

117. Thus the Gentiles do not become members of Israel, the people of God; together with the people of Israel they become members of the church.

he himself is the peace who is now experienced in the reconciliation of Jews and Gentiles (2:14). The author speaks of peace and of bearing with one another in love. Later it is clear that he is also concerned about the "unity of the faith" (4:13) in a situation where many find themselves "tossed about" by every wind of doctrine, by people's trickery and scheming (4:14). His principal exhortation is: Be "eager to maintain the unity of the Spirit" (4:3). Thus the parenesis returns immediately to the reality of salvation, for it is the Spirit who establishes peace. And instead of giving more exhortations, the author continues by praising the reality of the unity of the church in the style of an acclamation from the church's worship. "One body and one Spirit . . . one Lord, one faith, one baptism" (4:5). The acclamation calls attention to the reality that unity already exists and that first of all one must give thanks for it. One can experience it concretely. To the one Lord, the object of the worshiping praise, belongs the unity of his body into which all were baptized; the unity of the Spirit given to all in baptism; the unity of the confession of faith, for which the church gives thanks; and the unity of baptism, through which according to 1 Corinthians 12:13 all of this has taken place, so that in the body of Christ there is neither Jew nor Greek. Thus baptism stands at the beginning of unity; it is the basis and not the result of unity. Because the unity of the church expresses the unity established by Christ, human beings do not need to produce it; they can only give thanks for it.[118] The acclamation then continues — to God, the ground and the goal of all unity: "One God and Father of all, who is above all and through all and in all" (4:6). The author takes his stand here with the acclamation with which the community is familiar in its worship.

Here, too, the term "one," which appears in Ephesians for the first time in the New Testament in connection with church fellowship, is rooted in the liturgical acclamation of the *one* Lord and the *one* God (cf. 1 Cor. 8:6). Thus in this letter the word "one" plays an important role for the first time; the word "unity" also appears (Eph. 4:3). It is important to see that this root refers exclusively to the given unity of God, of Christ, of the Spirit, of baptism, etc. The already given unity is "kept" (4:3), not produced. On the human level, the movement toward fellowship, expressed in Ephesians 4:2 by love and peace, corresponds to unity. We will see that in the Gospel of John the root "one" also places the emphasis on "above" with the basic gift that is given. Ignatius will distinguish between the unity that is given and the process of unification the church has taken up.[119] In light of this clearly developing New Testament

118. Presumably the author could have said similar things about the Lord's Supper. It is too bad — for us — that he did not say it!

119. Cf. above, p. 125.

usage, we need to think carefully about talking about church unity as if it were something obvious. The unity of the church is *given;* it is not our *task* to produce it.

Ephesians gives us a basic model for thinking about the unity of the church. The universal church is understood dynamically, as the field of Christ's activity. Human beings are taken into this dynamic, and they put it into practice; but they do so by first of all giving thanks for the already existing unity and praising God. Thus thanking and praising are the most important things the Christian has to do about church unity. And this is in a letter in which the unity of the church is the first concern of parenesis! All of that is possible out of the knowledge that God and Christ *precede* human beings. That means that the faith given by God also precedes human interpretations of faith, the baptism instituted by Christ before human interpretations of baptism, and the body filled by Christ before human institutions. Ephesians says: the unity of the body of Christ *is* a reality, even though its members are "tossed about with every wind of doctrine" and even though in reality it obviously does not look very attractive with its unity. The reality of the church's unity is almost understood as a sacrament, but for that very reason it is dynamic. Ephesians speaks of this reality not with descriptive language but with prayer and praise. It thus makes clear that church unity is not an objective reality one can grasp from a distance but a dynamic reality one grasps only when one lets oneself be grasped by it in prayer, praise, and conduct.

The author could only think this way *after* Paul. Paul's engagement on behalf of the unity of Jews and Gentiles, his apostolic activity from Jerusalem to Rome, and his life lived out of the mystery of Christ have made it possible for him to comprehend Christ's activity on behalf of the unity of the church and to express it in words. It is as if Ephesians were the seal of Paul's life's work, and it expresses retroactively what Paul had lived without as yet grasping it in theological language.[120]

7.2. The Apocalypse of John

In Ephesians, looking back on Paul's missionary activity was a necessary prerequisite for theological reflection on the unity of the church. In the Apocalypse of John, by contrast, it seems to be external pressure that forces the churches of Asia Minor to expound theologically their own identity and their

120. On the theological deficiency of this view in Ephesians, cf. above, pp. 114-15.

unity. The prophet John, who may have emigrated from Palestine after the year 70, looks back on the separation of church and synagogue. The synagogue is a "synagogue of Satan" (Rev. 2:9; 3:9). The holy city of Jerusalem that crucified Jesus is no longer Jerusalem but "Sodom and Gomorrah" (Rev. 11:8). What is decisive for developing the ecclesiology of his book, however, is not the pressure from Judaism but the pressure from the state. In the mythical insertion of chapter 12, the state is seen as the representative of the heavenly dragon who has been cast out of heaven and who now is waging war on earth against the children of the heavenly queen, the church (Rev. 12:7-18). It is the beast from the abyss that oppresses the saints (Revelation 13).

In this situation, the Seer speaks to the local churches in the letters of chapters 2–3. Their situation varies from church to church. Even though John speaks to each church individually, he sends all the letters to all of the churches as part of a book. The problems of an individual church are the business of all of them: "He who has an ear, let him hear what the Spirit says to the churches" (Rev. 2:7, 11, 17, 29; 3:6, 13, 22). Thus the churches do not simply live for themselves; they are bound together. The whole church manifests itself in the local church.[121] That is the first level on which church unity is visible in the Apocalypse of John.

We see a second level in chapter 12 in the mythical figure of the heavenly queen. Primal mythological images emerge here. To whom do they refer? In the Bible and in Jewish texts, the image of a woman, especially a pregnant woman, often refers to Israel. The readers will initially have thought of Israel. In verse 5 the woman gives birth to a son "who is to shepherd the nations with an iron staff." That, too, could refer to Israel, out of whom the Messiah Christ comes, but the readers quickly notice that the text cannot be speaking of Israel, because the woman who gives birth to her son is threatened by the dragon. Her child is carried off to God and his throne. The dragon is cast down from heaven, and since it can no longer destroy the child it turns to the mother and threatens her. She flees to the wilderness and stays there safely during the time predetermined for her. All of that fits the church well. It is as if the church has imperceptibly moved into Israel's footsteps while the readers are forgetting about Israel. Thus the heavenly queen becomes the suffering church on earth.[122] She appears as a whole, something the traditional image of Israel permits. The church's individual members appear only at the end of

121. Peter Lampe, "Die Apokalyptiker — ihre Situation und ihr Handeln," in Ulrich Luz et al., *Eschatologie und Friedenshandeln: Exegetische Beiträge zur Frage christlicher Friedensverantwortung,* SBS 101 (Stuttgart: Katholisches Bibelwerk, 1981), p. 104.

122. Revelation represents a "hard substitution model" (cf. above, p. 99), although in chapter 12 there is a smooth transition in the image of Israel to the church.

the text as "the rest of her offspring, who keep the commandments of God and bear witness to Jesus" (verse 17). The dragon makes war against them, and many of them suffer martyrdom. Yet the church as a whole does not die; it is preserved in the wilderness "a time, and times, and half a time" (verse 14) — that is, during the predetermined 1,260 days of the tribulation. The distinction between the offspring, the individual Christians, and the woman (the whole church) offers a comforting perspective for the believers who are suffering. The church as a whole will be preserved, even if some of them have to die.

There is still another, a third way, in which the Apocalypse speaks of the one church. Visions of the heavenly church appear in the main section (7:1-17; 14:1-5; 15:2-4; cf. 19:1-8). They are not part of the horror visions John portrays in two passages beginning in chapter 6 and chapter 12. Instead, John sees the perfected church standing before the throne of God, and he hears it singing praises. It is the church of the people sealed by baptism (7:4-8), who, with white garments, will come out of the great tribulation to the throne of the Lamb. At their center is the Lamb enthroned on Mt. Zion, and they praise him (7:10-11; 14:2; 15:3-4). They sing a special song whose words the world cannot understand and learn, for they are redeemed out of the world (14:3-4). These visions are scattered among the images of terror as antitypes. They appear abruptly, as pauses for breath in the descriptions of the horror, as an invitation to look upward. When the author speaks of the 144,000 from the twelve tribes in chapter 7 (verses 4-8), he is not simply thinking of the Jewish Christians, to whom he then adds the countless number of Gentile Christians in verses 9-17. Instead, the subject in verses 1-8, as in verses 9-17, is the one, apostolic church. Its unity is not emphasized; it is assumed, reflecting the reality that divisions are not the Seer's main problem with his churches. Thus the believers in the seven churches who read or hear the Apocalypse look upon the one, heavenly church and know that they themselves will be preserved for the heavenly Jerusalem.

The heavenly Jerusalem then appears in chapter 21. It comes to earth when the new heaven and the new earth are created. Again, an image of Israel — indeed, for Israel, *the* image of Israel — is the image used for the church. When it is applied to the church the image is changed. Although the basic biblical text of Ezekiel 40–48 describes the new Temple, there is no temple in the new Jerusalem of John the Seer (Rev. 21:22). Instead, the dimensions and the description of Ezekiel's Temple have passed over to the city. The throne of God and of Christ the Lamb stands in the city. The holy city Jerusalem could be used to depict the church because, after the murder of the two witnesses, the "great city," whose name is not given in Revelation 11, has become "Sodom and Egypt" (Rev. 11:8). The new Jerusalem, this mighty picture of hope for a suffering and persecuted church, has a bitter aftertaste for us today.

For the suffering church, however, this picture is a picture of hope. It is *no more* than a picture of hope, because the new Zion has not yet come from heaven to earth. On the earth there are only the individual local churches whose situation and condition are not an occasion for joy. We can only hear the singing of the perfected ones, as though it constitutes the essence of the church, but the churches cannot yet join in the singing. Nevertheless, this church is for them not merely a dream church. Its center is the throne of the Lamb, who *is* already enthroned. The hoped-for *one* perfected church has already begun to live, and through John's visions its sounds reach the ears of the hard-pressed churches.

This view of the church is different from that of Ephesians; yet there are some common elements. As in Ephesians, the decisive reality is the *one* church created by God himself. As in Ephesians, here too worship is the place where one can sense something of it. As in Ephesians, here too the point is that the experience of what God has already given inspires and strengthens a movement. By looking to the coming Zion and to the throne of the Lamb, the Seer wants to encourage people to worship here on earth, to stay together, and to join in persevering. In the Apocalypse it is as if the one heavenly church has opened its window to earth.

7.3. *The Gospel of Luke and Acts*

Luke's two-volume work narrates God's history with his people, Israel, in the time when the promises began to be fulfilled. It is the history of a way that begins in Jerusalem, in the heart of Israel, and ends in Rome, the world capital. That is probably where we should look for the author, Luke, and his first readers. Luke attempts to make understandable the way the God of Israel and of Jesus has gone with them. He tells how Jesus has gathered his people of Israel[123] and how after Jesus' resurrection God has opened Israel for the Gentiles streaming to the nation. He tells how even after Jesus' martyrdom God remained true to his people, so that on his last arrival in Jerusalem Paul sees "many thousands among the Jews who have believed" — people who are zealous for the Torah (Acts 21:20). In the words of Simon, however, Luke also tells how Jesus "is set for the fall and rising of many in Israel and for a sign

123. Gerhard Lohfink, *Die Sammlung Israels: Eine Untersuchung zur lukanischen Ekklesiologie,* StANT 39 (Munich: Kösel, 1975).

that is spoken against," so that it will be as though a sword pierces Mary's heart (Luke 2:34-35). In the passion narrative, and then especially in the second part of Acts, Luke tells how the opposition to Jesus becomes more intense. In almost every city where Paul, the Diaspora Jew and apostle, first gathers God's Israel in the local synagogue, he meets with opposition from the majority of the Jews and is harassed and rejected. For this reason Acts ends with Paul reciting to the Jews of Rome the "hardening" quotation from Isaiah 6:9 — a text probably familiar to all Christians — and announcing the definitive transfer of "God's salvation" to the Gentiles (Acts 28:26-28).

The core concept of Luke's ecclesiology is the idea of the people of God. One could say that Luke represents something like a theology of substitution in stages. I think that is at most half right, however, because for Luke it is not simply the case that the church replaces Israel. Perhaps it is better to remember Paul's form of the people-of-God idea in Romans 9: "Not all who come from Israel are Israel" (Rom. 9:6). It is rather the case that, according to Luke, Israel's election is repeatedly a new event. It happens anew in the mission of Jesus, but after Jesus' death God also acts anew in history and calls Israel again. It is always only a part of the nation that embodies Israel. By acting anew, God also changes the shape of Israel. Thus one most likely cannot say that for Luke the church has replaced Israel. Instead, "the church [is] . . . the Israel that has arrived at its salvation-history destination."[124] Thus the form of the people of God changes in the course of its history. Unlike with Paul, however, for whom in Romans 11 there is an unapologetic hope for the Israel that does not believe in Jesus, based on God's faithfulness to his word, Acts ends with the Jews who do not believe in Jesus simply disappearing from salvation history. God's ways lead to the Gentiles, where Paul can preach the gospel unhindered and find a hearing (Acts 28:28, 31).

Thus Acts tells about the people of God within Israel and how it grew step by step beyond and away from Israel. It helps assure the readers of Luke's two-volume work of their identity. They are not in a tributary or in a dead backwater; they are in the mainstream of God's ways with his people. For this reason Luke tells in Acts how the church under the leading of the Spirit has crossed boundaries: the boundaries of Jerusalem, of Israel, of the Torah, of Asia. It describes how it moves beyond its beginnings to the capital city of Rome and to the pinnacles of society. It has gone this way harmoniously, without quarrels, ruptures, and dissonances, under the leading of the Spirit and the apostles. Thus the harmony of the church is like a basic motif that appears repeatedly in his portrayal of the church's way from Jerusalem to Rome.

124. Roloff, *Kirche,* p. 200.

This motif first appears at the very beginning of Acts. The two summary descriptions of the primitive church in Jerusalem (Acts 2:42-47 and 4:32-37) depict its fellowship in worship, in doctrine, in meals, and in possessions. The catchwords are: "were together," "had all things in common" (2:44; 4:32), "share" (2:45), "with one mind" (2:46; 5:12), and "one heart and one soul" (4:32). Luke describes here the all-encompassing fellowship of the primitive church in the spiritual and material areas. The leaders of this fellowship are the twelve apostles; the place where it meets is the Temple, the heart of Israel.

As Acts continues, it will be clear that this fellowship is also valid for the whole church. The harmony in the local church corresponds to the harmony in the oecumene. Here, for Luke, Paul is the most important figure. In Acts 8:1-3 he appears for the first time as a marginal figure in the stoning of Stephen and as a persecutor of the church. Then Luke portrays in detail his meeting with Christ near Damascus, followed by his first visit to the apostles (Acts 9). The narrative returns temporarily to Peter, but Paul never disappears completely from view (Acts 11:25, 30; 12:25). The missionary journey of Barnabas and Paul to Cyprus, Pisidia, Lycaonia, and Pamphylia (Acts 13–14) leads up to the Apostolic Council in Jerusalem, where the apostles and elders, on the basis of clear votes from Peter and James the Lord's brother, approve of the circumcision-free mission of Paul and Barnabas to the Gentiles and regulate the table fellowship in the mixed churches on the basis of the apostolic decree (Acts 15). Then the twelve apostles and Barnabas disappear from view. From this point on, the narrator is interested only in the apostle Paul. Now Acts shows that it is not, as the title later attached to it claims, a "history *of the apostles*"; rather, it is a history of Paul with a very long introduction. Throughout the entire book of Acts, Luke shows how Paul acts in accord with the twelve apostles and with James. Luke — probably quite consciously[125] — downplays, or completely omits,[126] conflicts in the church.

That was true already for the controversies surrounding the Stephen circle in Jerusalem in Acts 6:1–8:3 (for Luke there can be in Jerusalem only

125. Luke does not use Paul's letters. He does not even mention that Paul has written letters. In my judgment, it is inconceivable, however, that at the end of the first century an educated Christian knew nothing about Paul's letters — especially a disciple or Pauline sympathizer who did his research as carefully as Luke did. In my judgment, the conclusion is unavoidable that Luke intentionally said nothing about Paul's letters and intentionally refused to use this major source.

126. Luke accomplished this simply by reporting in detail only about the apostle's first visit in a church, wherever possible.

one individual church).[127] It is then true for the Apostolic Council (Paul's opponents become an insignificant marginal group, while James and Peter become Paul's defenders),[128] for the conflict with the emissaries of James and Peter in Antioch (Luke does not even mention it),[129] for the (only briefly mentioned) dispute between Paul and Barnabas (Acts 15:39), and for the delivery of the collection in Jerusalem (some scholars surmise, with good reasons, that Luke almost completely ignores it because he does not want to report that it was not accepted by the Jerusalem people).[130] What is especially noteworthy in comparison with Paul's letters is that Luke never speaks of opponents who followed Paul, never of opposing Jewish-Christian missionary activities,[131] and also never of inner conflicts in the Pauline churches. His portrait of Paul's mission is completely harmonious. The church — not only the earliest community — is united and harmonious. It completely supports the Pauline mission. There were never problems within the church — only problems outside the church, caused primarily by the Jews and by the Roman state.

By this time it is sufficiently clear that this portrait is fictitious, but there is disagreement about how much Luke knew of the historical reality. Even one who regards Luke as a largely reliable and informed reporter and probably even a companion of Paul must acknowledge that on this point his account is tendentious and ideal. Why? From history, from the struggle of the apostolic period on behalf of the fellowship of the church, and presumably from Paul himself Luke has learned that fellowship belongs to the essence of the church. The one Holy Spirit given to all disciples is active in the fellowship of the church. Thus Luke reported that the church had already achieved something for which in reality the apostolic church was still striving — something given by the exalted Lord and the Holy Spirit he had sent. Christ, the *one* Lord who reigns over the church, is portrayed in retrospect as having been victorious. Why does Luke describe the apostolic period this way? He is here not *only* interested in defending Paul. Luke would answer: because Christ, the one Lord who reigns over the church, intends to be victorious also in his (Luke's) present day. His own (post-apostolic) time was a time of "ravenous wolves . . . speaking perverse things, to draw away the disciples after them" (Acts 20:29-30). In this situation the *portrait* of the unity of the apostolic church that Luke paints becomes a power designed to help people strive for unity in their own

127. Cf. above, p. 43.
128. Cf. above, pp. 59-60.
129. Cf. above, pp. 66-68.
130. Cf. above, pp. 73-74.
131. Cf. above, pp. 69-70.

present. Thus the same thing is valid for Luke's *narrative* of the apostolic history that was valid for the conceptually designed ecclesiology of Ephesians or the Apocalypse: the *ecclesiology* that resulted from the experience of struggling for the unity already given itself became part of the basic gift that is a force in the struggle for unity. Thus the *narrative* of the unity of the apostolic church in Acts is less a representation of past reality than a model designed to cause something.

Is that a falsification of historical reality? Yes and no. If we judge Luke on the level of a historian — even an ancient historian — one will, depending on which idea of historiography one chooses, have to take seriously the charge of falsification. Luke, however, is not only a historian; he is also a believer. In his portrayal of apostolic history there speaks the faith that Christ, the one Lord of the church, will be victorious. History must be told from this perspective — that is, from the perspective of faith. Is that an illusion, or can we say that the power that has flowed from his texts in the history of the church has at least somewhat justified him?

7.4. The Gospel of John (with Anne Liedtke)

There is a widely accepted opinion among scholars today that the Gospel of John comes from a particular Christian group. The Johannine letters, which in my judgment come from the same milieu as the Gospel but were written later, show us a group of itinerant missionaries, who had a spiritual center in the person of the "Elder" (2 John 1; 3 John 1), but to which churches and sympathizers also belonged. In all probability, the group around the "Elder" comes originally from Israel's South, perhaps from Jerusalem. At the time the Gospel was written, the Johannine Christians lived outside Israel but presumably still within the compass of Judaism, for Jews repeatedly appear in the Gospel who have not yet decided whether they want to belong to the community (e.g., Nicodemus in John 3; cf. 7:50; 19:39), or who do not risk embracing the church openly for fear of being expelled from the synagogues (e.g., John 12:42-43). The Johannine Christians are no longer members of the local synagogues; they had been expelled (9:22; 12:42; 16:2), and this experience was for them the decisive event in their history. Nevertheless, their horizon extends far beyond Judaism. The Johannine message is "God so loved the world, that he gave his only Son" (3:16). Greeks come to Jesus, and he points them to the time when the Son of Man will be glorified (12:20-23). Not only Jews but also the world hates and persecutes the community (15:18-22), yet in the Gospel the Jews become the embodiment of the world that is hostile to God. Thus in the Gospel of John we meet "oppressed churches,"[132] which, much like the churches in the Apocalypse, are forced to articulate their own identity clearly. They do this by means of a quite special, "high," very exclusive Christology and in a special language that will be repeatedly misunderstood by outsiders.

How does the Gospel of John produced by these churches see the unity of the church? How are we to understand the relationship of these Johannine churches to the whole church? The Gospel of John does not answer such questions directly. I think the Gospel of John is not a book for an elite, perhaps a mystical or proto-Gnostic sect, but a book for the church. It is written for church-Christians who are familiar with one or more of the Synoptic Gospels, and it is designed to deepen their knowledge of Christ. It does this by deepening selected Jesus traditions, especially from the South of Israel, by means of Jesus' interpretations of himself. The primary configurations of his intended readers are the "ordinary" disciples — Andrew, Peter, Philip, and Nathaniel — whom Jesus calls at the beginning of the Gospel. The Gospel picks them up in their Jewish faith. They respond to what Jesus says, follow him, often ask him quite silly questions, and want Jesus to lead them into the deep things of faith without ever reaching these deep things. Among the configurations of the intended readers are also figures such as the Samaritan woman, Thomas, and Martha. They are joined in the second half of the Gospel by a special, nameless disciple, the "disciple whom Jesus loved" — a disciple whose identity the readers of the Gospel of John (unlike us) obviously know, but whose name they never mention. They always refer to him only with his title of honor.[133] He is close to Jesus and never asks silly questions.

In the following discussion (in the next five paragraphs), Anne Liedtke attempts to contrast the Beloved Disciple and Peter to gain further insights into the relationship of the Johannine Christians to the whole church.

We do not know for sure how much the figures of the disciples in John portray definite types of Christian faith at the time of the Gospel or how much they represent definite areas of the church. For at least two of them, Peter and the Beloved Disciple, that clearly seems to be the case. The Beloved Disciple appears for the first time in John 13:21-30. There he is lying next to Jesus at the farewell meal, and Peter asks him about the betrayer. In John 18:15-16 he arranges for Peter to gain entrance to the court of the high priest, Annas; he himself is an acquaintance of the high priest. In John 19:26-27 the

132. Cf. Klaus Wengst, *Bedrängte Gemeinde and verherrlichter Christus: Der historische Ort des Johannesevangeliums als Schlüssel zu seiner Interpretation,* BThSt 5 (Neukirchen: Neukirchener Verlag, 1981).

133. Much as the people in Qumran called their founding figure, whose name we also do not know, only by the honorary title "Teacher of Righteousness."

dying Jesus entrusts his mother to the care of the Beloved Disciple. John 19:35 also probably speaks of the Beloved Disciple. It is he who saw blood and water flowing from Jesus' side and had borne witness about it. John 20:2-10 is an especially important text. These verses tell how Peter and the Beloved Disciple race to Jesus' tomb. Peter arrives later but goes in first. Only the Beloved Disciple, however, recognizes what he sees in the tomb. He is the only one of whom it is said that he "saw and believed" (20:8). In the appended chapter, John 21, the story of the miraculous catch of fish at the Sea of Gennesaret is told. Jesus stands on the shore; the Beloved Disciple sees that the stranger is Jesus and tells Peter. Then comes the commission to Peter to feed Jesus' sheep (21:15-17). In this text it becomes clear that Peter, who in previous texts has often appeared as the spokesman for the disciples and in 6:68 also formulated the disciples' confession, is seen in the Gospel of John as the representative of the whole church. In 21:15-19 the leadership of the church is entrusted to him and martyrdom is predicted. In contrast to him, the Beloved Disciple will "remain until I come" (21:22). According to 21:24, he has also written the Gospel and left his true witness for the church. It is striking how often the Beloved Disciple appears with Peter.

The texts that speak of the Beloved Disciple are broken and uneven. For this reason people have often surmised that they could not have been an original part of the Gospel — that they were added by a later editor or reviser of the Gospel. Chapter 21 is in any case a later addition, although it is quite close to the Gospel. The style is almost identical, as is the way it views things. People from the Johannine church were probably involved in producing chapter 21. However, since the thesis that the Beloved Disciple passages in chapters 13–20 are also later additions of a reviser is difficult and can hardly be proven, we will interpret the Gospel in its present form.

Thus Peter represents the whole church. What then does the Beloved Disciple stand for? We can probably say two things. First, as a man from Jerusalem and an acquaintance of the high priest, he is understood as a guarantor of the tradition (cf. John 21:24-25 but also 19:35). As such he represents the Johannine group and is, so to speak, its ancestor. Yet that does not exhaust his meaning. The designation "the disciple whom Jesus loved" is a distinction that requires further explanation. People who know how frequently and with what importance love is mentioned in the Gospel of John cannot deny that precisely this substitute name says something quite important. In addition, there is the expression "lying on Jesus' breast" (13:23, 25), which, in spite of the different formulation, is reminiscent of Jesus' relationship to the Father (cf. 1:18). We are dealing here with a disciple who was especially close to Jesus. This closeness originated with Jesus, for Jesus loved the disciple, not vice versa. One sees it in the reality that the Beloved Disciple "saw and believed" (20:8) — that is, he has the true, deep knowledge of Jesus (cf. 20:7).

What then is the relationship between the Beloved Disciple and Peter? The Beloved Disciple always appears in a better light than does Peter. He can ask Jesus the delicate question about the betrayer (John 13:21-30); he is the first to come to the tomb and to faith (20:4, 8), and he recognizes the Risen One before Peter does (John 21:7). Is there an attempt here to portray Peter as inadequate or even as bad? Certainly not! It is precisely the Beloved Disciple who lets Peter go into the tomb first (20:5-6). In the Gospel of John, Judas is the negative example of a disciple. He is not only the betrayer; he also misuses the group's money (12:6). Peter is a good disciple who denies Jesus three times but also confesses his love to him three times (21:15-17).

Thus Peter and the Beloved Disciple are more than two individuals. They represent two ways of being a Christian: the way of the main church and the way of the Johannine circle. In the opinion of the Gospel of John, the way of the Beloved Disciple is the better way, with clearer understanding. Peter and the Beloved Disciple, however, are not antagonists; they remain respectful and friendly toward one another. The Beloved Disciple is there for Peter, and he shares with him his knowledge of Christ. In some such way we might think of the relationship between the Johannine church and the whole church. That also describes the purpose of the Gospel of John. It is the book the Beloved Disciple has written for the church (21:24), and in a sense it carries on his role in the church.

The Gospel of John speaks about church unity in several passages: in Jesus' great farewell prayer (17:11-12, 20-24), but also even earlier (10:16; 11:52). What does church unity mean in the Gospel of John?

1. On a first level we can give an obvious, but still very important answer. Church unity does not simply mean the unity of the Johannine circle; it means the unity of the *whole* church. John 10:16 already makes that clear. Here Jesus speaks of "other sheep that are not of this fold" who will hear his voice. "And there will be *one* flock, one shepherd." The thought is probably of Jewish and Gentile Christians; the horizon of John's understanding of the church is universal. The author also speaks of Gentile Christians at the end of John 11 by making use of the traditional concept of the gathering of the tribes of Israel from the dispersion. In a narrator's commentary on the word of Caiphas, that it is better for *one* person to die for the people than that the whole nation should die, he reveals its unintended ambiguity: "For Jesus should die for the nation, and not only for the nation but to gather into One the children of God who are scattered" (11:51-52). John expresses here the same idea that

Gnostics later interpret as the gathering of the sparks of light of the divine Spirit scattered in the dark world of matter into the heavenly *pleroma*. But John is no Gnostic. Unlike them, he is not primarily interested in the heavenly unity of the children of God lost in the world; he is interested in their coming together in the earthly church. This is why it is so important for him that his circle and the Petrine main church belong together. Therefore, in 2 John and 3 John the "Elder" sends his messengers to the local churches, even when, as in the case of the church of Diotrephes, they are not welcome there (3 John 9).

2. We penetrate a step deeper into Johannine thought when we say that the unity of the church in the Gospel of John is the unity of *love*. In the Gospel, brotherly love, the "new commandment" (John 13:34), is the identifying mark of the unity of the church. The church's brotherly love is not simply the central commandment; it is the only commandment of Jesus to his church. It directly corresponds to Christ's love for the church and to the love of the Father for Christ. The metaphor of the true vine in John 15 makes that clear. "I am the vine, you are the branches. He who abides in me and I in him, he brings much fruit" (15:5). *He* is the true vine, and it is through the relationship to him that his disciples are church. The relationship to Christ, however, is immediately given an ethical interpretation. "As the Father has loved me, so have I loved you. . . . This is my commandment, that you love one another as [Greek: *kathos*] I have loved you" (15:9, 12). Church unity is a process of love. The Father's love for the Son manifests itself in the Son's love toward the church. That in turn is realized in the brotherly love in the church. What looks like a relationship of analogy is in reality a relationship of identity. The church's brotherly love is made possible by the love of the Father and the Son to such an extent that finally it is nothing other than this love. It is "abiding in my love" (15:9). Therefore the church's brotherly love is its identifying mark for the world and its "means of proclamation" par excellence. "By this all will know that you are my disciples" (13:35; cf. 17:21b). In substance, that corresponds exactly to the Pauline understanding of *koinonia*. The "participation" in Jesus Christ and in his love is realized in the "fellowship" of Christians among themselves.[134]

In the post-apostolic period, this reification of the unity of the church exclusively as love may have received a new accent. The Johannine brotherhood lives *in* and *with* and *for* the main church but was not identical with it. In that day the main church already bore the weight of the ecclesiastical ministry. Peter does not represent only the church; he also represents the one who feeds the sheep (John 21:15-17). That church unity is concrete *only* in love in the Gospel of John may mean an implicit counter-position against a cur-

134. Cf. above, pp. 72, 83.

rently growing tendency to understand the church in terms of ministries. Here John shares a tendency of the Gospel of Matthew.[135]

3. But we have not yet reached the center of the Johannine understanding of church unity. The most central unity text in the Gospel of John is a prayer, John 17. It is thus clear that in the Gospel of John church unity is by no means "a moral or organizational accomplishment of the church; it is entirely a divine gift."[136] It is not "a unity that results from a consensus of the members"; it is something from which the church "always and already gravitates."[137] Church unity is "not a sociological reality," and it "does not consist in a . . . community in which the people involved have the same opinions."[138] Unity is unity *in Christ.* Christ is the power of life flowing through the branches. Without the vine they are nothing. Again, the Johannine "as" *(kathos)* emerges. It speaks of much more than a corresponding relationship; it designates a foundation — indeed, in a sense identical realities: "as you, Father, are in me and I in you, that they also may be in us" (17:21). Ultimately, the unity of the church is nothing more than the Father being one with the Son. One can only pray that the disciples will be "in" this unity. Their unity is that the Father and the Son let their power become active in the disciples.

We can compare the Johannine metaphor of the vine and its branches in John 15:1-8 with the Pauline idea of the body of Christ in 1 Corinthians 12:12-31. Paul reflects on the relationship of the members to one another. John, on the other hand, uses one of the great biblical images for Israel — Israel is God's vine (Isa. 5:1-7 and elsewhere) — but he does not use this image for the church; he applies it to Jesus himself, and he reflects exclusively about the relationship of the disciples to Jesus. Thus he can also speak of the disciples and in them think of the church. He uses — not without good reason — the word "friends" for the disciples, but he does so in the christological sense rather than in the ecclesiological sense. They are not friends among themselves; they are "my friends" (15:14). Decisive here is hearing. Disciples are those sheep "who will hear my voice" (10:16), who "abide in me and my words in you" (15:7), and who pray as Jesus himself prays (15:7). Thus ultimately unity in Christ means hearing the word and prayer.

135. Cf. Matt. 18:15-20; 23:8-10; and above, p. 120.

136. Josef Blank, *Das Evangelium nach Johannes,* GSL 4/2 (Düsseldorf: Patmos, 1977), p. 282.

137. H. F. Weiss, "Ut omnes unum sint: Zur Frage der Einheit der Kirche im Johannesevangelium und in den Briefen des Ignatius," *ThV* 10 (1979): 74.

138. Gerhard Friedrich, "Die Einheit der Kirche nach dem Neuen Testament," in *The New Testament Age: Essays in Honor of Bo Reicke,* 2 vols., ed. William C. Weinrich (Macon, GA: Mercer University Press, 1984), vol. 1, p. 182.

That idea speaks to the deepest dimension of the unity of the church in John. Yet we should not misunderstand it in an individualistic sense. The point is not that the unity of the whole church is exhausted in the love of brothers and sisters in a small group. And it is certainly not that even the love of brothers and sisters is finally made relative through the individual's relationship to Christ. Instead, the point is that the fellowship of the believers awakens to the reality in which it lives. Thus the christological text of the vine takes an ecclesiological turn. Abiding in Christ means that Jesus' disciples keep Jesus' sole commandment: "that you love one another as I have loved you" (John 15:12). Thus unity with Christ not only makes possible the movement to brotherly love; it is itself this movement. The "abiding" of the disciples in the vine of Jesus, which establishes the unity of the church (John 15:4), is an abiding in him who, according to John 14:6, is at the same time the "way" (that one *goes*), the "truth" (that one *recognizes* and *does*), and the "life" (that is both *promised* and *given*). Thus it is not "mystical" in the sense of something internal, isolated, and removed from the world. And yet it *is* "mystical" in the sense that it is the deepest and most fundamental experience of God — an experience one can never "make" oneself. Therefore, Jesus' farewell prayer closes with a sentence that brings together love and the hearing of the word and at the same time is a petition and its fulfillment: "I have made known to them your name and will make it known, that the love with which you have loved me may be in them and I in them" (17:26).

We began by trying to understand the whole-church-universal, the brotherly-fellowship, and the Christological-individual dimensions of unity as different steps. That has now proven to be overly hasty. The three steps are more like aspects of the same thing. The unity with and in Christ cannot be separated from brotherly love, and this in turn cannot be separated from the integration into the whole church. The depth of the Johannine view proves itself by not spiritualizing Christ, the basic gift of unity. Instead, it draws him into the love lived in the local churches and in the whole church.

8. The Second Basic Conflict: Church Fellowship in the Controversy with Christian Gnosticism

8.1. Introduction

For the church, the second century was a century of major internal conflicts. There were essentially three of them: the conflict with the Gnostics; the conflict with Marcion; and the conflict with the so-called "New Prophecy," the Montanists. Of these three conflicts, only the conflict with the Gnostics left traces in the latest New Testament writings. The other two conflicts came in later years. That is also true in the main of the conflict with Gnosticism. It begins in the latest New Testament writings and then comes to a head in the second half of the second century. In the first half of the second century it left definite traces only in canonical and other church writings; unfortunately, we cannot date the extant writings of the Christian Gnostics with any precision. The problem is that the New Testament texts seldom make clear what their opponents' positions were. Usually, therefore, we cannot be certain that the opponents are actually Gnostics, and we have no choice but to make use of later texts for our description of the Gnostic side of this conflict.

In addition to all of these difficulties, there are the unresolved problems in the study of Gnosticism. Today there is hardly any consensus about what one meaningfully can call "gnosis." An era of research influenced largely by Adolf von Harnack understood "gnosis" as a Christian heresy or, more precisely, as the acute secularization and Hellenization of Christianity.[139] In the first half of the twentieth century, this understanding was replaced by the view that gnosis was a complex Oriental syncretistic religious phenomenon that was not limited to Christianity. It had various pre-Christian roots and a similarly structured redeemer myth.[140] Today the pendulum is tending to return to the first position, but at the same time people have recognized that "gnosis" is a label for a "movement" that never understood itself as a unified movement. More precisely, this label was used for the first time by the author of the Pastoral Epistles when he admonishes Timothy: "Avoid the godless chatter and polemics of the falsely so-called gnosis" (1 Tim. 6:20). This label may have been part of the self-understanding of the author's opponents. Then the church father Irenaeus made use of this label in his major five-volume work against the heretics to lump together a whole series of different groupings and schools that in any way at all were similar to Christianity and therefore dangerous. In this way he actually created "Gnosis."[141]

139. Adolf Harnack, *History of Dogma*, vol. 1, trans. Neil Buchanan (1896; repr. New York: Dover, 1961). [The English translation is of the third German edition. A fourth German edition was published in 1909.] For the relevant texts, see Kurt Rudolph, ed., *Gnosis und Gnostizismus*, WdF 262 (Darmstadt: Wissenschaftliche Buchgesellschaft, 1975), pp. 142-73.

140. Wilhelm Bousset, *Hauptprobleme der Gnosis*, FRLANT 10 (1907; repr. Göttingen: Vandenhoeck & Ruprecht, 1973). One can find a modern version of this position in Kurt Rudolph, *Gnosis: The Nature and History of Gnosticism*, trans. Robert McLachlan Wilson (San Francisco: Harper & Row, 1984).

141. The distinction between "gnosis" (in the phenomenology-of-religion sense of a saving religious knowledge) and "Gnosticism" (in the sense of a Christian heretical or religious-syncretistic movement predominantly of the second century A.D.) has not been widely accepted

There was indeed one group of people — but only one — that called itself "Gnostic."[142] The word "Gnostic," however, does not appear in the manuscripts found at Nag Hammadi. Justin is revealing when he says, speaking of those people he calls (based on the names of their leaders) Marcians, Valentinians, Basilidians, Satornilians, etc.: "They call themselves Christians."[143] That certainly does not apply to all the groups and schools that we, following Irenaeus and often going beyond him, call "Gnostics," but it is true of many of them.

When we survey all of the texts and groups that people call "Gnostic" today and that also exhibit "Christian" contents,[144] we find a great deal of variety. I would suggest the following rough division of types:

1. *"Pre-Gnostic" or "proto-Gnostic" Christian writings, groups, or teachers* who are to be located in the foreground or in the wider surroundings of Christian gnosis and who exhibit only some of the characteristics that are definitive of Gnosticism.[145] To this group belong, for example, the Jewish Christian Cerinth[146] and other early "Gnostic" teachers down to Basilides[147] and perhaps Valentinus,[148] *The Gospel of Thomas,* and *The Odes of Solomon.*

2. *Christian Gnostic writings, groups, or teachers* who exhibit a majority of the characteristics definitive of gnosis and who also make considerable use of Christian traditions and understand themselves to be Christian. Examples of this group include many of the pupils of Valentinus, Gnostic writings such as *The Gospel of Philip, The Gospel of Truth, The Epistle to Rheginos,* and the *Testimonium Veritatis, The Apocalypse of Peter,* and *The Interpretation of*

---

by German-speaking scholarship. Therefore, I use "gnosis" in the sense of "Gnosticism" and thus maintain the terminology of Irenaeus.

142. Cf. Irenaeus, *Adversus haereses* 1.25.6, on the followers of a certain Marcellina who was said to have venerated icons of Christ.

143. Justin, *Dialogue with Trypho* 1.35.6. On the self-designations of Gnostics, cf. Folker Siegert, "Die Selbstbezeichnungen der Gnostiker in den Nag Hammadi Texten," *ZNW* 71 (1980): 129-32.

144. I am leaving out of consideration the Mandaean writings, the Hermetic writings, the Manichaean texts, and all works in which no Christian revealer plays a role as, e.g., *Zostrianos, The Apocalypse of Adam,* and other writings (e.g., "Sethian" works) that only marginally make use of Christian traditions.

145. Cf. here below, p. 146.

146. Cf. Winrich Alfried Löhr, *Basilides und seine Schule: Eine Studie zur Theologie- und Kirchengeschichte des zweiten Jahrhunderts,* WUNT 83 (Tübingen: Mohr/Siebeck, 1996).

147. Cf. Christoph Markschies, *Valentinus Gnosticus? Untersuchungen zur Valentinianischen Gnosis mit einem Kommentar zu den Fragmenten Valentins,* WUNT 65 (Tübingen: Mohr/Siebeck, 1992).

148. In all of these cases, the judgment must be based on the few fragments that actually come from them. It cannot be based on the church fathers' organizing of their ideas into a "Gnostic" system.

Gnosis. In the case of the school of Valentinus, one could also speak of an increasing "gnosticizing," while with other Christian teachers — for example, Clement of Alexandria — there was a decisive return to Christian tradition. From among the so-called "Barbeliot" or "Sethian" Gnostic writings one might attribute several writings given a strong Christian flavor to this group, such as *The Apocryphon of John* and related writings.[149]

3. *Principally anti-church Christian Gnostic writings or groups* that exhibit most of the characteristics definitive of gnosis and that refer to a great deal of Christian tradition but sharply reject it and have a polemical relationship to the Christianity of the church. Until recently the only known example of the type was *The Second Logos of the Great Seth,* but now there is also the *Gospel of Judas.*[150]

4. *Syncretistic Christian Gnostic writings or groups* that exhibit a majority of the characteristics definitive of Gnosticism but refer to Christian traditions only among others. Thus they are more "syncretistic" than Christian. For the most part they belong to a later phase of the Gnostic movement in which individual Gnostic groups understood their symbolic world as "a subsystem of a more universal sign world" that in many religions and philosophical systems "was present . . . as images and symbols of a process of self-discovery."[151] To this type belong, in my judgment, such writings as the *Trimorphic Protennoia* and the *Pistis Sophia.*

Of course, this evolution of the Christian Gnostic movement to the point of an increasing loss of identity and an increasing universalizing is, in my judgment, only *one* of the possible ways Gnostic movements developed. Another is that they organized themselves into independent churches with their own rituals, doctrines, and institutional forms. Among "Gnostic" movements that have originated in Christianity, this is the case with the Marcionites and the Marcosians. In a sense it is also true of the Manichaeans, who have roots among the Elkesaites.

Following Christoph Markschies,[152] I will select the following features

149. Since in *The Apocalypse of John* the Christian traditions appear almost exclusively in the narrative framework, while the content of the revelation largely appears to be non-Christian, I am inclined here and with related works to speak of Sethian missionary writings or introductions for Christian readers. Their authors could have been either inside or outside the Christian communities.

150. Cf. below, p. 157.

151. Gerd Theissen, *The Religion of the Earliest Churches: Creating a Symbolic World,* trans. John Bowden (Minneapolis: Fortress, 1999), p. 237.

152. Christoph Markschies, *Gnosis: An Introduction,* trans. John Bowden (London: T&T Clark, 2003), pp. 16-17.

as *typological characteristics* of "gnosis" that, taken together, permit us to designate a group or a writing as "gnostic."

1. the experience of an other-worldly, distant, supreme God;
2. the introduction conditioned by this experience of further divine figures that are closer to human beings than the supreme God;
3. the estimation of the world and of matter as evil creation and the related experience of the alienation of the gnostic in the world;
4. a variously expressed tendency toward dualism in cosmology and anthropology;
5. the introduction of an ignorant or malicious creator God who in the Platonic tradition is called "craftsman" *(demiurgos);*
6. the assumption of a fall of a divine element into matter that is told in a mythological drama and that explains the present condition of the world and of human beings;
7. the knowledge *(gnosis)* of this state that is mediated by a redeemer figure from the other world and that leads to salvation.

The preceding excursion into gnosis scholarship should make clear how complex is the task of dealing with church fellowship in the "parting of the ways" between Gnosticism and orthodox Christianity. From the very beginning we must expect that there will be many different developments and forms of conflicts. That depends a great deal on the local churches and on the type of so-called Gnostics one meets. Concerning the latter, we can assume that before 150 we will be dealing primarily with the first group — thus, with "pre-" or "proto-Gnostics." It seems that, as the decades went by, the gnosis that originated in orthodox Christianity relatively often emancipated itself from Christian faith; thus it has made itself "Gnostic," as one sees, for example, in the school of Valentinus. This development will have been intensified by the accelerated "parting of the ways." Presumably there was also the reverse movement in which an originally non-Christian gnosis moved in the direction of orthodox Christianity, as, for example, in the so-called Sethian or Barbeliot schools. In this case, however, the presumably oldest extant documents are largely non-Christian and do not come into consideration for our theme.[153]

On the Christian-orthodox side, our sources are those we have already considered: the New Testament texts and the Apostolic fathers. On the Christian-Gnostic side I have had to draw on writings that may have origi-

153. E.g., *The Apocalypse of Adam* (NHC V, 5) or *Zostrianos* (NHC VIII, 1).

nated after 150, because there are no other sources. We will examine first the orthodox (= 8.2) and then the Christian-Gnostic side (= 8.3). On both sides we will see, on the one hand, various possible ways of reacting, yet on the other hand clearly dominant tones. They will then lead to some closing considerations of our own (= 8.4).

8.2. *The Gnosticizing Opponents as Seen by Church-Christians (with Andreas Karrer)*

The opponents combated by the New Testament authors show "gnosticizing" features only in the latest New Testament texts, shortly before the turn of the century.

We recognize almost nothing of them in the only text where Luke speaks of such opponents — in Paul's farewell address to the elders in Ephesus in *Acts 20:17-38*. In Paul's speech, Luke admonishes the elders, whom the Holy Spirit has appointed to be overseers *(episkopos)* over the local churches, to shepherd God's flock with vigilance (20:28). We learn that some of the opponents are "devouring wolves" who have come into the church from the outside (thus perhaps itinerant teachers). Others have come from the local churches and obviously with no little persuasive power have drawn the believers to their side (20:29-30). We do not find out who they are and what they teach. The label "devouring wolves" is enough to call forth the necessary defensive reflexes from the readers. Are they people with affinities to later Gnosticism? One could conclude that this was the case from verse 20, where Paul protests that there was nothing secret in his preaching. Is that an allusion to the favorite Gnostic practice of appealing to secret traditions and teachings of the risen Jesus? Or is it simply a traditional topos of asserting one's innocence? It is certainly that, but its repetition in verse 27 could indicate that in that situation this topos was especially important. Thus we have no more than a vague suspicion that the combated "wolves" might have been precursors of the Gnostics. In this speech of the Lukan Paul, there is no theological debate with the opponents, only an appeal to the officeholders and an emotional reminder of the apostle Paul's sacrificial concern for his church during the time he was with it (20:31). In many ways it is reminiscent of the picture of Paul in 2 Timothy (cf. 2 Tim. 3:12; 4:9-18).

The *Pastorals* give us a clearer picture. Here we learn not only that the opponents are very proud of their spiritual knowledge *(gnosis)* but that they may even call themselves "Gnostics" (1 Tim. 6:20). They claim that they "know" God (Tit. 1:16). We also hear that they teach in houses, perhaps for payment (Tit. 1:11).[154] They are of Jewish origin (Tit. 1:10), claim to be teachers of the Torah (1 Tim. 1:6; cf. Tit. 3:9), and teach "Jewish myths" or "myths and endless genealogies" (1 Tim. 1:3-4; cf. 4:7; 2 Tim. 4:4; Tit. 3:9). They prohibit marriage and require the observance of food regulations (1 Tim. 4:3; cf. 4:8). Some of them teach that the "resurrection has already happened" (2 Tim. 2:18) — that is, perhaps a spiritual resurrection in the here and now such as one finds in the Valentinian letter to Rheginos[155] and such as Paul confronted with the Corinthians. All of this would fit well with an early form of Gnosticism with a Jewish imprint that may have come into the churches from the outside.

The author of the Pastorals refuses to be drawn into a discussion of the issues of these opponents. He disqualifies them with deprecating comments such as "foolish," "babblers," "corrupters," etc., and with a harsh catalogue of vices (2 Tim. 3:2-5). Even the label "Jewish" (Tit. 1:14; cf. 1:10) does not have a friendly sound. He cannot refrain from a harsh insult in the form of an obscure prophetic saying (Tit. 1:12). He turns to Timothy and Titus and — through them — indirectly to the ministers of the local churches, who are very important in this situation. They should pay special attention to what is going on "in the houses." Both here and later in the history of the church, "house groups" often are seen as potential breeding grounds of immorality and heresy. A substantive theological debate with the opponents is lacking. Instead, the author urges people not even to respond to their foolish controversies (Tit. 3:9). After one or two reprimands, one should simply break off fellowship with them (Tit. 3:10), as obviously had already been done in the case of Hymenaeus[156] and Alexander (1 Tim. 1:20). Thus the unity of the local church is to be achieved by administrative measures! That is logical, since one cannot even raise for discussion the tradition that is to be preserved uncorrupted and unchanged until the last day.

There is a similar situation in *2 Peter* and in the *Epistle of Jude,* the latter of which underlies 2 Peter as a source. I will deal with them only briefly. Who the opponents are, whether they are the same in both epistles, and whether they belong in the context of nascent Gnosticism are questions we cannot answer with certainty. Although both authors revile the opponents prolifically, they give scarcely any information about them. With many of the insults, one can hardly determine whether they have any basis in reality or whether the

154. This would best describe itinerant teachers who have come into the church from the outside and who earn money with their "gnosis."

155. *The Treatise on the Resurrection* (NHC I, 4).

156. Who advocated a false doctrine of the resurrection (2 Tim. 2:18).

negative names the opponents are called simply come from a standard repertoire of invectives. The author of Jude appeals to the "most holy faith," the foundation on which the church is built (Jude 20), "which once for all has been delivered to the saints" (Jude 3). It is worth noting that the opponents obviously still participate in the church's love *(agape)* feasts (Jude 12) and that the author does not stop trying to save the people who have fallen away. One should snatch those who are in danger from the fire and pray for the hopeless cases while protecting oneself from contamination by their spotted garment (Jude 22-23).[157] The author of 2 Peter no longer makes such attempts. He appeals to the "holy commandment delivered" — that is, to tradition — and, in addition, to the authority of the "holy prophets" and the apostles, especially to his own authority, which is strongly emphasized in this letter, written as a testament of the prince of apostles.

The *Johannine epistles* are the most interesting case.[158] According to 1 John 2:19, the opponents "went out from us." Thus at one time they had belonged to the Johannine group. They do not know the truth because they deny that Jesus is the Christ (1 John 2:22). In other texts this is made more precise: they deny that Jesus Christ "has come in the flesh" (1 John 4:3; 2 John 7). Thus they advocate a "docetic" Christology. Are they Gnostics? In my opinion that is not certain, although many later Gnostics (not all!) advocated a docetic Christology because they regarded the union of heavenly spirit and earthly matter as the deepest ground of the hopelessness of the human situation, and they wanted to keep the savior who had come from the other world free from being ensnared in earthly matter.

If we follow the clue Irenaeus gives us in *Adversus haereses* 3.3.4, according to which Cerinth was the main opponent of John the disciple in Ephesus, we discover affinities. Cerinth is said to have denied the virgin birth and to have claimed that the Spirit came down at the baptism in the form of a dove onto the human Jesus, the son of Joseph and Mary (Irenaeus, *Adversus haereses* 1.26.1). The only thing that is certain is that Irenaeus understood Cerinth to be a Gnostic. He could also have been a Jewish Christian[159] whose Christology was later given a Gnostic interpretation.

The author of the Johannine letters denounces them harshly (cf. 1 John

157. Thus the most probable interpretation of "to have pity"; cf. Anton Vögtle, *Der Judasbrief: Der zweite Petrusbrief,* EKK 22 (Neukirchen: Neukirchener Verlag; Solothurn: Benziger, 1994), pp. 106-7.

158. I am proceeding here on the assumption that they were written *after* the Gospel of John and that their author, the "Elder," was not the author of John 1–20.

159. Thus Christoph Markschies, "Kerinthos," in *Reallexikon für Antike und Christentum,* vol. 20 (Stuttgart: Hiersemann, 2004), pp. 755-66.

2:21, 17). Indeed, they are "the antichrist," who, as the believing readers know, will come in the last hour (1 John 2:18, cf. 22; 2 John 7). It is the last hour, and now many antichrists have appeared who lead the churches astray. One can no longer have fellowship with them in the church; indeed, the author says, since they did not remain with us, they never did belong to us (1 John 2:19). They are of the world, not of God (1 John 4:5). In 2 John the "Elder" gives the church clear guidance: "If anyone comes to you and does not bring this teaching, do not receive him into the house and do not greet him" (2 John 10). Even the universal commandment of hospitality is not to be observed when one is dealing with false teachers.

Where did the author see the boundaries of the church? Andreas Karrer writes on the subject (in the next five paragraphs):

The author appears to be aware of two criteria. The first is brotherly love. "By this are the children of God and the children of the devil manifest: Whoever does not do righteousness is not of God, and whoever does not love his brother" (1 John 3:10). The author cites this criterion, however, only in the non-polemical, parenetic parts of his letter. The second criterion is significantly more important. It is the confession: "This is the antichrist, he who denies the Father and the Son" (1 John 2:22). That is the confession the church has "heard from the beginning" (1 John 2:24). This is where the spirits go their separate ways. Only those people are part of the fellowship who confess that "Jesus Christ has come in the flesh" (1 John 4:2). Those who speak differently exclude themselves from the fellowship. Thus, unlike the texts we have previously considered, the author of 1 John has a clear, substantial criterion for what is true doctrine. At first glance, this use of the confession makes sense, but it carries with it the following difficulties.

1. According to the author of 1 John, one is to hold fast to the confession just as it was from the beginning, without changes (2:24). One's own possession of the Spirit confirms that this is the true way (1 John 2:27; 4:2). It follows that without the Spirit the wording of the confession cannot guarantee the truth. The authority to which the author appeals is one's own possession of the Spirit. Yet the apostates also claim to have the Spirit (1 John 4:1). Thus there is a face-off between Spirit and Spirit.

2. The confession bears witness to God's love and at the same time clearly separates those whom God loves from the children of the world and the apostates. Thus it no longer opens itself to include others. It is scarcely able any longer to testify to and in the world about the Jesus who with his love transcends all boundaries. Instead, it places limits on God's love. It is no longer granted the freedom to embrace the apostates. Judgment is given; even God's love can no longer — indeed, may no longer — overturn it. Thus the

believer is now able to pass judgment about the range of God's love and in the name of that love exclude people from fellowship.

3. As a result, love is limited to one's own ranks. Love is determined as the love of brothers and sisters. The "children of the devil" are not brothers. God's unconditional acceptance of people is made conditional on the right confession. The second letter gives an example of how this is practiced. There the Elder even forbids extending hospitality and greeting people whose confession is different. Loveless behavior is demanded as a sign of the confession. There is tension between confessing God's love and accepting it in one's own life.

4. That also changes the confession's function. Instead of calling attention to Christ as the basic gift who creates fellowship, it now designates the boundaries of fellowship by unmasking false brothers. When it is passed on, especially in a canonical text, it permits or forbids fellowship in new situations. One can clearly see in what direction it is developing. The content of faith has moved from bearing witness to Christ himself to a rigidly formulated and unchangeably transmitted confession. No longer is the living Christ confessed; now a confession formulated for all times is believed.

We can quickly bring our *tour d'horizon* to a conclusion. Opponents who advocate a docetic Christology also appear in some of the *letters of Ignatius of Antioch,* especially in the letter to the Smyrnaeans (chaps. 1–8) but also in the letter to the Trallians (chap. 10). How they are related to the opponents in the letter to the Magnesians, who live as Jews do (*Magnesians* 8–10; *Philadelphians* 5–9), is controversial. It is worth noting, however, that Ignatius breaks off fellowship in principle only with those Christians who deny that Christ has come in the flesh and has truly died and been raised — not, however, with "Judaizing" opponents.[160] Only of them does he say: "I did not think I should write their names as unbelievers. Indeed, I would prefer not even to remember them" (*Smyrnaeans* 5.3). Since they also do not participate in the eucharist,[161] there is no fellowship with them: "So it is right to keep our distance

160. The different attitudes toward the docetic Christians in the *Smyrnaeans* and the "Judaizing" Christians in *Magnesians* and *Philippians* is one of the reasons why I surmise there were two different groups of opponents. *Philadelphians* 6.1 could indicate where Ignatius sees the limit of church fellowship. "When both of them (that is, Judaizing Gentile Christians and Jewish Christians) do not speak of Jesus Christ they are for me tombstones and sepulchers of the dead."

161. We do not know why they did not. There are three possibilities: (1) Had they been shut out? (2) Did they belong to a different house church from that of the bishop? (3) Did their Christology lead them to reject the eucharist? The third possibility is improbable, because according to *Smyrnaeans* 7.1 they also do not participate in the prayer.

from such people and to speak about them neither in private nor in public" (*Smyrnaeans* 7.2). In only one place does he make the concession that one might pray for them (*Smyrnaeans* 4.1). The standard of measurement Ignatius uses is the confession he quotes, for example, at the beginning of his letter to the Smyrnaeans. Admittedly, he does not leave it unchanged; he accentuates it much as Paul had done earlier: "*Truly* of David's family according to the flesh . . . *truly* born of a virgin. . . ." And, looking to the future, he also interprets it, for example, with the claim that Jesus Christ "was in the flesh even after the resurrection" (*Smyrnaeans* 3). Ignatius is not merely a traditionalist; he is a great creative theologian.

Polycarp's letter to the Philippians is interesting for our theme because in 7.1-2 he cites a number of "basic beliefs" that are part of "the word delivered to us from the beginning" and that are essential for Christian identity. They are: the belief that Jesus Christ has come in the flesh, the testimony of the cross, and the belief in resurrection and judgment. Believing these truths separates true Christians from the "foolishness of the crowd."

We bring the section to a close with a small prosopographic note. Marcion, who had come to Rome from Sinope in Asia Minor and taught there in the Roman church, was excommunicated in A.D. 144, and he immediately founded his own church. Valentinus, who later was represented by Irenaeus as the "father of the so-called Gnostic heresy" (*Adversus haereses* 1.11.1) came to Rome before A.D. 140 and worked there as a teacher of the church for at least fifteen years. According to Tertullian (*Adversus Valentinianos* 4.1), he even sought the office of bishop. We never hear that the Roman church excommunicated him. In the time of Bishop Victor, at the end of the second century, the Valentinian presbyter Florinus was even active in the Roman church (Eusebius, *Historia ecclesiastica* 5.20).

We summarize: the gospel and love — the truth of the confession and the fellowship of believers — were the two focal points of the ellipse that represents the church in early Christianity. In the slowly evolving conflict between the church's Christianity and nascent Christian Gnosticism, it seems that in the church the confession took precedence over church fellowship. The confession that was evolving into an unchangeable tradition became the condition of church fellowship. Former brothers became heretics with whom one was to break off all fellowship — indeed, about whom one did not even speak or whom one insulted in an extremely loveless way.

This picture is certainly right in its broad strokes, but only in its broad strokes. There are different shades of color and small exceptions. Among them is the firmly held admonition in the Epistle of Jude and Ignatius to pray for the heretics as well. It is also important that the traditional confession was not only retained and repeated; sometimes, as with Ignatius, it was also theologically interpreted. It is also not unimportant that not *all* of the church's convictions became divisive truths. Ignatius and Polycarp show that with special clarity. And, finally, one must remember that one did not always, everywhere, and immediately excommunicate enemies or suspect teachers. Sometimes one waited patiently, even in Rome.

8.3. The Church-Christians as Seen by Their Christian-Gnostic Opponents

We begin by remembering a daring hypothesis. In 3 John the author, the "Elder," complains to his addressee, Gaius, that a certain Diotrephes, who "likes to be first," does not receive his messengers and "expels from the church" those members who do extend hospitality to them (3 John 9-10). According to Ernst Käsemann, Diotrephes is the orthodox bishop of a local church, and the "Elder" is a gnosticizing presbyter[162] whose sympathizers were expelled by the bishop from his church. If this bold hypothesis were correct, we could see in the Johannine letters the conflict between the Gnostics and the church as it might have looked from the other side. For several reasons, however, the thesis is improbable.[163] That means that we have no Gnostic sources contemporary with the New Testament texts that would permit us to have this view from the other side. Thus we have to make use of later sources.

As a general observation, we can say that in the extant Christian-Gnostic texts the polemic against the church-Christians does not play nearly as important a role as does the polemic against Gnosticizing Christians in the later New Testament texts or in the writings of the Christians who combated heretics.[164] The church father Irenaeus says clearly why that was the case. The Gnostics — he is speaking here of the Valentinians — work *in* the church. Their lectures are intended for the simple church-Christians; they want to win them and not repel them. "They complain . . . about us that we avoid their fellowship without reason, since their teaching is similar to ours, and that we call them heretics, even though they teach the same and have the

162. Ernst Käsemann, "Ketzer und Zeuge," in Käsemann, *Exegetische Versuche und Besinnungen,* vol. 1 (Göttingen: Vandenhoeck & Ruprecht, 1960), pp. 168-87.

163. The "Elder" is not a Gnostic. In my judgment, there was not yet a full-blown Gnosticism in the context of the Johannine writings. Still, Käsemann's thesis was very attractive, because it suddenly brought the texts of Christian Gnostics into the church's canon.

164. The most important book on the theme is Klaus Koschorke, *Die Polemik der Gnostiker gegen das kirchliche Christentum,* NHS 12 (Leiden: Brill, 1978).

same doctrine" (Irenaeus, *Adversus haereses* 3.15.2). They feel that they are part of the church. They confess the same Christ. Justin also says that these people are confessing Christians and that they believe in the crucified Jesus as Lord and Christ (*Dialogue with Trypho* 35.2).[165] And they really believe what they say. The church father Tertullian complains in *De praescriptione haereticorum* 41 that the Gnostics have no sense of hierarchy and church discipline. That is understandable. Most Christian Gnostics are laypersons. At best, they are going to suffer under the church's official leadership. As we will see, their understanding of the church is influenced by the Pauline principle of fellowship in the body of Christ and by Jesus' principle of humility and rejecting status. Tertullian then continues: "As for peace in the church, they are peaceful with everyone, without distinction" (*De praescriptione haereticorum* 41).[166] They recognize no church divisions and act humbly (42.4.6). That is true not only of their relationships among themselves but also of their relationships with the Catholic Christians. They emphasize the "*common* faith" (Tertullian, *Adversus Valentinianos* 1).

My general impression is that polemics of genuine Christian Gnostics against the church are primarily a reaction. That is to say, they engage in polemics only when they must, and they do so as a reflection of their own experiences in the church. Of course, strictly speaking, there is little firm proof for that statement, because normally Gnostic texts reveal little about the context in which they are written. In the following comments I will give several examples of quite different reactions.

The work *The Interpretation of Gnosis*[167] is possibly a Valentinian writing that may date from as early as the middle of the second century. In its second part it contains a charismatic church order that closely follows 1 Corinthians 12. According to Koschorke's interpretation, the issue here is the relationship between church members who have full knowledge and the "ignorant" — that is, normal church-Christians. The author writes with the "knowing ones" in mind: "How do you know that someone is ignorant of the brethren? For you are ignorant when you hate them" (17.25-27). And to the "ignorant" he says: "But is someone making progress in the Word? Do not be hindered by this; do

165. Similarly, Irenaeus, *Adversus haereses* 5.18.1: "The heretics also confess the crucified one."

166. Tertullian adds: "In fact, although they have divergent doctrines, there is no difference between them."

167. NHC XI, 1. Cf. Klaus Koschorke, "Eine neugefundengnostische Gemeindeordnung: Zum thema Geist und Amt im frühen Christentum," *ZThK* 76 (1979): 30-60. The translation is by John D. Turner, in *The Nag Hammadi Library in English*, ed. James M. Robinson, 3d ed. (San Francisco: Harper & Row, 1988), pp. 472-80.

not say, 'Why does he speak while I do not?', for what he says is also yours" (16.31-36). The text is an impressive attempt to strengthen the relationship between Gnostics and non-Gnostics in a local church under the signature of Paul's teaching about charismata.

The Gospel of Philip is certainly a Valentinian text from the second century.[168] Logion 26 contains a variation of the Gnostic doctrine of the various forms of Christ that explains their background: "Jesus took them all by stealth, for he did not appear as he was, but in the manner in which they would be able to see him. . . . He appeared to the great as great. He appeared to the small as small. He appeared to the angels as an angel, and to men as a man. Because of this his word hid itself from everyone. . . . When he appeared to his disciples in glory on the mount he was not small. He became great, but he made the disciples great, that they might be able to see him in his greatness." Here we are far removed from Paul's firm statement that other people proclaim "another Jesus." "Other Jesuses" are accommodations that correspond to the various human capacities for understanding. This means that there can hardly be a limit to Jesus' variability. In principle, every view of Jesus is possible.

We find harsher tones in *The Apocalypse of Peter,* [169] a short, impressive text, perhaps still from the second half of the second century. The author speaks on behalf of the "little ones" who have been captured and oppressed. Who are the people who oppress the little ones? Initially, the Savior, speaking to Peter, leaves it open. "Some who do not understand mystery speak of things which they do not understand, but they will boast that the mystery of the truth is theirs alone." They oppress their brothers by saying to them: "Through this our God has pity, since salvation comes to us through this." Thus the Savior is speaking here against an *exclusive* claim of salvation that leads to oppression. At the end of the vision he says openly: "And there shall be others of those who are outside our number who name themselves bishop and also deacons, as if they have received their authority from God. They bend themselves under the judgment of the leaders. Those people are dry canals."[170] It is characteristic of Gnostic polemics against the church that they are seldom directed against the "little ones" — that is, against laymen, only against the officeholders.[171]

The *Authentikos Logos*[172] is a relatively early, in any case still second-

168. NHC II, 3. Translation by Wesley W. Isenberg, in *Nag Hammadi Library,* pp. 139-60.

169. NHC VII, 3. Translation by James Brashler and Roger A. Bullard, in *Nag Hammadi Library,* pp. 372-78.

170. Quotations: 76.27-34; 79.13-16, 22-31 (allusions to Matt. 23:6 and 2 Pet. 2:17).

171. Koschorke, *Polemik der Gnostiker,* pp. 80-85.

172. NHC VI, 3. Translation by George W. MacRae, in *Nag Hammadi Library,* pp. 305-10.

century, work that presumably is to be located at the margin of Christianity. In its closing part it deals with a basic principle of Christian Gnosticism, the principle of seeking. We find it frequently, following Matthew 7:7, in Gnosticizing texts, such as, for example, in the opening of *The Gospel of Thomas:* "Jesus said, 'Let him who seeks continue seeking until he finds. When he finds, he will become troubled. When he becomes troubled, he will be astonished, and he will rule over the all'" (logion 2). Tertullian formulates the most expressive of the church's polemics against this principle: "One must seek until one finds, and when one has found, believe, and then there is nothing more to do than to hold fast to what one has grasped in faith" (*De praescriptione haereticorum* 9). It is the same as with the woman in the parable of the drachmas: those who have found no longer need to seek. Now in the *Authentikos Logos* we find the Gnostic counter-polemic against this polemic. Once again the ecclesiastical officeholders are in the author's sights: "But these — the ones who are ignorant — do not seek after God. Nor do they inquire about their dwelling place, which exists in rest, but they go about in bestiality. They are more wicked than the pagans, because . . . they do not inquire about God, for their hardness of heart draws them down to make them their cruelty. . . . If they find someone else who asks about his salvation, their hardness of heart sets to work upon that man. And if he is not silent as he asks, they kill him by their cruelty, thinking that they have done a good thing for themselves. . . . For even the pagans give charity, and they know that God who is in the heavens exists, the Father of the universe, exalted over their idols, which they worship" (33.4-32). This is the voice of a man who has been excluded from the fellowship of the church.

The anti-church polemic in *The Second Logos of the Great Seth*[173] is part of a Gnostic system. The Gnostic work is perhaps to be dated sometime after 200, and it has in the broadest sense of the word a "Sethian" background. Formally, it is a revelation of the heavenly Son of Man, Christ, but the people who believe in this Christ have nothing more to do with the church-Christians since an intensive quarrel that led to persecution against the Gnostics. "We were hated and persecuted, not only by those who are ignorant, but also by those who think that they are advancing the name of Christ, since they were unknowingly empty, not knowing who they are, like dumb animals" (59.22-29). The Gnostics belong to the heavenly *ekklesia* (50.1-7), and they live in its "ineffable Monad" (51.16-17): "Then before the foundation of the world, when the whole multitude of the Assembly came together upon the places of

173. NHC VII, 2. Translation by Roger A. Bullard and Joseph A. Gibbons, in *Nag Hammadi Library,* pp. 362-71.

the Ogdoad, when they had taken counsel about a spiritual wedding which is in union . . ." (65.34–66.2). Although their Christ, the heavenly Son of Man, came to earth and performed miracles, he did not reveal himself to the inhabitants of these regions "in the love which was coming forth" (52.5-7). He remained a stranger to them. The archons created for them "an imitation, having proclaimed a doctrine of a dead man and lies so as to resemble the freedom and purity of the perfect assembly and joining themselves with their doctrine to fear and slavery, worldly cares, and abandoned worship" (60.20-29). Thus the *one* true heavenly church of the Gnostics has nothing to do with the visible, earthly church. The latter is only an imitation, much as the entire visible world is an imitation of the heavenly world above, created by the ignorant and arrogant demiurge, Yaldabaoath.

What may have been the harshest anti-church polemic appears in the *Gospel of Judas.*[174] It is a relatively early work, probably to be dated shortly after the middle of the second century, and a work of which Irenaeus had already heard.[175] It comes from a Gnostic group that also is to be assigned to Sethian Gnosticism. What sets this gospel apart is that the "arch-betrayer," Judas,[176] was chosen to be Jesus' conversation partner and to receive the Great Revelation[177] from the heavenly Jesus. His "betrayal" made it possible for Jesus to leave his body and to return to the Pleroma. For Judas it also meant his ultimate salvation. In this gospel the visible Catholic Church is represented by the twelve foolish disciples. They have a vision and see a temple with twelve priests who sacrifice, some of whom "sacrifice their own children, others their wives, in praise and humility with each other; some sleep with men; some are involved in slaughter; some commit a multitude of sins and deeds of lawlessness. And the men who stand before the altar invoke your name" (38). Jesus' interpretation is: "You are the twelve men you have seen. The cattle you have seen brought for sacrifice are the many people you lead astray" (39). Thus the church is an earthly apparition in the service of the lie, but the true church is the heavenly house that Judas, the "thirteenth spirit," sees in his vision, the dwelling place of the great men, the generation of Seth (44-45). The

174. Translation by Rodolphe Kasser, Marvin Meyer, and Gregor Wurst, in *The Gospel of Judas,* ed. Kasser, Meyer, and Wurst (Washington: National Geographic, 2006), pp. 19-45. *The Gospel of Judas* belongs to group 3, above, p. 145.

175. Irenaeus, *Adversus haereses* 1.31.1.

176. The work presupposes the Judas traditions of the canonical Gospels and turns them on their head.

177. This revelation is a short version of a Sethian cosmogony of a type such as one finds in *The Apocryphon of John* and in the so-called *Gospel of the Egyptians,* thus in the two classical writings of Sethian Gnosticism.

polemic against the church is similar to, but even sharper than, that of *The Second Logos of the Great Seth.* The difference is that here the Catholic Church of priests is morally slandered, much as were the Gnosticizing opponents of the church-Christians in the Pastorals or in 2 Peter. I can imagine that behind this text there is a group of Sethian — thus, in my opinion, originally non-Christian — Gnostics who tried to find a place for themselves in the early Catholic Church and were expelled from it.

In summary: in sociological terms, most Gnostic Christians were educated or partly educated laypersons, and often they were Christian teachers who tried to connect their Christian traditions with the material known to people familiar with popular philosophy. Initially, they had a clear tendency to believe that it was more important to maintain fellowship in the local churches than it was to prevail with their own doctrine. The nature of Gnostic thought facilitates this, since, as a basic principle of Gnostic thinking, asking and seeking salvation make it impossible to regard any knowledge as something definitive and final, as an "unalterable truth." The multiformity of Christ, the traces of which Gnostics discovered not only in the different interpretations of Christ in the churches but also in their philosophical traditions and in other religions, led them to understand all linguistic formulations of divine truth merely as symbolic approximations or as metaphors and "myths." For this very reason Gnostics continually had to turn to new formulations of artificial myths, none of which could serve as an adequate expression of eternal truth.[178] All of this led Gnostics not to be inclined to orthodoxies; they were tolerant both with their own kind and with the church-Christians. From the "Gnostic" perspective, that was the starting situation of the encounter between early Catholic church-Christians and pre-Gnostic church-Christians.

These encounters were often very difficult. From the side of early Catholic church-Christians, especially from the side of their officeholders, the leading impulse was a "hermeneutic of suspicion." One smelled the scent of apostasy and false doctrine everywhere. People did not know the free teachers who came into the local churches from the outside; for that reason alone they were suspicious. Frequently the "hermeneutic of suspicion" simply meant not understanding and not wanting to understand. That led to rejections and exclusions, and they in turn to insults and calumnies. That is not to say that the suspicion was always without foundation. Texts such as *The Second Logos of*

178. Naturally, "the inconstancy of their teaching" (Irenaeus, *Adversus haereses* 1.11.1) is a constant irritant for the people who combat heretics. They contrast the Gnostic innovations with the *one* and *invariable* rule of faith.

the Great Seth and the *Gospel of Judas* show that in fact non-Christian Gnostics repeatedly tried to make their way into local Christian churches and then failed to do so. But of course, in many cases the situation will have been reversed: The hermeneutic of suspicion and not wanting to understand among Christian brothers and sisters in the same local church sooner or later *caused* dissension and led to a break. One sees that in the history of the schools of the church teacher Valentinus. It is a history that shows how free Christian schools increasingly evolved into religious associations with their own rites alongside the church (or how they were forced into this development!) or how they even became separate churches.[179] Exclusions do not strengthen unity; they increase and harden the divisions — divisions the Christian Gnostics had not even wanted. That led finally to what one sees in *The Second Logos of the Great Seth* and in the *Gospel of Judas:* the anti-church polemic of the Gnostics who had been thrown out of the church largely became the mirror image of the church's anti-Gnostic polemic.

8.4. *Final Observations*

That brings us again to the fundamental problem we have already seen in Paul:[180] How does one reconcile the reality that Christ, who embodies God's unlimited love, is a power that tears down barriers and creates community with the reality that this same Christ also limits the community he has created? In Paul's case the question was: To what degree may — indeed, must — Christ be *interpreted anew* so that he becomes recognized as one's own Christ no longer "according to the flesh" but "in the Spirit" (2 Cor. 5:16)? Or to say it differently: When does one reach the point at which the newly interpreted Christ becomes "another Jesus" (2 Cor. 11:4) — the point at which every fellowship must end, because it no longer has the same basis? Paul answers this question formally: whoever makes God's grace depend on conditions other than Christ has betrayed Christ. Yet in reality Paul's answer was not formal; it presupposes an interpretation of Christ. Whoever, for example, was of the opinion that Jesus has "fulfilled Law and Prophets" (cf. Matt. 5:17) may well have disagreed with Paul in the Galatian controversy where the question was whether Torah and Christ can be combined.

A half-century after Paul, this same question began to be raised in the controversy with the Christian Gnostics. Again it was a question of the rela-

179. Thus probably in the case of the Marcosians.
180. Cf. above, pp. 89-90.

tionship between confession and fellowship. The church-Christians tended to make the confession the criterion for fellowship. They did not recognize that in so doing they called into question the Christ who was confessed, for the Jesus who had come in the flesh has demonstrated just how much God "has loved the world" (John 3:16). Jesus has broken down religious boundaries, not built them up. With this critical statement we are not saying that the complementary Christian-Gnostic position would be true to the gospel. Its weakness was that it often obliterated the clear grounding of church fellowship in the activity, death, and resurrection of Jesus of Nazareth and increasingly replaced it with one's own spirituality as the basis of fellowship. That had ecclesiological consequences. For many Gnostics, for whom it was not difficult to live at peace with all people in the church regardless of the doctrine they advocated or the ethos they practiced, the true church could *only* be the heavenly church. We have found such a position in *The Second Logos of the Great Seth.* As a consequence, they were able to accept their excommunication, since in any case the visible unity of the church in this world was not important. A further consequence was that the basis of their tradition soon became every bit as arbitrary as their interpretations of the tradition. If ultimately it made no difference how Christ was interpreted, then it also made no difference what basis people chose for their interpretation. Thus many Gnostic schools and churches increasingly lost their Christian identity and disappeared into a general syncretism. Historically, that had the consequence that many of the Gnostic schools and groups that were forcibly expelled from the church went under relatively soon, because after their separation from the church they did not form a new whole church. The Marcionites and Manichaeans, groups that emerged from the orbit of Gnosticism, are here the great exceptions.

The difficulty of the orthodox position as it appears in 1 John is more interesting for us, because *mutatis mutandis* it still is the difficulty most churches have in the struggle for unity with sisters and brothers "who went out from us but were not of us" (1 John 2:19). Today, too, it is either a confession, a dogma, or a doctrine that precludes church fellowship. Almost always such confessions serve as *boundaries* for God's love, even though they confess him who lay down his life for God's unbounded love. Since love crosses boundaries and the drive toward community constitutes the essence of the church,[181] the contradiction is deep. Or it is the office that was created as a *ministry* to preserve the church's unity that serves as a boundary. It evolved from a ministry to a basic gift of unity that then became for others a precon-

181. Cf. above, p. 41, nos. 3 and 4.

dition of unity. Here, too, there is a deep contradiction. The ministry originally designed to serve community — from the priesthood to the papacy — makes unity impossible.

The first epistle of John says, "Whoever does not love God does not know God, for God is love" (1 John 4:8). The truth is also part of knowing God, and the truth includes negations. How then are truth and love, confession and fellowship, related to one another? Perhaps we can say: where a confession becomes the standard, subject to human control, that sets out the limits of community once and for all, beyond the concrete situation in which it has spoken, there it destroys the power of the living Christ to *create* community. Thus, in my judgment a confession can in a given situation prevent community, but it cannot define the condition of the possibility of community for all time, for the living Christ is not a condition but a basic gift — that is, *ground* and *power* — for his children to become one. Or one can also say: where a confession loses its relevance to life and becomes something other than a thanksgiving for the love of God one has received, or where a confession loses its *analogical character* and tries to define the living God instead of merely approaching him in metaphorical, provisional, human language, it threatens to become a precondition of unity rather than its basic gift.

All of that will be the subject of reflection in the systematic part of this book. We close the New Testament part with a quotation that in a different way tries to reflect the relationship of knowledge and fellowship from Paul's perspective.

> He who has knowledge of the truth is a free man . . .
> He who is really free through knowledge
> is a slave because of love for those
> who have not yet been able to attain
> to the freedom of knowledge . . .
> Love never calls something its own,
> and yet it may actually possess that very thing.
> It never says "This is mine" or "That is mine," but "All these are yours."

This text comes from someone who probably had been expelled from the church — the Gnostic author of *The Gospel of Philip* (logion 110).

PART THREE

The Unity Movement: Church Fellowship in the Oecumene

Christian Link

1. On the Way to Unity

In the New Testament, the whole church was a reality one could experience. People may have argued about its unity, but they bore living witness to it as a unity to which they aspired just as they bore witness to the one Lord, Jesus Christ, whose living presence turned the fellowship of Christians into the church. How shall we deal with this witness in view of more than a thousand years of church schisms?

Yet we must ask: Who, or what, is the whole church? If we want to talk about it, we need a concept of church, but what constitutes the church — its "truth" — is always something we see only in perspective, never in concepts or tenets, because we meet it only in a particular historical or cultural form. Nevertheless, it is the task of theology to analyze the traditions, experiences, and doctrinal systems of the church's various denominations, which come to expression precisely in concepts. When we try to express the situation in concepts modern people can understand, there are three levels or ways of looking at it.[1]

Externally, from the perspective of the neutral observer, we ask about the *that* of the church — its empirical reality. Here one describes its social appearance, its structure and its organization, its diaconal activity, but also its attitude toward such things as war, power, and poverty as well as its alliances with might and money and its proximity to national interests.

At the boundary where the external and internal perspectives meet, there is the question of the church's *how* — of how it looks when seen with the eyes of a concerned party, or perhaps also a committed observer, who

1. Cf. Dietrich Ritschl and Martin Hailer, *Diesseits und Jenseits der Worte: Grundkurs Christliche Theologie* (Neukirchen: Neukirchener Verlag, 2006), pp. 44ff.

wants to gain a deeper understanding of the life of his own denomination and beyond that maybe even a responsible picture of the universal church, the oecumene. This is always a theological question, for it assumes God's presence and the activity of his Spirit, even when it does not itself have to make use of the themes of formulated church doctrine. Here one is dealing — in the context of one's own denomination — with its lifestyle, its involvement in society, its understanding of its own life, also the form and meaning of devotion down to questions of the legal system — in other words, with themes of church membership, participation in the eucharist, etc.

Finally, looking at the church from the inside, one asks about its establishment, its *why.* Why is the church there? Why does it exist? How is it different from other groups and social alliances? Here we face the question of its *constitution* — a strictly theological question that the church's tradition has answered by creating doctrines. It has done so with different models of explanation that are inseparably bound to biblical motifs: election, assembly, community/fellowship. In this book we have posed the question of the church's unity primarily on this level, at least to begin with. On what is it based as "unity" with God, as unity with Israel (without which we would have no right to appeal to the inseparable connection of the Old and New Testaments of our Bible), and as an ecumenical unity of the individual denominations with one another?

The following reflections begin at this level. In the process we will see that they cannot be isolated from the question of the *how* — of the cultural contexts and conflicts in which the church's unity must prove itself.

1.1. Unity as Process

That church unity is not possible without the unity of faith appears to be immediately obvious, even if individual believers and groups strongly differ about which contents are central or should have priority, for one of the comprehensive expressions for the church is also that it is the "community of believers" *(coetus fidelium).* It is further clear that one cannot simply divorce this faith from the standard ways of knowing, such as when one says, "Oh, that's just what you believe." Faith has a definably specific fixed point to which it knows it is bound and with which in some measure it forms an alliance. It is, in the words of Dietrich Ritschl, "'standing in' and remaining in a story and the attitude appropriate to it."[2] This story determines the perspec-

2. Dietrich Ritschl, *The Logic of Theology: A Brief Account of the Relationship Between Basic Concepts in Theology* (Philadelphia: Fortress, 1987), p. 28.

tive in which Jews and Christians interpret their own situation, their memories and possibilities, and beyond that their social and political environment. Communities of faith are communities of interpretation. They are rooted in and appeal to a common story, and they try to bring it up to date in a suitable way — that is, in keeping with its origin. From this perspective, the New Testament section of the present volume has developed the theme "church unity as process," and we will begin by recalling its results.

(1) *Jesus Christ as the church's basic gift.* The community of the church — thus the point of departure — has its origin in the story of Jesus,[3] in the symbolic gathering of the Twelve and the group of followers in which important features of the later church are modeled: the personal attachment to Jesus, the ministry of preaching, the task of living as if one portrayed the coming kingdom of God in one's own life, and — probably the most important characteristic — the fellowship of brotherly love. By raising the crucified one from the dead, predicating him as Christ, the God of Israel has joined himself inseparably to the man Jesus of Nazareth. Thus the model of obligatory fellowship initiated by him becomes the permanent standard, rescued from the death of historical insignificance, by which in the future any history beginning in his name is to be measured. It established the continuity between Jesus' way in Israel and the way of the Jerusalem church "to the end of the earth" (Acts 1:8). If we were to ask the New Testament witnesses who the founder of the church was, they probably would not say who *has* founded the church but perhaps: "The risen Lord Jesus is its *foundation*."[4] It is in this sense that we understand him to be the church's basic gift (not its prerequisite or precondition). Yet how is he present in the church? How does the church experience him? Answer: in the form of the Holy Spirit. The presence of the kingdom of God that Jesus proclaimed and by which he knew himself to be authorized for his work remains a living force in the church's midst as the presence of the Spirit. Only in this form can his earthly life lived in the small land of Palestine become *universally* effective. The Spirit creates a new form of existence for the Jesus who has been taken from us — a form Paul describes with the metaphor of the "body of Christ" (1 Cor. 12:12-31). Although, as with all living things, this body is subject to tensions and crises, it still appears as the center of an action that is inwardly coherent. That is why the theme of church unity can be portrayed only in the form of a moving story.

A picture of Mother Teresa of Calcutta hangs in the room in which we

3. Above, Part Two, pp. 34-43.
4. Above, p. 37.

conducted the conversations that led to this book. Below the picture there is a quotation from her that reads: "Here in the slums we see and touch Christ in the broken body, in the children." One can speak that way only when one knows the story told in the New Testament and its continuation in the history of the church. The risen Christ continues to be active as a present, experienced reality, not only in the apostles (Col. 1:24-25); in the church's very existence — when Christians are there for one another, when they celebrate, pray, and work together — the story bears witness to his living presence. The New Testament "basic gift" meets us only in this historical form.

(2) *Unity.* In the New Testament story we see two strong trends moving in opposite directions. From the very beginning, early Christianity was subjected to tensions that could lead to divisions. The earliest witness is the conflict between Peter and Paul at the Apostolic Council.[5] Then, when we take a somewhat wider view, we are faced in the post–New Testament age with the picture of a church characterized by diversification. Today it can be compared to a tree that, since the western schism of 1054, is divided into two large branches (Orthodoxy, the Western church). Then, since the Reformation, these large branches in turn put forth more branches and twigs: the Byzantine and Oriental churches in the East; and in the West, Roman Catholicism and the churches of the Reformation.

Yet, from the very beginning there have also been strong tendencies toward keeping the followers of Jesus together. Nevertheless, there never has been unity. When people affirm it (in the Apostles' Creed, in ecumenical declarations) they are talking about a "virtual" reality. One can see that in nearly all expressions of the church's life. *Fellowship* looks different in Jerusalem than it does in Corinth or in a modern metropolis. Its forms change just as do the culture and society out of which they arise. The *Lord's Supper* is celebrated according to a different ritual depending on whether it is celebrated in Athens, Rome, or Geneva. *Prayer,* the most flexible of these elements, is more strongly subjected to the changes of time than are any of the others.

Moreover, there is not always agreement about what one is looking for in unity; it has been and still is a matter of controversy among the churches. One can realize it only in the "process of struggle for unity"[6] — that is, less in formal theology than in historical "movements" in which fellowship is experienced. Still, one will be able to say that where there are such movements, people have appealed — on the basis of the New Testament — to the story of Jesus as the "basic gift" of unity, even if it is understood and interpreted dif-

5. Above, pp. 58-60.

6. Above, pp. 31-34.

ferently with Paul, in the Pastorals, or with Ignatius. On the other hand, the lived story is the place where it has been most vividly experienced, and that has inspired the unity movement.

(3) *Doctrine.* Unity that is practiced and given as a gift, but also intensively sought, is accompanied by a process of theological reflection that today (differently than in the New Testament) is by no means "something secondary or tertiary."[7] In view of the real discord, theology's task is not only to explain; it also has "nothing short of a 'therapeutic', a healing function."[8] Whether this healing ever is successful is another matter. In any case, it is a mistake to think — and historically it has long since been demonstrated — that one cannot simply attribute the differences that divide the various denominations to *doctrinal* causes. Differences in one's social world — factors that belong to the church's *how,* such as particular forms of worship, different rules and customs, or attitudes toward economic and social politics — often are more important here. The historian Hermann Heimpel has expressed this reality in the formula: "As little as he could have wanted to do so, Luther created a Protestant world and brought about a Catholic world."[9] On the other hand, the motto of the early ecumenical movement, "Doctrine divides, service unites" (Life and Work) is certainly too simple to resolve these differences. Does the debate about the way of unity not *also* always pass through "articles" (that is, "doctrine") we have received from tradition? From the very beginning, has not one element of the church's firm existence and way of living been the *confession,* which, with a minimum of central formulations of faith, has laid out the space we obviously need in order to assure our fellowship? We understand *doctrine* here as the result of experiences, thus *contextually.* It, too, is part of a process, and it cannot simply — a danger of classical dogmatics — be divorced from its historical context without calcifying into an abstract "truth."

In the "therapeutic" view, one cannot dispense with the theological-critical question about the identifying marks *(notae)* of unity, which, to mention an extreme example, make it possible to differentiate the Christian church today in its many forms from esoteric religions, from scientology, or from the Mormons. It is also helpful to formulate criteria, minimal conditions that must be fulfilled before one can even begin the way of unity. Dietrich Ritschl names them: "1. Worship; 2. The retelling of the story from

7. Cf. above, p. 33.

8. Thus correctly Ritschl, *Diesseits,* p. 41.

9. Hermann Heimpel, *Der Mensch in seiner Gegenwart: Sieben historische Essais* (Göttingen: Vandenhoeck & Ruprecht, 1954), p. 57.

Abraham to Jesus and down to the present; 3. Personal commitment to this story; 4. Vicarious support of other people; and 5. Freedom to see only the church as the matrix for the discovery of ethical criteria."[10]

(4) *Flash points.* With regard to the unity for which we are looking, however, it is not as if we had to "reinvent the wheel." There are places where the power of Christ as the basic gift has always been intensively experienced with special clarity — baptism, the eucharist celebrated in all churches, but also the confession or the ecclesiastical ministry. We speak of crystallization points or flash points of unity, and yet at the same time these are the very things that confront us with a remarkable paradox. On the one hand, they are like pillars of certainty: "This is where we have always experienced Christ." On the other hand, they have become the occasion for bitter controversies that continue to divide the denominations even today. When we look for reasons for this puzzling contradiction, we get the following explanation: precisely because of their salient importance, people have tried to secure these flash points dogmatically — the *eucharist* with the theories of concomitance, of transubstantiation, of the real presence, and of the ubiquity of Christ; *church ministries* with the idea of divine hierarchy, the doctrine of apostolic succession, or the church's calling — doctrines that have little to do with creating living unity (or at the most do so with complicated distractions) and now oppose one another as literally "abstract" truths.

Parallel to these classical conflicts, there are historically contingent flash points at which the process of unity must prove itself. In the New Testament period, one had the controversial table fellowship between Jews and Gentiles or the question of eating meat from the altars of heathen idols.[11] In the ancient church, there were the Donatist struggles over the validity of the official functions of clerics who had avoided martyrdom in the time of persecution, or the strong controversies over the veneration of icons in the Eastern churches. The Reformation in Zurich — with church schism as a consequence — was set off when medieval fasting regulations were broken. Later, in the Leipzig Interim (1548), people argued passionately about whether one might continue to observe Catholic rites and ceremonies as indifferent matters, as *adiaphora.* Remembering these long-settled controversial issues leads us to ask where there are basic conflicts today in which the unity of the church is at stake. One will have to think of the *peace issue* that has led the Executive Committee of the Reformed Church of Germany to declare military (atomic) rearmament to be a *status confessionis,* a situation or status of con-

10. Ritschl, *Logic,* p. 133.
11. Above, pp. 68-69, 86.

fession.[12] Or one thinks of the economic and political *North-South conflict* and the liberation theology that Rome has suppressed. Or one thinks of the integrity of *creation*, threatened by ecological collapse — an issue the World Council of Churches (Vancouver, 1982) made the guideline of an ecumenical process. These challenges also have two sides; they can divide the churches, but they can also bring them closer together.[13]

(5) *The process — a model.* How does the process sketched here happen? How *could* it happen? We accompany it with the hope that it will loosen hardened fronts and bring the separated churches closer together. They must portray the basic gift, Jesus Christ, emphatically in their confessing and their teaching, in their acting and their common life, in a way that inspires and renews. Only then can such a process take place at all. The churches must cooperate. The metaphor of a game can serve as a model that once again summarizes and makes clear what the historical unity movement means and what its goal is. When we speak of portraying Christ in the life of congregations and churches, this has — as is the case with every artistic portrayal, whether contest, drama, music, or dance — something of the nature of a game. Or to come at it from the other direction, in every game something is portrayed. The game follows its own rules, but the decisive thing is what the players do with the rules — how they shape reality under the given conditions; or, in the case of the oecumene, how they create a space for new forms of action and for inviting patterns of identification, open themselves to different experiences, and in the process develop scenarios of unity never tried before. Here the rules are only one element of the game. They are formulated in articles (*regula fidei* or "rule of faith"). This is where the confessions have their place. They retain the decisions made in the journey thus far, the church's experience in its dealings with the New Testament, and they do so not to keep them as norms for all later ages, but to orient the direction of the process anew on the standard of its basic gift, and perhaps even to correct it. For there is no confession that cannot be repealed or is incapable of improvement, as if a confessing church were *standing* somewhere rather than *going* somewhere.

One may be permitted to ask the critical question whether in the present official oecumene people do not talk too much *only* about the rules and not enough about the game. The game takes place on the playing field, and often that is where what is decisive happens. Although some are still busy making up new rules, others are already playing the game of the ecumenical church.

12. *Das Bekenntnis zu Jesus Christus und die Friedenverantwortung der Kirche: Eine Erklärung es Moderamens des Reformierten Bundes* (Gütersloh: Gütersloher Verlag, 1982).

13. See below, section 1.3, pp. 173-79.

Of course, how the process develops is also determined in part by other factors — by the given historical situation as well as by the behavior of the players. As every chess player knows, one can observe the basic rules and still make false moves. Dogmatic correctness, such as the joint recognition of the Augsburg Confession by both sides, was no more able to prevent the division between German Christians and the Confessing Church in the Third Reich than in its day the Westminster Confession could prevent the separation between black and white churches in South Africa. Yet can such so-called false moves not be corrected? Must they of necessity lead to a definitive and final abrogation of fellowship? Although in fact the chess game does compel this consequence — false moves end the match — the events set in motion by the story of Jesus are a process that has no losers.

1.2. *Which Fellowship Do We Mean?*

The Greek word *koinonia* is a key concept in the New Testament. In its vertical dimension it designates the "participation in Christ," in its horizontal dimension the believers' "fellowship" among themselves. "Fellowship and love," it is said in the New Testament section of this volume, "are the essential features of church that most clearly correspond to the gospel of Jesus Christ it proclaims."[14] The Western church has translated the Greek word with *communio*, a similar multilayered concept, and has developed a distinctive *communio* theology. Yet here we already have a serious change in meaning. *Communio* is understood primarily as a fellowship of the "mysteries" — that is, of the sacraments. Decisive for all subsequent developments, it refers primarily to the *vertical* dimension of the connection between God and humankind. Since the second century, the celebration of the eucharist with the bishop at its head has increasingly — and intentionally — become its most important sign and bond. *It* establishes the fellowship of the churches *(communio ecclesiarum)* that is the standard for their unity. Correspondingly, the Pauline "body of Christ" is interpreted in eucharistic-sacramental terms, even when one still maintains that the church is the "real body" of the risen Christ — his presence in history translated into the social (horizontal) dimension. As the Roman church rose to a prominent position, the picture changed once again. With a certain consistency, the Roman primacy has been integrated into the *communio* conception as the protector and guarantor of the unity understood thus. Yet "from the fifth century on its actual arrangement contributed

14. Above, p. 41.

substantially to the gradual dissolution of the *communio*-structure."[15] No longer do local churches and parishes provide its decisive framework. The result of this development is then that fellowship becomes a legal concept; its *idea* must increasingly yield to Roman centralism.

With the Protestant Reformation, there came on the Protestant side a development in the opposite direction that is most clearly reflected in the reversal of the concepts. While the Apostles' Creed takes up the ancient church's designation of the church as a "communion of saints" *(sanctorum communio)*, the Augsburg Confession speaks of the church as a "congregation of saints" *(congregatio sanctorum)* (*CA* 7). The result is a by-no-means insignificant displacement of the accents. The concept of "assembly" or "congregation" no longer reflects the content of fellowship as it was understood by the ancient church, even when it is further defined with "word" and "sacrament" (*CA* 7). It contains "an element of actuosity . . . that is foreign to the original texts."[16] It in fact means the assembly of faith in the here and now, but, in the words of an expert in ecclesiastical law, it has not been able to develop "the spirit, the drive, the understanding, the dimension of a *communio*."[17] It is closer to the brotherly love of the New Testament than to the common sharing in the sacrament. It is not a concept one can grasp in the terms of ecclesiastical or canon law (the church's ministry is not one of its constituent elements), but it makes clear that the visible unity of the church cannot be reduced to word and sacrament.[18] The result of this development can then be summarized in the words of an ecumenist thus: "Unity is of the order of faith; union or communion of the order of love. Unity is the vertical dimension of the church; union or communion the horizontal dimension."[19] In Protestant thought, what the New Testament concept of *koinonia* contains is divided into two dimensions. This is the source of the difficulties in coming to an ecumenical understanding. In the

15. Joachim Drumm, in *LThK*, 2d ed., vol. 2, p. 1281.

16. Hans Dombois, *Das Recht der Gnade: Ökumenisches Kirchenrecht*, 3 vols. (Witten: Luther-Verlag, 1961-83), vol. 3, p. 85.

17. Dombois, *Recht der Gnade*, vol. 3, p. 98. For this reason, Dietrich Bonhoeffer again built his theory of the church on the concept of *communio*. See *Sanctorum Communio: A Theological Study of the Sociology of the Church*, trans. Reinhard Krauss and Nancy Lukens (Minneapolis: Fortress, 1998).

18. Lukas Vischer (". . . satis est? Gemeinschaft in Christus und Einheit der Kirche," in *Christliche Freiheit im Dienst am Menschen: Deutungen der kirchlichen Aufgabe Heute: Zum 80. Geburtstag von Martin Niemöller*, ed. Karl Herbert [Frankfurt: Lembeck, 1972], pp. 243ff.) has avowed this with the excellent dictum: "*satis est* non *satis est*" ("It is sufficient is *not* sufficient").

19. Gérard Siegwalt, "Authority in the Church," in *The Gospel and the Ambiguity of the Church*, ed. Vilmos Vajta, The Gospel Encounters History Series (Philadelphia: Fortress, 1974), pp. 161-210, quotation p. 203.

eyes of the Roman Catholic as well as the Orthodox churches, the Protestant concept of fellowship — broad and socially anchored, yet juridically vague — is not a concept that can be theologically satisfying.[20]

Where do we stand today? In its decree on ecumenism *(Unitatis Redintegratio = UR),* the Second Vatican Council intentionally took up again the ancient church's *communio* theology and in so doing moved significantly in the direction of the non-Catholic churches. The Council clearly emphasized the incarnation of the Son and the sending of the Spirit as the high point of God's activity in creation and history. Since the Holy Spirit has made it possible for *all* people to share in God's life and love, the church is also "called and empowered as an image and parable — indeed, as a 'sacrament' of this divine *communio* — itself to be a *communio* among men, both in its own social condition as well as in the ministry to the universal reconciliation of humanity and of all creation."[21] Here one energetically draws from the vertical dimension of fellowship its implications for the horizontal dimension. Here the church that really exists is rediscovered also in its diaconal and social activity as a *communio.* With its statements about the Holy Spirit as the author of a fellowship of faith, hope, and love,[22] the groundwork is laid for recognizing the "ecclesial reality of the non-Catholic churches"[23] and for opening the ecumenical conversation on a basis of equality ("among equals," *par cum pari, UR,* 9). The decree commends the churches of the Reformation for professing that the Lord's Supper "signifies life in communion with Christ" (*UR,* 22), and in the chapter on realizing ecumenism it expressly advocates the "promotion of peace" as well as active efforts to relieve "the afflictions of our times," such as "illiteracy and poverty" and the "unequal distribution of wealth" (*UR,* 12). With one exception — admittedly a decisive point — the decree reaches the breadth and depth of the New Delhi declaration.[24] What is missing is the recognition of non-Catholic ministries.

20. All of the endeavors of the ecumenical dialogue to find a consensus in questions of faith and doctrine cannot obscure the reality that the area of ecclesiastical or canon law that is *decisive* in a conversation with Rome is here notoriously ignored. Without it, however, we will never, *rebus sic stantibus* (as things stand today), arrive at a unity of the churches. To its loss, the Protestant oecumene has thus far completely ignored the pioneering beginnings at arriving at a theological basis of ecclesiastical law (Karl Barth, Erik Wolf).

21. Medard Kehl, *Die Kirche: Eine katholische Ekklesiologie* (Würzburg: Echter, 1992), p. 66.

22. The decree on ecumenism, *UR,* no. 4; similarly also *LG,* nos. 39 and 40.

23. Thus Johannes Feiner, *LThK,* supplementary vol. 2, pp. 47-48. Thus *UR,* no. 3 says that their members "have a right to be called Christian, and so are correctly accepted as brothers by the children of the Catholic Church."

24. Quoted in Part One, above, p. 21.

This disagreement about the fundamentals of *communio* blows through the open-minded decree like a cold undercurrent. The Christians of the non-Catholic oecumene are still "separated brothers" *(fratres sejuncti)*, for no matter how intensive is the horizontal fellowship of common prayers or assemblies, nothing compensates for the reality that "we believe them to be deficient in some respects" (*UR*, 3), in particular "the absence of the sacrament of Orders" (*defectus ordinis, UR*, 22). "Worship in common *(communicatio in sacris)* is not to be considered as a means to be used indiscriminately for the restoration of Christian unity" (*UR*, 8).

The problem that even criticism within Catholicism has pointed out for some time is the strong over-legalizing of community. It has found its most pointed expression in the concept of the hierarchical community *(communio hierarchica)*, explicitly in the *Dogmatic Constitution on the Church* (*Lumen Gentium*, 18). The primacy of the pope's unconditional jurisdiction is firmly established in the "approach of the First Vatican Council."[25] One spoke of a "juxtaposition" — in reality it is a tension that in theory can hardly be resolved — of sacramental *communio* ecclesiology and juristic ecclesiology, of pastoral life and doctrine. Otto Hermann Pesch argues that even within Catholicism the paradoxical relationship between partial church structures and universal church structures can be solved practically only "by rules of cooperation and conflict management . . . supported by faith's insight into what the church is."[26] Achieving *koinonia* would depend on connecting the independence of the *local* church with the unity of the *one* church of Jesus Christ. That would require taking up the early church concepts once again, much as John D. Zizioulas has attempted to do in an exemplary way for the Orthodox churches.[27]

1.3. *Dealing with Church Schisms: Basic Conflicts*

The "most difficult problem" the churches have faced in their history and occasionally still face today "lies in deciding when for the sake of the truth of

25. Thus also in the *Corpus Juris Canonici (CIC)* of 1983, canon 330.

26. Otto Hermann Pesch, *Das Zweite Vatikanische Konzil, 1962-1965: Vorgeschichte Verlauf — Ergebnisse Nachgeschichte* (Würzburg: Echter, 1993), p. 191. Cf. here Johannes Brosseder, "Koinonia," and Joachim Track, "Hermeneutik des ökumenischen Gesprächs," in *Kein Anlass zur Verwerfung: Studien zur Hermeneutik des ökumenischen Gesprächs: Festschrift für Otto Hermann Pesch*, ed. Brosseder and Markus Wriedt (Frankfurt: Lembeck, 2007).

27. John D. Zizoioulas, *Being as Communion: Studies in Personhood and the Church* (Crestwood, NY: St. Vladimir's Seminary Press, 1985). Cf. also Nicolae Manole, *Ekklesiologische Perspektiven im Dialog zwischen den orthdoxen und reformatorischen Kirchen*, Ökumenische Studien 31 (Münster: Lit, 2005), pp. 360ff.

faith fellowship can no longer be continued and when, on the other hand, refusing fellowship destroys the truth of faith."[28] The former and much more frequent case has its historical models in the great Western schism of 1054 and in the Reformation, the latter in the forced separation of the black South African churches from the Dutch Reformed Church.[29] In both cases we are faced with the question: Is there an inner necessity to maintain these divisions, or are they part of a historical inheritance that must be eliminated? In their day they may have been right and necessary, but are they today? Do they still matter?

In the New Testament section of this volume, the basic pattern of these separations has been analyzed with the example of concrete church conflicts.[30] There we saw that it is the "interpreted Christ" who becomes the dividing wall. The two quarreling parties interpret and appropriate him so differently that one can no longer recognize him as *the same* Christ. He now appears as "another Jesus" (2 Cor. 11:4) in a form that does not create fellowship; it abolishes it. Here one sees the root of the paradox of all church divisions. Christ, who tears down all barriers between Jews and Greeks, slaves and free (Gal. 3:28), is taken over by church groups (and interests) in such a way that he *limits* the fellowship he has created. In the age of the great Gnostic crisis this conflict was intensified, and it took on the form in which the later church inherited it down to our own day. It is the *conflict between confession and fellowship.*

If we ask why the church has experienced such conflicts, we will — from the context of today's discussion — have to distinguish between *dogmatic* and *ethical* motives. Not all schisms are equally severe and long-lasting. In the controversy over the dogma of Mary, the issue is obviously quite different from that in the discussions about the apartheid previously practiced in South Africa. There we are dealing with a dogmatic conflict, here with the extremes of an ethical conflict. Both resulted in the termination of church fellowship. In the case of *ethical* controversies, a changed historical situation may, as a rule, heal the rupture. The unity of the Evangelical Church of Germany that had been disrupted over the persecution of Jews and the deification of the state was in fact restored after the collapse of the Third Reich. *Dogmatic* differences, however, seem to affect the structure of the church quite differently. It is obviously of the nature of every reformation that it brings about a break with tradition that history alone does not heal.

(1) The *dogmatic* conflicts are especially severe — one might think of

28. Above, p. 90.

29. In the view of the black churches, the manifesto of this separation is the KAIROS document of 1985, in *Challenge to the Church: A Theological Comment on the Political Crisis in South Africa* (Geneva: WCC, 1985).

30. Cf., e.g., above, pp. 58-73, 142-59.

the Trinitarian and Christological conflicts of the ancient church — because they touch on the images of God and Christ themselves and thus call into question the doctrinal foundation of the church, its *confession,* thus its own truth. People will go their separate ways for the sake of the truth. The basic gift (Vor-*gabe*) has become its precondition (Vor-*bedingung*) according to the frequently varied pattern: "Whoever does not confess that God's Son has suffered in the flesh . . . let him be anathema."[31] Here the contentious point is seen on a level that has nothing directly to do with the way the quarreling parties lead their lives. It is true that confession and doctrine, understood as a "rule of *faith,*" are essential if the church wants to remain "in Jesus' word" (John 8:31), but when dogma moves out of the life of worship and community to the halls of the academy, it is in danger of ossifying into a formula that is ineffective and empty because it no longer speaks of a reality.

(2) *Ethical* conflicts — the controversy about military rearmament, about measures to prolong life in terminal illnesses, or (in fundamentalist circles) about alcohol and dancing — flare up on the question of the relationship between the church's truth and its lifestyle.[32] In the language of the Barmen theological declaration: the church's faith and its obedience, its message and its regulations, can become caught up in an intolerable contradiction that destroys not only its credibility but also its foundations. Already in the New Testament, the unity of the church is much more (if not only) a question of its common *life* than it is a problem of *doctrine.* Especially today, the questions about its way of life confront it with the greatest challenges. For even here it is true that life-and-death situations — be they the prevention of wars, the reduction of the crying injustice in the distribution of goods between rich and poor, or the preservation of the earth from ecological collapse — confront it with the necessity of confessing. If the church wanted to refuse to intercede for the needy and the victims of government or economic power, it would have to deny Christ as its "basic gift." At issue here is its capacity for telling the truth. Since today the process of unity is increasingly decided on these kinds of conflicts, *basic conflicts of modern societies,* the situation calls for special attentiveness.

So how shall we resolve the conflict-filled tension between confession and fellowship? How shall we deal with the divisions it creates?

(1) In an article that is still relevant today ("On the Question of Church

31. Thus the Council of Ephesus (431), in Heinrich Denzinger and Adolf Schönmetzer, *Enchiridion Symbolorum,* 34th ed. (Freiburg: Herder, 1965), no. 263.

32. See here Wolfgang Huber, *Folgen christlicher Freiheit: Ethik und Theorie der Kirche im Horizont der Barmer Theologischen Erklärung* (Neukirchen: Neukirchener Verlag, 1983), pp. 183ff.

Fellowship"), written at the peak of the struggles over the life of the church in the Third Reich, Dietrich Bonhoeffer points out that even dogmatic controversies, as harshly as they may be fought and defended, are historically conditioned: "The same article that today leads to church schism may tomorrow no longer be important enough to cause a separation."[33] When in 1999 Catholics and Protestants agreed on their joint declaration on the doctrine of justification,[34] this classical battle over seemingly insurmountable differences was officially ended. Or at least it was shifted. This example shows that one cannot use the (traditional) confession to build a theoretical model outlining the scope of a church and then use it to design the church definitively. The confession is not "a compilation of dogmatic statements from which one then draws all possible consequences."[35] It leaves open the question of its boundaries. The church does not establish boundaries for itself; that would be a "legal" self-misunderstanding! Instead, it bumps up against boundaries imposed on it from the outside, by its opponents, and then it must decide in an "evangelical council" whether to accept or reject them. The church cannot avoid the truth question without ceasing to exist. At the same time, it may not pose the question abstractly; it must "take seriously the specific situation and leave it up to God to make of it what he will."[36]

That is especially true for *abolishing* a separation that already exists. There has been a great deal of movement here since the Leuenberg Agreement (1971) made church fellowship possible between Lutherans and members of the Reformed churches, communions that had been separated for centuries,[37] and even more so since the study *The Condemnations . . . Do They Still Divide?*[38] was produced jointly by Catholic and Protestant theologians. Both sides have developed a remarkable ecumenical hermeneutic of conflict:

33. Dietrich Bonhoeffer, "Zur Frage nach der Kirchengemeinschaft" (1936), in *Illegale Theologen-Ausbildung: Sammelvikariate, 1937-1940*, DBW, vol. 14 (Gütersloh: Kaiser, 1996), pp. 655-80, quotation p. 664.

34. In Karl Lehmann, *Einig im Verständnis der Rechtfertigungsbotschaft? Erfahrungen und Lehren im Blick auf die gegenwärtige ökumenische Situation* (Bonn: Sekretariat der deutschen Bischofskonferenz, 1998), pp. 35-58. ET: *Joint Declaration on the Doctrine of Justification* (Grand Rapids: Eerdmans, 2000).

35. Bonhoeffer, "Frage," p. 664.

36. Bonhoeffer, "Frage," p. 667.

37. One can find the text of the revised edition of 1973 in Marc Lienhard, *Lutherisch-reformierte Kirchengemeinschaft heute: Der Leuenberger Konkordienentwurf im Kontext der bisherigen lutherisch-reformierten Dialoge*, Ökumenische Perspektiven, vol. 2, 2d ed. (Frankfurt: Lembeck, 1973), appendix.

38. Karl Lehmann and Wolfhart Pannenberg, eds., *The Condemnations of the Reformation Era: Do They Still Divide?* trans. Margaret Kohl (Minneapolis: Fortress, 1990).

Against whom is a concrete condemnation directed? Did it correctly describe the other person's position? Does it still today describe the position the partner holds?[39] Furthermore, in both communions a "process of further and continuing interpretation" has been taking place for some time, so that the opposing positions held in the sixteenth century "no longer confront one another in unaltered form."[40] Not least of all, since the Second Vatican Council a great deal of attention has been given on the Catholic side to the role of *Scripture* as the basis of agreement in whose light, according to the Protestant understanding, all doctrine and its continuing interpretation is to be tested.[41] The study speaks of a "fundamental agreement" on this point, even if "there is as yet no explicit consensus about the critical function of Scripture."[42] Still, it too has smoothed the way for overcoming denominational barriers in the post-conciliar age.

(2) No one will ever be able to establish a uniform Christian *ethic* that gains an ecumenical consensus, even if all the churches try to base their activity on the story that begins with Israel's election and derives its special character from the offer of fellowship with Jesus Christ. For to a great degree ethical decisions are situational. Yet this is where the intractable modern conflicts flare up. To be sure, they lead to an actual church schism only when the cause people are expected to profess is declared to be an occasion or a situation requiring confession (*casus* or *status confessionis)* — that is to say, when it becomes a question that touches on or threatens the substance of faith. If the church's unity is to be preserved in an ethical conflict, one must first of all clarify when one can responsibly require a *status confessionis,* for a *question* of confession (Bekenntnis*frage*) does not necessarily have to be elevated to an *occasion* of confession (Bekenntnis*fall*).[43] A situation that justified — indeed, demanded — such a move was created under Germany's National-Socialist dictatorship, when state action subjected an entire group of people to criminality, and it did so with the approval of part of the church. This is a good example of how the *status confessionis* has its origin in social-political conditions. In responding to a single pointed question, it confronts the church's confessing life with a particular challenge that in no way is to become perma-

39. Lehmann and Pannenberg, *Condemnations,* pp. 8-9. In modern language this is the attempt to find the deep structure of the text beneath its surface structure. In the former one can often find a common *intention.*

40. Lehmann and Pannenberg, *Condemnations,* p. 19.

41. Thus in the Dogmatic Constitution, *DV,* no. 10: "This teaching office is not above the word of God, but serves it."

42. Lehmann and Pannenberg, *Condemnations,* pp. 26, 27.

43. Cf. the illuminating discussion by Huber, *Folgen,* pp. 25-264.

nent.[44] That includes the understanding that it is to be clearly separated from partisan politics and that its rational justification is to be grounded in categories of Christian doctrine. It carries with it the risk of separation, but it is in no way designed to cause a separation. Its initial purpose, rather, is to achieve an accommodation with the opposing position. Thus understood, it can "only be the result of a process over which it has no control."[45] For this reason Wolfgang Huber has suggested that we speak of a "process of confession" *(processus confessionis)* rather than of a status or situation of confession.

Church unity can survive the challenges of serious modern conflicts only when people jointly examine the differing, perhaps even opposing, consequences that arise from a given situation instead of excluding from the community of faith those who arrive at a different opinion about how one is to act with regard to such questions as the peace issue or solving ecological problems. Saying Yes to the fellowship established by Christ and No to all forms of our civilization's injustice and decay have the same goal. They want to find ways of speaking and acting jointly and to clarify steps that lead to a solution of substantive problems. Following Bonhoeffer, who suggested an "evangelical council" as the place for such work, the ecumenical movement has initiated a conciliar process designed to lead to the reconciliation of churches torn asunder by these questions.

There is also a New Testament *regula fidei* ("rule of faith") for this process of reconciliation. Just as in following Jesus there *can be* no fellowship between "God and mammon" (Matt. 6:24), in the ranks of the churches there can be no reconciliation between lawlessness and justice, between love and hate, between repression and liberation, between the wealth of the North and the poverty of the South. Without political and social justice, without the active abolition of existing injustice, the reconciliation for which Jesus "gave" his life is not possible. Thus the unity of his body can be made real only by a church that, with the same partisanship he had, sides with the God who "brings justice to the oppressed and gives bread to the hungry, [who] frees the prisoners, . . . supports the downtrodden, protects the stranger, helps orphans and widows, and blocks the path of the ungodly."[46] It was not in vain that J. B.

44. "It can happen that positions are taken in public that provoke an unqualified no, because they call into question or deny faith in Jesus Christ and the love of neighbor. In such a situation Christians may not remain silent, even when this . . . might lead to a rupture with Christians who think differently *(status confessionis)*." Thus the opinion of the Theological Commission of the Arnoldshain Conference: *Möglichkeiten und Grenzen eines politischen Zeugnisses der Kirche und ihrer Mitarbeiter* (Neukirchen: Neukirchener Verlag, 1982), p. 15.

45. Huber, *Folgen*, p. 260.

46. From the draft confession of the Dutch Reformed Mission Church, in J. D. Cloete

Metz specified "that 'foreign world' the Son reclaimed as his own property,'" as the primary "theological place *(locus theologicus)* of the Christian's lost and longed-for unity."[47]

2. The Church's Unity with Israel

From the very beginning, the oldest theologically important designations of the whole church have pointed in two seemingly different directions. On the one hand, they emphasize that "the *Christ*-fellowship belongs to Christ ('body of Christ'; 'disciples')." On the other hand, "they associate the Christ-fellowship with the people of God/*Israel* ('elect,' 'holy ones,' 'temple,' 'assembly')." The strong tensions suggested here led to the "first basic [ecumenical] conflict," solved at the Apostolic Council (Galatians 2; Acts 15) more by pragmatic means than by theological arguments.[48] As a result, in the two-thousand-year history of the two faith communities, the conflict grew into that irreconcilable hostility that reached its terrible peak in the attempted annihilation of European Judaism. Since the way the Christian churches and their oecumene understood themselves — positively as well as negatively — is decisively related to the controversial question of their unity or solidarity with Israel, we will attempt to offer a theological clarification of this relationship before turning to other considerations.

2.1. *With Which Israel Is the Church Dealing?*

After a centuries-long history of pogroms against Jews and of discrimination against Judaism, in recent decades the relationship between the two faith communities has been placed on a new basis. Christians understand that their historical guilt has a theological dimension. "In dealing with the Jews the act of election, the covenant and faithfulness of the God of Abraham, Isaac, and Jacob, the Father of Jesus Christ, was abandoned. In the center of his self-revelation as a true and living God he was attacked and denied."[49] "We have

---

and D. J. Smit, eds., *A Moment of Truth: The Confession of the Dutch Reformed Mission Church* (Grand Rapids: Eerdmans, 1984), p. 3. Cf. also the so-called Kairos Document (above, n. 29).

47. Johannes Baptist Metz, *Reform und Gegenreformation heute: Zwei Thesen zur ökumenischen Situation der Kirchen* (Mainz: Grünewald, 1969), p. 36.

48. See above, Part Two, pp. 57-61.

49. Friedrich-Wilhelm Marquardt, *Von Elend und Heimsuchung der Theologie: Prolegomena zur Dogmatik* (Munich: Kaiser, 1988), p. 77.

not recognized," wrote H. J. Iwand, as if he were thinking of the theme of this book, "that by being uprooted from Israel we should lose and would have lost our ecumenicity as a church."[50] With its confession of Christianity's complicity in the Holocaust, the 1980 synod of the Evangelical Church in Rheinland conspicuously opened the way to a "renewal of the relationship of Christians and Jews." In its theses it speaks to the dogmatic misunderstandings and controversies of the past and declares, among other things:

> 4.3 We affirm our faith in Jesus Christ, the Jew, who as Israel's Messiah is the savior of the world and who unites the peoples of the world with the people of God.
>
> 4.4 We believe in the continuing election of the Jewish nation as God's people and acknowledge that through Jesus Christ the church is incorporated into God's covenant with his people.[51]

No less important is the document that appeared in September 2000, *Dabru Emet* ("Speak Truth"), in which a group of American rabbis and scholars formulated a programmatic response to the Christian efforts toward understanding. They speak of a "dramatic and unprecedented shift in Jewish and Christian relations." In spite of their insurmountable differences, Jews and Christians worship the "same God" and his mystery, "seek authority from the same book — the Bible (*Tanakh* or 'Old Testament')," acknowledge the "moral principles of Torah," and recognize that they must work together for "justice and peace."[52] This view of Christianity is *programmatic,* because it goes beyond the traditional distinction between Israel and the nations, and, *against* the experiences of history, it dares to affirm a genuine kinship of the two groups.[53]

What conclusions can we draw from these two declarations for an ecumenically thinking church? How far may (and must) it go in this direction?

50. Hans Joachim Iwand, "Antwort: Ein Brief an J. L. Hromádka," *CV* 2, nos. 2-3 (1959): 130. Cf. here Bertold Klappert, "Israel — Messiah — Kirche," in Klappert, *Miterben der Verheissung: Beiträge zum jüdisch-christlichen Dialog,* Neukirchener Beiträge zur Systematischen Theologie 25 (Neukirchen: Neukirchener Verlag, 2000), pp. 322-47, esp. beginning p. 324.

51. "Zur Erneuerung des Verhältnisses von Christen und Juden," in *Handreichung der Evangelischen Kirche im Rheinland,* no. 39 (Düsseldorf, 1980), p. 10.

52. *New York Times* and *Baltimore Sun,* 10 September 2000. One can find the English text on numerous sites on the Internet.

53. For a German translation of the text, see Rainer Kamplin and Michael Weinrich, eds., *Dabru emet — redet Wahrheit: Eine jüdische Herausforderung zum Dialog mit den Christen* (Gütersloh: Gütersloher Verlagshaus, 2003), pp. 9-12. Cf. the contributions to the discussion in that volume by Hans Hermann Henrix and Michael Weinrich.

Few people seriously deny today that the church's relationship to Judaism is of the highest order.[54] The faith of the Jews to which the Bible bears witness is also the foundation of the Christians' own faith. According to Ephesians 2:12, to belong to Christ is to live in the "commonwealth of Israel." We would not have to waste words on the truth of this statement if Christians had not forgotten and denied and betrayed it for centuries. Jesus himself understood himself as a messenger for *Israel.* When the Christians' Easter confession appeals to the story of Jesus of Nazareth as the basis of the church, it takes the God of Israel at his word. "Christian faith calls the Jew, Jesus, the Son of God, and in so doing it stands in a relationship of grateful dependence on the history of the Jewish people. It calls Jesus the 'Christ' and thus professes the truth of the messianic hope from which the faith of the Jews lives."[55] Thus understood, Israel is a special gift that the church, for the sake of its own election, may not forget. It lives with Judaism not as with another religion but as a branch of the tree lives from its "succulent root" (Rom. 11:17). It is the rainbow of the one covenant that arches over Jews and Christians, church and Israel.[56] Therefore, the church cannot regard its witness to the Jewish people in the same way it regards its mission in the Gentile world.

Nevertheless, in view of the present situation of this people, today we must ask specifically: With which Israel is the church dealing? When we use the name "Israel" in our church and theology, it is a *cipher* we take from the language of the New Testament. But whom do we mean when we use it? A historical nation? Only the Jews who confess the one and only God of Abraham, Isaac, and Jacob? All the people who are born of a Jewish mother or who become "Abraham's descendants" by converting to Judaism? And where does the modern state of Israel fit in? Is it also part of the church's basic gift? These are questions that after the Shoah, the annihilation of the Jews in Nazi Germany, are a special concern of European theology.

54. Among the pioneering works are, in particular: Franz Mussner, *Tractate on the Jews: The Significance of Judaism for Christian Faith,* trans. Leonard Swidler (Philadelphia: Fortress, 1984); Marquardt, *Elend* (above, n. 49); and not least the three-volume work by Paul M. van Buren: *Discerning the Way* (New York: Seabury, 1980), *A Christian Theology of the People of Israel* (New York: Seabury, 1983), and *Christ in Context* (San Francisco: Harper & Row, 1987). Reprinted as *A Theology of the Jewish-Christian Reality* (Lanham: University Press of America, 1995).

55. Wolfgang Huber, *Kirche,* Themen der Theologie, supplementary volume (Stuttgart: Kreuz-Verlag, 1979), p. 71.

56. This thesis was formulated by Karl Barth (*CD,* II/2, p. 200 [§34.1]), following John Calvin (*Institutes of the Christian Religion,* II.10.2 and 4). For a valuable period commentary, see Eberhard Busch, *Unter dem Bogen des einen Bundes: Karl Barth und die Juden 1933-1945* (Neukirchen: Neukirchener Verlag, 1996).

There are historical reasons why it is difficult to answer these questions with clarity. In late antiquity, "Israel" and "the church" evolved so differently that they developed almost incomparable profiles. The churches became a *religion* as a trans-national, universal reality whose identity is determined by a faith stance, confessions, rituals, and ecclesiastical institutions. In spite of its Diaspora existence, Israel's way led to a *national* cohesion, of which one is a part not by virtue of a confession but by birth. One cannot be expelled from this nation, either because of false doctrine or because of false practice. It no longer defines itself by means of faith or religion; it understands itself as a secular reality, albeit one that is held together by an unmistakably unique culture and tradition. We must accept the reality that this nation does not fit the pattern of the object of theological reflection or of the conversation partner of theological discourses. It is neither the recipient nor the sender of theological messages. Of course, that does not exclude the possibility that within this kind of association there is a living religious tradition that is cultivated and passed on in synagogues of all persuasions and shades. The contemporary Judaism that lives in this tradition and that knows itself to be bound to the confession of the God of Abraham is the church's conversation partner here. As the document *Dabru Emet* indicates, it may be understood as a religious entity and as such, according to its own self-understanding, as a theological challenge to the church. Therefore, in the remainder of this study (and in the consensus of most Christian theologians), this Judaism will be called by the traditional name "Israel." The *theological* problem this creates for us is then: Was the coming of Jesus of Nazareth really the fulfillment of the promises that biblical Israel had received? Is the judgment of the primitive church, its *credo,* right when it says that the God of Israel in his essence is present in Jesus? Or are the Mishna and Talmud in truth a continuation of the Old Testament? Is the suffering of this people down to the Holocaust in truth God's passion narrative?

I would add here two necessary observations.

(1) It is difficult to draw a clear dividing line between Israel, or Judaism, as we understand it here and the *state of Israel,* especially when for many Jews such a line does not even exist. Still, this state and secularized Judaism do not stand before the church merely as neutral entities.[57] Although it is true that we can hardly see the founding of the state of Israel in an apocalyptic, eschatological sense as a sign of the imminent return of Christ and his messianic glory (as

57. See Ulrich Luz, "Israel und sein Land — aus der Sicht des Neuen Testaments," in *Israel und Palästina: Der nahe Osten im Konflikt der Meinungen,* ed. Lukas Vischer (Basel: Reinhardt, 1983), pp. 145-55.

often happens in evangelical and fundamentalist circles), we can also not dismiss it as an event of purely secular world history and deny it theological significance out of hand. By its very existence this state confronts the church with the question of the validity of the promises to "Israel according to the flesh." It forces the church to examine the idea that Israel's God also keeps modern Judaism (even where it thinks it can live without God) in his service and uses it to testify that he lives. It thus may be seen as a sign of God's faithfulness to his people — an idea that, after all, reflects the self-understanding of most Jews. It was no accident that the Exodus tradition, a central part of Jewish hope, has found wide ecumenical acceptance. In Africa and in Latin America it has become the most effective bearer of the hope for justice and peace, even if a large part of the present-day oecumene regards the state of Israel as one of the powers that keeps the exodus to new shores from happening and thus holds it at arm's length.

(2) Since Paul, the church has been defining itself with regard to Israel, but it does so without consulting Judaism. Must — indeed, can — these attempts be any concern of Israel's? *Historically,* it seems that there is an asymmetrical relationship, with the unavoidable consequence that the church is always in danger of talking past Israel. In the words of Jeshajahu Leibowitz: "For Christianity, the very existence of Judaism is a frightening problem; for us, on the other hand, Christianity does not matter at all."[58] There is an undeniable element of truth in this rebuff. Christian faith cannot dispense with the Jewish tradition, but the reverse cannot be said for the Jewish credo. It is all the more significant that the document *Dabru Emet* principally disavows the idea of asymmetry, because it overlooks the actual course of history: "Jews and Christians worship the same God" — and they have done so from the very beginning.[59] Seen *theologically,* it is the question of a simply unique relationship with the unavoidable consequence that the church would betray itself if it no longer were to stand by this root. Nevertheless, this tension is still virulent, and the question remains: How are we to overcome it?

On the Christian side, Rolf Rendtorff, probably correctly, sees the heart of the problem in approaching the question from a falsely chosen point of de-

58. Jeshajahu Leibowitz (with Michael Shahar), *Gespräche über Gott und die Welt* (Frankfurt: Insel, 1990), p. 73.

59. *Dabru Emet* (above, n. 52). Peter von der Osten-Sacken ("Zum gegenwärtigen Stand des jüdisch-christlichen Dialoges," in Kampling and Weinrich, *Dabru emet,* pp. 206-18) says: "As far as their 'primeval' origin and their eschatological future is concerned, Jews and Christians are *one* religion. In the present, in their historical manifestations, they are *two* religions. The beginning and ending unity is an object of faith . . . the duality is a historical fact and in all probability cannot be eliminated historically" (p. 212).

parture, and he argues for a radical change of perspectives. "We usually try to define Israel from the perspective of Christian theology. Stated somewhat pointedly: We try to assign Israel a place in the Christian conceptual structure . . . , but as long as we do that we can in no way speak of a 'radical change of thinking.' The radicality must lie, rather, in a reversal of perspectives, defining the church in light of the continuing existence of biblical Israel."[60] Thus my second step will be to turn to the question of Christian-church identity.

2.2. *Christian Identity in the Mirror of the Jewish-Christian Dialogue*

At a time when the National Socialist persecution of the Jews was in full swing, Karl Barth said, in a lecture before his fellow citizens in Switzerland, that the Christian community "would have to be blind if its first and only thought in this matter were not that its own Lord, Jesus Christ, was not himself a Jew; that its own roots were not the people of Israel, chosen and called by God; that the gospel from which it lives were not the message that was delivered first to the twelve tribes of this people. . . . The Jewish question is the Christ question."[61] To speak and think through these sentences (which were so clear-headed then) in the opposite direction — that is, to recognize that we cannot even ask and answer the Christ question on which our identity as a church depends without making sure of its Jewish background — is one of the tasks to which remembering Auschwitz obligates us. Here the Jewish-Christian conversation of recent decades has changed directions. Now the church is challenged in its self-understanding as the nucleus of the new people of God and thus in its Christology. In the words of one of the protagonists of this dialogue: "Part of the Christian self-understanding, the necessary response to the question of its own identity, is not only the careful interpretation of the Old Testament but also the conversation with [contemporary] Judaism," the community that since Abraham and Moses stands in a "continuous history," in an "enduring relationship," in the "unbroken covenant with the God to whom for the sake of Jesus the Christian faith listens."[62]

Fidelity to the historical tradition itself requires that we recognize that

60. Rolf Rendtorff, "Christliche Identität in Israels Gegenwart," *EvTh* 55 (1995): 3-12, quotation p. 8.

61. Karl Barth, "Verheissung und Verantwortung der christlichen Gemeinde im heutigen Zeitgeschehen (1944)," in *Eine Schweizer Stimme 1938-1945*, 3d ed. (Zurich: Theologischer Verlag, 1985), pp. 307-33, quotation p. 318.

62. Jürgen Seim, "Zur christlichen Identität im jüdisch-christlichen Gespräch," *EvTh* 51 (1991): 458-67, quotation p. 462.

Jesus of Nazareth is to be found only in Israel. We must immigrate into this "foreign territory," not to become Jews ourselves but to hear in Jesus Christ the message of Israel's God to the nations of the world. For Jesus spoke and thought in Jewish categories. He measured his task and his mission solely against the "scriptures," our Old Testament.[63] One can see that clearly enough in the mainstream of the New Testament tradition. It wants to connect the person of Jesus with Israel's election (messianic motif: Luke 1:68-79). It wants to show — explicitly in Paul (Phil. 2:7-8) — that, with and in Jesus, God himself shares in humanity's suffering and death (the motif of the *Shekhina*), and it wants to call attention to God's therapeutic activity in the Spirit (the Elijah tradition: Luke 1:17). Christology must be developed in this Old Testament–Jewish context, for its language draws on Moses and Elijah as well as on the apocalyptic figure of the Son of Man. The basic problem also appears in a question that is understandable only against this background: "Are you the one who is to come, or shall we look for another?" (Matt. 11:3 and parallels). Luke, who thought in Greek terms, puts an echo of this question in the mouth of the Emmaus disciples: "But we had hoped he would redeem Israel" (Luke 24:21), and he adds the last word the disciples direct to the risen Lord: "Lord, are you going to restore at this time the kingdom for Israel?" (Acts 1:6). The two questions are neither rejected nor corrected. They summarize the world of hope in which the early Christian communities still thought of Jesus.

Given its origins in the ancient church, later dogmatics never dealt with these questions. And the fact that their theological claims might be measured by their continuity with the historical Israel also never became a problem for the churches of the Reformation. For the strong bond connecting the nascent church with the people of God/Israel had already been intentionally severed in the treatments that came after Paul and James. In Matthew and John, Israel appears as the disinherited nation from whom the kingdom of God is taken (Matt. 21:43). This is the beginning of the history of disqualifying Judaism as the unrepentant synagogue with all its well-known legal and political consequences. In the language of the New Testament, the "Jews" are the Israel that has lost its election. It is henceforth theologically irrelevant. It is true that the community of the Epistle to the Hebrews understands itself as the "wandering people of God," but it does so *without* any reference to the historic Israel that is still in existence. And when the Epistle of James addresses the "twelve

63. Recognized thus already by Hans Joachim Iwand, *Gesetz und Evangelium*, in his *Nachgelassene Werke*, vol. 4 (Munich: Kaiser, 1964), pp. 176-77: "The witness of scripture . . . is the only witness Jesus Christ accepts about himself, in contrast to every human witness (and thus to every interpretation applied to him)."

tribes in the Diaspora," it obviously means the church. When it speaks of the "royal law" (Jas. 2:8), it is thinking just as obviously of the moral law established by Christian faith without considering the question of its relation to the Mosaic Torah. Neither Hebrews nor James is anti-Jewish here. On the contrary! Undoubtedly, however, the church was already putting itself in Israel's place and making use of its language, obviously without recognizing the problem involved. Here historical developments simply obliterated and repressed a central claim of Jesus.

Today we are slowly beginning to recognize that in truth this loss affects the church most of all. We face the task of restoring in a changed situation what has been lost, but we cannot simply follow here the mainstream of tradition. Too much damage has been done, initiated by the New Testament itself, for us to follow in the future the "solutions" of Matthew and John or of Acts.

It is not the least of Jürgen Moltmann's contributions that in his dogmatic sketch *The Way of Jesus Christ* (1989; ET 1990) he uncovered the world of Israel's buried hope and restored it to its rightful place. "There is no such thing as a Christology without presuppositions; and its historical presupposition is the messianic promise of the Old Testament, and the Jewish hope which is founded on the Hebrew Bible. We can only truly and authentically understand Jesus if we perceive him and his history in the light of the Old Testament promises and the history of hope of Israel today. . . . 'The Christ' is Israel's messiah." "In Jesus, Israel herself encounters the Gentiles — Israel with her whole history, in a nutshell and in messianic form."[64] Here Christian identity receives a new point of reference. One finds what is probably the most important evidence for this thesis in the titles — "Messiah," "Son of David," "Kyrios," "Son of God" — with which the early churches interpreted the unique significance of the figure of Jesus. Even if he himself already may have established or suggested them in their essential parts, they are *confessions* of these churches, their response to God's raising Jesus from the dead. They are the earliest expression of the newly found theological language with which Christians reacted to this event for which there were no analogies. They are — although in their importance hardly recognized as such by earlier scholarship — thoroughly biblical (that is, Jewish) names, and as such they are keepers of Jewish identity. Thus the title "Son" carries with it the mystery of Israel's sonship. As the "Son of God" (Hos. 11:1), Israel is present in Jesus.[65] In

64. Jürgen Moltmann, *The Way of Jesus Christ: Christology in Messianic Dimensions,* trans. Margaret Kohl (San Francisco: Harper, 1990), pp. 1, 36.

65. See here Hans-Joachim Kraus, *Systematische Theologie im Kontext biblischer Geschichte und Eschatologie* (Neukirchen: Neukirchener Verlag, 1983), p. 367.

Romans 8:32, a literal quotation from Genesis 22:16 (LXX), the title recalls Isaac's binding, the symbol of Jewish martyr theology, and in Luke 1:32 it incorporates Jesus into Israel's sacral tradition, the enthronement of the Jewish king as the bearer of the promise. The Hebrew Bible is the *grammar* on which primitive Christianity understood the resurrection of Christ and from which it derived the elementary forms and structures of its Christology. One need think only of the formative power of Isaiah 53 ("lamb of God") or of the doctrine of the threefold office (king, priest, prophet). In the words of Hans Urs von Balthasar, Israel is "in its essence *formal* Christology."[66] The Old Testament is given to the Christian community along with its Easter faith as an essential element of its own identity.

On the other hand, the Christian self-understanding must also be subject to correction here. Even in its absence, Israel has an irreplaceable critical function for the church that the church must acknowledge. Martin Buber has stated the Jewish objection to Jesus' messiahship with exemplary pointedness:

> We, Israel, are not able to believe that. Deeper, more authentically, we know that world history has not reached its end, that the world is not yet redeemed. . . . For the salvation of the world is inviolably one with the completion of creation, with the establishment of the totally unhindered . . . unity that is realized in all its diversity, one with the fulfilled kingdom of God. We simply are not able to conceive of anticipating any part of the already-carried-out redemption of the world such as a salvation of the soul.[67]

Later Gershom Scholem and Schalom ben Chorin offered similar arguments: in Jewish terms, redemption means redemption from everything evil, an event "that takes place publicly, on the stage of history . . . and that cannot be conceived apart from such a visible appearance."[68] Reinterpreting the prophetic promises to make them refer to an inner life must appear to Jewish thought as an illegitimate hope. This is where the difference lies. With its never-abandoned messianic hope, Judaism offers a corrective to the self-assurance with which the church claims that in Christ it already has salvation.

66. Hans Urs von Balthasar, *Einsame Zwiesprache: Martin Buber und das Christentum* (Cologne: Hegner, 1958), p. 83.

67. Conversation with Karl Ludwig Schmidt, 14 January 1933, in the Jewish *Lehrhaus* in Stuttgart, in Martin Buber, *Der Jude und sein Judentum: Gesammelte Aufsätze und Reden* (Munich: Kösel, 1964), p. 562.

68. Gershom Scholem, "Toward an Understanding of the Messianic Idea in Judaism," in Scholem, *The Messianic Idea in Judaism and Other Essays on Jewish Spirituality* (New York: Schocken, 1971), p. 1.

It exposes the church's absolute claim in the theological as well as in the political and cultural realms as a betrayal of the grace that is for all people. It reminds Christians that the kingdom of God has not yet achieved its final goal. At the same time it asks our theology if it does not go too far when it thinks it can discern more in Jesus' appearance and proclamation than an anticipation in the "context of Israel's history of hope."[69] For the "synagogue's main question to the church is . . . this: Is the world really redeemed? In which sense is it redeemed? Where can we see the *signs* of its redemption?"[70] The question posed to us by Judaism is the question of the *future* of creation and of its completion. Even more, it is the question kept open by the very existence of Judaism. What the Israel that lives today and that hopes with the Hebrew Bible gives us is *future* eschatology in the widest sense of this word. It thus impresses on us what Paul also taught: the promises have not even come close to being redeemed. Can the savior himself have come into the world before the real salvation of the world has happened? From Judaism's perspective that is for Christians the question of their very existence.

How are we to deal with the Jewish No to Jesus' messiahship, since, as Buber says, it is based on an "inability" and therefore is not to be condemned? It is doubtless true that people who are satisfied with an internalized salvation, with the soul's "already savedness," relinquish the real future hope of the kingdom of God. Here Christian theology will have to make more precise the basis of its conviction and say that the Messiah who has come and whom we confess is the "suffering servant of God" (Isaiah 53), not the Pantokrator of the parousia. He is the "Lamb of God," not yet the "Lion of Judah."[71] That too is not yet the risen Lord. He bears the scars of the cross on his body; he is still with us on the way to the completion of his rule. We believe in *reconciliation,* but — with Judaism — we are waiting for the *redemption* of the world. The Christian Yes to Jesus as the Christ is not self-contained; it looks beyond itself to Jesus' messianic future. Therefore it is able to acknowledge the Jewish No, based on the experience of an unredeemed world, without echoing it.

For redemption, the great hope of Judaism, needs its *sign.* This sign is humanity's reconciliation with God that began with the way of the earthly Jesus. From the Jewish root of the church (Rom. 11:17-18) Paul derived the hope that in the eschaton the two groups, Jews and Christians, will make up a

69. Bertold Klappert, "Reich gottes und Gerechtigkeit," in Klappert, *Miterben,* p. 30 (above, n. 50; refers to Robert Raphael Geis, *Gottes Minorität: Beiträge z. jüd. Theologie u. z. Geschichte der Juden in Deutschland* [Munich: Kösel, 1971], p. 227).

70. Hans-Joachim Kraus, *Reich Gottes, Reich der Freiheit: Grundriss systematischer Theologie* (Neukirchen: Neukirchener Verlag, 1975), pp. 75-76.

71. In the felicitous expression of Jürgen Moltmann, *The Way,* p. 32.

unique people of God. This hope is part of the church's identity. It is the mustard seed that must become a tree if its shade is to reach historical Judaism. In the limited time available to it, the church thus would have to become the sign of the times and make true what it believes. In the world not yet redeemed, it would have to raise visible signs of reconciliation that in the here-and-now speak on behalf of the kingdom of peace for which we both hope.

2.3. *Israel and the Oecumene*

In its *Declaration on the Relation of the Church to Non-Christian Religions* (*Nostra Aetate,* no. 4), the Second Vatican Council stated its position on Israel. At the same time, the World Council of Churches relegated the dialogue with Judaism to the section on "other faiths." As if it were something quite obvious, the two churches shared the theory of substitution that is deeply rooted in their tradition — the conviction that the churches that appeal to the New Testament are the legitimate successors and heirs of Old Testament Israel and as such have replaced the biblical people of God. This problematic thesis, however, is not simply the result of an ecclesiastical closing of the mind; it has reasons that go back to the New Testament.

In his mission, Jesus did not consider what would change if all Israel or almost all Israel rejected his message, but his critical attitude toward the practice of the Mosaic Law along with the Pauline interpretation of justification as the "end of the law" (Rom. 10:4) soon confronted the churches with the question "whether they could still maintain their previous understanding of themselves as the core of the eschatological people of God/Israel."[72] That led to the beginning of the influential thesis that the church was Israel's salvation-history replacement. The theme was consistently carried out in the Gospel of Matthew and in the Lukan history. Here it is the historical experiences with the gospel that moved the churches a noticeable distance away from Israel, and this step was later justified in Acts with an intentional portrayal of the attitude of the Jews as deprecatory, even hostile. Thus from the very beginning the later church's problematic understanding of itself as a "new Israel" or even as the only people of God appears to be a reaction against its image of contemporary Judaism, yet Paul expressly addresses this Israel as "of the seed of Abraham" (Rom. 11:1), as the bearer of the same *permanent* election and promise as the church. Thus if the church does not want to deny its origin in Jesus' mission to gather Israel — it would otherwise lose

72. Part Two, above p. 58.

the right to appeal to Jesus as its Lord — then it cannot define itself without also defining its relationship to today's Judaism. Otherwise it would be an inner impossibility.

The Old Testament of our Bible could have opened our eyes to this reality, for Israel's election is not an end in itself; it has a goal. The view of the prophets roams from Israel's center to the farthest reaches of the inhabited world. "You shall call peoples you do not know, and nations who did not know you shall run to you . . . for the sake of the Holy One of Israel" (Isa. 55:5). The nations are not standing aloof; they are included in the prophetic word. The promised new Exodus (Isa. 52:10) is not a private event of Jewish history. The New Testament develops this line to its fullest implications. Will not the people of God who are hidden in the world and in a sense still sleeping become visible in the "men of Nineveh" who, according to Jesus' vision of the last judgment (Luke 11:30 and parallels), will occupy the place of the righteous along with the legendary queen of Sheba (1 Kings 10)? Does not the much older vision of the eschatological pilgrimage to Zion (Isa. 2:2-5) envisage a summons that greatly exceeds the boundaries of Israel?

As was described in the New Testament section of this volume, there are two early ecclesiological sketches that take up and extend these lines.[73] *James*, the brother of the Lord, whose voice we hear only indirectly through Paul's letters, presumably had a direct connection to the movement of the historical Jesus. He sees the church developing in unbroken continuity with Israel and thus conceives of its unity as a unity *in* Israel with Jerusalem as its center. Even if we can no longer go back to James, his model can remind us that as a church *without* Israel we are a damaged, at best an amputated people of God.

Fundamental for *Paul* is the certainty that Christ creates an inviolable fellowship between Jews and Gentiles whose visible sign is the church. He differs from James in his understanding of the church's stance toward the part of Israel that does not believe in Christ. In Galatians (6:16) he can even refer on one occasion to the church in polemical exaggeration as the "Israel of God," but he speaks much differently in Romans. He understands his Gentile mission vis-à-vis Israel without thinking that the newly established churches could replace Israel. They remain Israel's vis-à-vis, but at the same time they are a church *for* Israel. They are an "ecumenical fellowship between Jewish and Gentile Christians." Although they are "temporarily divorced from Israel," they remain "disposed toward Israel" and will "be with Israel again in the eschaton."[74] For Paul, too, church unity *without* Israel is unthinkable,

73. Above, pp. 61-66, 74-76.

74. Above, p. 75.

even if it can no longer represent itself as a unity *in* Israel. What that means, however, is that even if Rome, Constantinople, Wittenberg, and Geneva were able to proclaim their unity, the ecumenical movement would not yet have reached its goal; its catholicity would not yet be complete. For even in the totality of Christian churches we are not yet the whole people of God. We are simply joining it. Only by joining it do we *become* what Israel has always been and even without us will never cease being: God's people.

Of the theologians who think ecumenically, Karl Barth was the first to call attention to this state of affairs that the church had repressed from its consciousness.

> For it belongs to its [the church's] nature and situation as the community in the world to be separated from all kinds of religions and religious communities. . . . But . . . the existence of the Synagogue side by side with the Church is an ontological impossibility, a wound, a gaping hole in the body of Christ, something which is quite intolerable. For what does the Church have which the Synagogue does not also have, and long before it (Rom. 9:4-5) — especially Jesus Christ Himself, who is of the Jews, who is the Jewish Messiah, and only as such the Lord of the Church? The decisive question is not what the Jewish Synagogue can be without Him, but what the Church is as long as it confronts an alien and hostile Israel.[75]

It is Israel's hope, born of its election, that enabled Barth in the middle of the century to pose the ecumenical question in a more far-reaching way than any theologian had previously dared to do: "The problem of the church's unity with Israel is the first problem of ecumenical unification."[76] He later observed, "even the modern ecumenical movement suffers more seriously from the absence of Israel than of Rome or Moscow."[77] It will not reach its goal until Israel joins it. The unification of the churches has its center in the meeting with Israel, yet in the organized ecumenical movement this principle has not yet prevailed.

A materially relevant objection comes from the very people who are involved in the Christian-Jewish dialogue: Is it possible even to speak of incorporating the nations into God's covenant with Israel? Is there a single Old

75. Barth, *CD*, IV/1, p. 671. Cf. here Bertold Klappert, *Israel und die Kirche: Erwägungen zur Israellehre Karl Barths [in Memoriam Hans Joachim Iwand (1899-1960)]*, TEH 207 (Munich: Kaiser, 1980). Also: Thomas Herwig, *Karl Barth und die ökumenische Bewegung: Das Gespräch zwischen Karl Barth und Willem Adolf Visser 't Hooft auf der Grundlage ihres Briefwechsels 1930-1968* (Neukirchen: Neukirchener Verlag, 1998), pp. 178ff., 221ff.

76. A suggestion of the systematic-theological seminar of the University of Basel for the full assembly of the WCC in Evanston (1954), quoted in Herwig, *Karl Barth*, p. 221.

77. *CD*, IV/3, p. 878.

Testament text that could justify it? For this reason Paul van Buren has objected strenuously to speaking of the "one people of God [from Israel and the church]."[78] Yet if Jesus had not opened the covenant with Israel for Gentile Christians, what could we say about the legitimacy of the Pauline mission? To get out of this dilemma we must distinguish between the *Sinai Covenant,* the prerogative of Israel alone, and the *New Covenant* promised by the prophet (Jeremiah 31) as the place of the ecumenical church drawn from all nations.[79] Only then can we exclude the mistaken idea that the nations newly arrived under the sign of the gospel could ever replace Israel. To the degree that they are "chosen by grace" (Rom. 11:5), they can only enter Israel's providential "place" — that is, *into* its history and its promise made to them with Abraham (Gen. 12:3).

Thus no one is elected in the place of, and certainly not *against,* Israel. If they are elected, it is in continuity *with* Israel, and that means to the benefit of and *for* Israel. For in its relation to Judaism the church of the Gentile world is not to contrast a false God with a true one, not to proclaim a true faith against a false faith. To the Jews, Paul argues, belongs the "adoption as sons," the presence of God's glory in the world. To them belongs the covenant, the gift of God's life-ordinance, and to them belongs first and foremost the Christ who is born of their flesh and blood (Rom. 9:4-5). Only those can be chosen who are called to become part of this history.

Even today, therefore, we can say no less than Paul has said, and this necessary minimum embraces the recognition that Israel is not the church's negative antitype; it is what we are lacking as a church in order to grow to the biblical perspective of election-faith and "to confirm" our own election (2 Pet. 1:10). It is an insight that not only involves examining the covenant with Israel that has not been abrogated; it also includes the unity and reconciliation between Jews and Gentiles that has scarcely been accepted by Jews or practiced by Christians. Thus solidarity with the Jewish people, no matter how controversial it may be on the political stage, is one of the permanent constants of the church's historical way.

Now that we have performed the necessary theological task of expanding our horizons, in the following section we must unavoidably narrow our purview to the problems of the Christian oecumene that is still in its beginning stages.

78. Van Buren, *Jewish-Christian Reality* (above, n. 54), esp. vol. 3, pp. 10-18, 137. Cf. here Klappert, "Paul van Burens Theologie im christlich-jüdischen Kontext," in Klappert, *Miterben,* pp. 272ff.

79. Thus Bertold Klappert's well-founded suggestion in "Israel und die Kirche in einem Gottesbund," in Klappert, *Miterben,* pp. 348-70, esp. 368-69.

3. Flash Points of Unity

The widely held idea that an originally existing unity was destroyed in the course of the centuries due to the guilt of Christians is much too simple, and we need to abandon it. The New Testament shows us a different picture. Even stronger than the unifying forces, there are sundering centrifugal forces that determine the earliest stage of Christianity. Yet the diverging forces (apart from false doctrines) come not from the obstinacy or mischief of specific groups; they have their roots in necessary, carefully considered decisions in response to new religious and cultural conflicts such as the tension between Jewish and Gentile Christian churches or the debate about the position of slaves in these churches.

Moreover, explicit reflection about the whole church does not happen right away; only in the post-apostolic period does it take on obvious contours. In the New Testament section of this volume, we have seen elements around which the consciousness of unity has grown.[80] First, there was the orally transmitted *Jesus material* along with the unifying bond of the *apostolic figures,* then the first *ecclesiological sketches* that helped the (separated) churches understand themselves as the one people of God (Luke) or as the one body of Christ (Paul; Ephesians). Further, there was the development of a *structure of ministries* that was the same throughout the entire church, and — remarkably, the chronologically last thing — the New Testament *canon* as the result of the mutual struggle for unity. I am calling these elements *flash points* of unity, but in view of our present ecumenical situation I am intentionally discussing them in a different selection and order. For initially these flash points, figuratively speaking, are not the places where something is burning. The metaphor is drawn from the field of optics, and it suggests that rays of light are collected and bundled here as in a lens, in this case the *experiences* in which Christ has proven himself to his churches as a living basic gift: "This is where he has always met us." The forms of meeting of which we will speak here are even today in the ecumenical discourses the centers around which the churches have gathered, in which they have assured themselves of their unity.

In substance we are talking here about the same things that in a more structured consideration have been represented as "unity-promoting forces" or as the "rules of the game" for the process that make the event of the church possible only when they work together. Now, the view is that these forces or rules are not our invention; they must conform to the content of the basic gift. But do they? Is that what they have been from the very beginning, or have

80. Part Two, section 2.2, pp. 43-54 as well as sections 6.4–6.6, pp. 100-126.

they perhaps been that only in the apostolic beginnings? The very fact that in almost every century the flash points named here have broken out and been tested (and therefore chosen by this criterion) shows that we cannot answer the question with a simple Yes or No. It has long been a controversial question and is thus part of every generation's ecumenical self-examination. We cannot say the same thing of the previously mentioned[81] *ethical* conflicts that erupt in every age (apartheid, militarism, etc.), even though from experience "burning" is more likely to happen there. They are more the field where *previous* decisions are tested, as if they were derived, secondary conflicts. They reveal whether what is meant in Scripture, in the confession, or in the eucharist is preserved or betrayed. Seen this way, we will now, to put it carelessly, be dealing with the unity discussion's "slow combustion" issues fed by denominational controversies. In reality, the flash points discussed here are also the places where differences and church schisms are concentrated. Accordingly, we will now focus the light on various specific experiences of their "basic gift." That has the advantage of letting us describe the decision about how to understand unity with examples.

Flash points belong together, even if we see them at different places as the position of the sun changes. They also interact with one another in the life of the church. One cannot speak of Scripture without ministries, and one cannot have ministries without an outline or a concept of the church. Even the list we have put together is not complete. Not only the past, but to a much greater degree the church's present situation determines what can (and perhaps also must) become a flash point of unity. The *Lima texts* concentrated on baptism, eucharist, and ministry. Churches of the *Third World* experience the much older motif of liberation (Exodus) as a living bearer of the reality of Christ and as a key to unity. What interests us is in what manner these historical basic gifts have been further developed and actually used. That they belong together has never kept them from being preserved and passed on in quite different relationships to one another in different denominations — from achieving a different importance in the new association so that finally they are able to become the hallmarks of separated churches. The best known and most influential example is the role of *Scripture and tradition,* already analyzed in the introductory section of this volume. Two originally converging factors of unity have become independent and thus apparently irreconcilable opposites. It is an opposition that even until today has been able to separate the Roman and Protestant churches — as a consequence also in their view of eucharist and ministry. Our reflections must begin at this point.

81. Part Three, section 1.3, above, pp. 175-77.

3.1. Scripture

Scripture, the canon of the Old and New Testament books of our Bible, is the uncontested basis of all churches and church groups, no matter how much they might differ from one another. Yet appealing to Scripture alone — we are not the first to be in this situation — does not yet enable us to overcome the existing divisions, for we continue to read it with different presuppositions. It does not stand above the different traditions as a neutral referee.[82] The hope that in the denominational disputes Scripture could decide whether the one baptism, the one faith, or the standardized ministry, whether the eucharistic fellowship or the bonding in witness and service is a sufficient criterion for unity simply cannot be realized. It proceeds from a false conception, albeit one that is widespread in the Western churches. We are accustomed to asking Scripture about doctrine — enlisting its help in establishing the conditions for faith and life, for truth and unity, as if they were for all time. We read Scripture as a basic text for dogmatic theology. Is this the form, however, in which it can bring its authority to bear on our issues, or in which it even wants to do so?

We can overcome the battle lines of the past only by starting to ask new questions. There are two insights in particular that make it necessary for us to move beyond the previous positions. When Scripture is taken seriously as the "witness of an active history,"[83] the question of its authority is different than it is when we make of it a doctrinal document. Likewise, when the church is understood as a living process that by no means ended with the closing of the canon, we must expect the function of Scripture also to change in this process. The first stage is well known. The New Testament takes its place alongside the church as a separate entity. In the hindsight of later people, its active history is frozen. Scripture becomes tradition, and its authority is based on the "true tradition" it contains. The church can be understood as process, however, only when, in a second step, the opposite movement takes place from time to time. What is rigid must become fluid. The living Christ must, so to speak, be liberated from the "frozen stage" of Scripture. Since whenever that happens Scripture is suspected of separating itself from the original witness, we must ask how that kind of fixed Scripture relates to the process. The decisive question has been stated sharply in the first part of this book: "How [can] one distinguish between true tradition and distorted tradition and what role [does] the witness of Scripture

82. Part One, pp. 10-11.
83. Part One, pp. 12-15.

play in this task?"[84] We will use the classic models to look at the problem in its present form.

3.1.1. Scripture and Tradition

(1) In *Catholicism,* Scripture and the ongoing history (tradition) are balanced in a way that approaches a basic equality. Conciliar decisions, dogmas regarded as "inspired," in later times also individual unwritten apostolic traditions, and further dogmatic developments constitute the heart of the church's tradition as an instrument of interpreting Scripture. Following the Council of Trent, one spoke of two channels into which the one fountain of the gospel flows. That led to the concept of the *two* sources of revelation that was resisted by the Reformation. Tradition is to supplement and interpret the "insufficient" Scripture. The Second Vatican Council is more reserved but also less precise when it understands tradition as the church's Spirit-inspired and lived faith that is passed on in its life, doctrine, and cult.[85] Here the basic idea is that Scripture is dependent on the continuous encounter with the church's tradition and the intellectual trends of the times to get its message across; tradition is to "interpret and make [the testimony of Scripture] understood,"[86] for Scripture cannot be understood apart from the history of its own influence *(Wirkungsgeschichte).* Thus the Catholic solution is tantamount to saying that the transmitted Word interprets itself "correctly" in the historical process of the church.

What does that mean for the process of the church and its unity? If one were to try to paraphrase the issue in a traditional Catholic approach, one might think of the old concept of the church's *indefectibility* ("It can err, but it cannot be lost"). It expresses the confidence that on its way the church will be kept in the truth in accordance with the promise that "the gates of hell will not overcome it" (Matt. 16:18). Many of its ways will turn out to be dead-end roads, but the determinative direction itself, its "basic line," will not be revoked. That does not exclude the possibility, however, that this model will run the risk of declaring a particular instant of the process as *the* tradition "by divine right" *(iure divino),* as normative (such as in the question of ministries), and in so doing terminate its progress.

(2) In the *Orthodox Church,* we see a similar picture that may have an even sharper contour. In its essence, writes Georges Florovsky, tradition is "the

84. Part One, p. 9.

85. *DV,* no. 8.

86. Peter Lengsfeld, "Tradition und Heilige Schrift — ihr Verhältnis," in *Mysterium Salutis: Grundriss heilsgeschichtlicher Dogmatik,* ed. Johannes Feiner and Magnus Löhrer, vol. 1 (Einsiedeln: Benziger, 1965), pp. 463-96, here p. 493.

uninterrupted life from God, the permanent presence of the Holy Spirit."[87] This presence is claimed not only for Scripture but in the same way for the seven ecumenical councils, the consensus of the church fathers, and in a larger sense for the liturgies and ordinances of the ancient church. In recent times people have begun to make a critical distinction between the basic (definitive) tradition and the tradition of the church, but they continue to maintain that both serve to convey and interpret Scripture.[88] They are the "extension of the divine action in Christ," and as such they "supplement" Holy Scripture. Correspondingly close, if not to say indissoluble, is the relation of Scripture, tradition, and church. The authentic content of Scripture is not only preserved and interpreted by the church through the tradition that lives in it; the church itself is formed and maintained by tradition. It lives — so the exalted claim — "within revelation and on the basis of revelation."[89] Here the contrast with the churches of the Reformation shows up most clearly in the understanding of ministry and ordination.[90]

(3) In *Protestantism,* Scripture and tradition are in principle set over against one another. The written text of the Bible is the *sole* standard ("by Scripture alone" = *sola scriptura*) on which the historical form and order of the church and its doctrine are to be measured. The *principle of Scripture,* thus understood, denies to developed tradition — at least in theory — any right to be an independent conversation partner in questions of interpretation and doctrine. In its extreme ideal it makes of the church a reality that is always new and thus always calls into question its own history; it is a continually reforming church *(ecclesia semper reformanda).* We act as if the New Testament were immediately applicable to our situation, and thus we keep ourselves from recognizing what we *are.* We are neither the church of Paul nor that of the Reformation. Seen in this way, the Protestant model results in a critical attitude toward the church's process — in regarding it as something remote from its origin that is to be regarded with suspicion and in retreating to Scripture as if it were a simple "preserve." Now we can — again the extreme result — react to a new situation at most with a "scriptural" self-delimitation.

87. Georges Florovsky, *Orthodoxy: A Faith and Order Dialogue,* with introduction by Keith R. Bridston, Orthodox Consultation Kifisia, Greece, 1959, Faith and Order Paper No. 30 (Geneva: WCC, 1960), p. 40.

88. Dumitru Staniloae, *Orthodoxe Dogmatik,* trans. from Rumanian by Hermann Pitters (Zurich: Benziger; Gütersloh: Gütersloher Verlagshaus, 1985), p. 64: "If scripture had only a narrow, literal-static meaning, it would not need tradition as the interpretation that preserves its original, apostolic understanding."

89. Staniloae, *Dogmatik,* p. 72.

90. Manole, *Ekklesiologische Perspektiven,* pp. 352ff., esp. p. 356.

It is an old problem. In 1 John one can already see an example of what it means to demand too much of the principle of Scripture this way when it tries to fix the church's boundaries in terms of confession (by excluding the "apostates").[91] In any case, one may ask whether Protestantism has not often enough approached Catholics with the Bible in hand this way without noticing how potentially liberating faith in Christ can be in history. Protestants still know that councils can be wrong, but they no longer know where and in what form the word of Scripture they quote against them is realized — in what form and in what structures its truth becomes binding. The result is Protestantism's formlessness, which is often, and justifiably, criticized. In the best cases people rely on the regulating power of the biblical word without, however, giving a definite direction to the process in which it takes shape. It has been largely forgotten here that the incarnate Word needs a historical and thus well-structured body in order to be effective in history.

Yet if we want to read Scripture in order to keep the process of the church moving — and moving toward the goal of unity — we must decipher it as a document that in fact has let this church come into being as a *creatura verbi*, a creation of the Word, and that means as a historical body. Then, however, we cannot refuse to appeal to the tradition from which we come. In fact, for the Reformers themselves the maxim *sola scriptura* never did mean sawing off the entire tree of tradition above the last New Testament branch. Nor with their acknowledgment of the Bible as "the sole rule and standard according to which all dogmas . . . should be estimated and judged"[92] have they wanted to repudiate all of faith's later witnesses, certainly not the ancient church's confessions. The idea has been, rather, that one decides on the basis of the biblical root whether individual branches on the tree of tradition have to be cut off. In other words, "the content of scripture, the *solus Christus* ('Christ alone'), keeps the *sola scriptura* ('by scripture alone') from becoming merely a formal principle."[93] For to interpret Scripture by the standard of Christ means to derive impulses and models from it that enable us to continue on the way of Jesus under changed conditions and thus to test and, when necessary, to correct every traditional understanding of the church.[94] Instead of entering a closed

91. See here Part Two, above, pp. 149-51.

92. The introduction to the Epitome of the Formula of Concord (ET: Theodore J. Tappert, ed., *The Book of Concord: The Confessions of the Evangelical Lutheran Church* [Philadelphia: Fortress, 1959], pp. 464-65).

93. Ritschl and Hailer, *Diesseits*, pp. 214-15.

94. Frank Crüsemann, "Jenseits der Gemütlichkeit: Allein die Schrift!" *Zeitzeichen* 5 (2007): 41: "The Protestant principle of scripture also consists of taking a fresh approach to scripture and thus contributing to the renewal of tradition in all its forms."

building for which we already have the key ("grace" or "justification"), we retain the freedom to try new keys ("exodus," "covenant," "community," etc.) to make sure the house is habitable — that it has integrating power, even in a changed situation. Since and with the declaration of the World Conference on Faith and Order in Montreal (1963), what appeared to be the churches' insurmountable difference over their understanding of the *relationship* of Scripture and tradition has lost its sharp edge.[95]

We mention here only in passing a difficulty that affects all churches in the same way. The principle of Scripture suffers a serious crisis as the result of a phenomenon to which it itself contributed — the emergence of historical-critical scholarship.[96] The meaning of the words of Scripture and their historical content — which for the Reformers were still one and the same thing — are torn apart. New Testament scholarship has been forced to abandon the old concept of the canon in which they understood it to mean that the contents of the biblical works are in full agreement with one another. It distinguishes among the biblical works on the basis of their different historical settings *(Sitz im Leben)* and their no less different interpretations of the way of salvation. "As a consequence the hope that the churches would find themselves to have in the near future the basis of a common understanding of the one biblical message has been fading, even to such an extent that in the eyes of some the new exegetical developments seem to undermine the raison d'être of the ecumenical movement."[97] Scripture, read historically, can no longer serve as a common frame of reference.

3.1.2. *The Authority of Scripture*

In the first part of this book, the question was raised whether it is even appropriate to use the term "authority" in connection with Scripture. "Does this term do justice to the close connection, indeed, the blending of Scripture and tradition?"[98] Karl Barth has already pointed out that Holy Scripture, a book written by human beings, is not identical with the Word of God. "The Bible is

95. Cf. the discussion in Part One, pp. 8-10.

96. See Wolfhart Pannenberg, "The Crisis of the Scripture Principle," in Pannenberg, *Basic Questions in Theology,* trans. George H. Kehm (Philadelphia: Fortress, 1970), pp. 1-14.

97. Ellen Flessemann-van Leer, ed., *The Bible: Its Authority and Interpretation in the Ecumenical Movement,* Faith and Order Paper No. 99 (Geneva: WCC, 1980), p. 40. These reflections were stimulated by the article by Ernst Käsemann that attracted a great deal of attention in its day: "The Canon of the New Testament and the Unity of the Church," in Käsemann, *Essays on New Testament Themes* (Philadelphia: Fortress, 1982), pp. 95-107.

98. Part One, p. 10.

God's Word to the extent that God causes it to be His Word, to the extent that He speaks through it"[99] — that is, when the biblical word actually becomes the event of God's Word. Thus the authority of the Word of God cannot unconditionally be transferred to Scripture as such. Instead, the much-discussed problem of the "authority of Scripture" must be directed to the circle of people to whom the Scripture was originally addressed as the place where such an event can actually take place and where the question of authority is first raised. In substance, what is at issue here is how one deals with Scripture, a question that cannot be separated from the subject of its hearers and readers — that is, from the community as the bearer of the process of tradition. Thus, if we can claim Scripture as a flash point of unity, it must be read and interpreted in the church. Its historical setting *(Sitz im Leben),* the setting in which the question of how one deals appropriately with the texts first makes sense, is the "wandering people of God," the church on the move. Although the Catholic tradition turns Word and Scripture over to the teaching ministry, and the Reformation also has assigned both of them primarily to the "preachers lawfully called,"[100] today everything depends on making the church the primary place and subject of the interpretation of Scripture. For preaching is a community happening, a happening of the entire congregation. That is something the Protestant theology of the Word has constantly obscured. The Word does not merely "create" the church; it also presupposes it.

To rule out an obvious misunderstanding: the problem to be addressed here is not the mere vis-à-vis between Scripture and church, between Scripture and tradition. If the process is not to run wild, if claims to power and mistaken developments in the tradition are to remain subject to criticism, then we need the opposition of Scripture. It cannot simply get lost in the process, for that would make impossible the necessary debate about the truth. The decisive question is rather: Whose opposite number is Scripture? In Protestantism the special subject of scriptural interpretation is the trained exegete or the educated pastor. That is, of course, a far cry from the Reformation principle according to which every Christian can read the Bible without a tutor, trusting the plain sense of the Bible *(claritas scripturae).* It is understandable, however (or at least practically unavoidable), when, according to this principle, Scripture is understood as its own interpreter *(scriptura sui ipsius interpres).* One must know the Bible, and in the age of enlightened criticism

99. Barth, *CD,* I/1, p. 109. Cf. also Ritschl and Hailer, *Diesseits,* p. 207, as well as Kurt Schori, *Das Problem der Tradition: Eine fundamentaltheologische Untersuchung* (Stuttgart: Kohlhammer, 1992), pp. 50ff.

100. *Confessio Helvetica posterior,* chapter 1 (ET: Arthur C. Cochrane, ed., *Reformed Confessions of the Sixteenth Century* [Louisville: John Knox, 2003], p. 225).

that means that one must know it also in its historical connections in order to discover its authentic meaning.

In this model, however, the situation of the interpreter and with it the situation of the church play next to no role at all. They have basically no significance for investigating the meaning of biblical texts, and as a result they are methodologically not part of the interpretation. This is where our problem lies in dealing with Scripture. We must learn anew that every text has a context — not only in the lives of its authors but also in the lives of the people to whom it speaks today. Part of interpreting Scripture is interpreting the situation into which it wants to speak.[101] Who is to say that Scripture cannot have a completely different potential meaning from the one we already know from the church's history? If we can succeed in coming to an understanding about the present relevant contexts, we should also be able to come to a new agreement about the old *sola scriptura.*

Then, however, one will have to answer the question of scriptural authority differently from the way it has been defined in the history of the church. The idea of the norm is not an adequate justification — either in terms of its *form,* for which one customarily has appealed to Scripture's clarity and self-evident nature, or in terms of its *content,* as guidance for doctrine and life. For authority, which can never be a matter of compulsion, depends on free acceptance. In the world in which we are accustomed to live, "authority" is a term of relationship. It presupposes an encounter with persons and circumstances. If, when thinking about the process of the church that unfolds in the freedom of the Holy Spirit, we ask for authority, we certainly cannot disregard the event of encountering other people. And in significant contrast to the way scriptural authority has traditionally been justified, that means we cannot disregard the community of the church. The church encounters Scripture. It is an indispensable presupposition for the life of the church that the community enters into a conversation with Scripture. Like every genuine conversation, however, this conversation lives from mutual understanding, not from the exchange of information or norms. It carries its evidence in itself. For its part, understanding means to come to an agreement about the subject matter, the factuality, not to empathize with other people and to repeat their experiences.[102] This subject matter — the floor, so to speak, on which understanding takes place — is the reality of Christ, which, like the canon, is a mutual gift to us. The encounter with Scripture leads us to Christ,

101. Cf. the impressive attempt by Ernesto Cardinal, *The Gospel in Solentiname,* 4 vols., trans. Donald D. Walsh (Maryknoll, NY: Orbis, 1976-82).

102. Cf. Hans-Georg Gadamer, *Truth and Method* (New York: Seabury, 1975), pp. 403-4.

moves us to join him so that we are taken into his own movement. This process does not happen of its own accord; it is a work of the Holy Spirit.[103] It substantiates the authority of Scripture, which is therefore never the authority of a document of the past; it is the authority of the Spirit that makes this past present in our midst and with its overwhelming power draws us into the past's still unfinished history.

3.1.3. The Differences

People have not always made the best use of the freedom to take a fresh approach to Scripture in the spirit of the *sola scriptura* and to try out new keys to its understanding (as happens in the "theology of hope" [Jürgen Moltmann] or in contextual theology). In fact, that freedom has often been squandered. One can see in two extreme forms the differences in understanding Scripture that still exist within the oecumene.

(1) The *Protestant* misunderstanding of Scripture is the widespread phenomenon (in the countries of Africa and Asia as well as in the United States) of *fundamentalism*. Here the appeal is to the doctrine of inspiration worked out by "early Protestant orthodoxy" that draws exclusively on the biblical texts and attributes to them per se authority for faith and life, "authority causative and normative" (*auctoritas causative* and *normativa*) or self-efficacy with regard to future salvation *(efficacia)*.[104] Now, we will certainly not deny Spirit-filled inspiration to the biblical prophets and evangelists. But when one objectifies this gift and declares it to be the qualifying characteristic of letter and book as *verbal* inspiration, then one makes of the Bible a magical book that confronts us in "wooden objectivity" (Barth) as a kind of "paper pope." The result is a biblicism that, with sovereign contempt, disregards the historical place and context of the text, and that, entirely under the widespread modern watchword of the "inerrancy of Scripture," leads to absurd consequences.

A by now classic example is so-called *creationism* and its modern variant, the idea of *intelligent design*. Here scientifically based biological evolution is challenged by what is alleged to be a true-to-the-Bible "theory" according to which the natural world came into being exactly as it is described in Genesis 1. What is wrong here? With their opinion that they have to defend the

103. Calvin developed this idea impressively in his discussion of the *Testimonium Spiritus Sancti internum* (*Institutes*, I.7, esp. 4 and 5, trans. Henry Beveridge [reprinted Grand Rapids: Eerdmans, 1989], vol. 1, pp. 71-73; here and below, quotations of Calvin's *Institutes* are cited according to this translation). This is the only really new approach the Reformation brought in support of the authority of Scripture.

104. Cf. the cautious criticism of Ritschl and Hailer, *Diesseits*, pp. 215ff.

"truth" of the Bible against a godless enlightenment, the advocates of this view brush aside the thrust and thus the intention of the ancient text, which does not purport to give information about the cosmological origins of the earth. It thinks instead of the world's threatened future. They falsify the point of the text by historicizing what was never meant to be historical.[105] It is quite obvious that one cannot ask about Adam and Eve in the same way one asks about David or Isaiah. They are not historical individuals; they are representatives of the human race. These theses are not only scientifically obsolete; they are also, and especially, theologically untenable.

Fundamentalism does not take seriously the historicity of biblical texts. It confuses the Bible's declarations of faith couched in a historically conditioned worldview with historical conclusions, and it may well be the "most dangerous poison for church and Christianity" (Dietrich Ritschl). To cite another example, can one still cling to a sentence such as "Let the woman be silent in the church" (1 Cor. 14:34)? Today that is clearly a heretical sentence. To understand means to be aware of one's own place in history and to include it in what comes to us from the biblical as well as from every other tradition.

(2) The *Catholic* misunderstanding of Scripture manifests itself in the administration of the church's teaching ministry *(magisterium)*. It alone has the task of "interpreting the word of God, whether written or handed on."[106] It is true that, according to the declaration of the Second Vatican Council, the teaching ministry "is not above the word of God, but serves it, . . . guarding it scrupulously and explaining it faithfully in accord with a divine commission and with the help of the Holy Spirit."[107] In reality, however, it is independent of the Word in a way that noticeably limits its free unfolding.[108] Here the process of unity that "should be accommodated" by this institution (M. Löhrer) is to an extent threatened from the other side. Instead of being kept in the truth, it is channeled through the teaching ministry. The promise given to the church (Matt. 16:18), a promise no one can guarantee, is from the very beginning directed into the riverbed of proven traditions. As a result, the move-

105. See Christian Link, "Schöpfung: Schöpfungstheologie angesichts der Herausforderungen des 20. Jahrhunderts," *HST* 7/2 (Gütersloh: Gütersloher Verlag, 1991), pp. 351ff., esp. p. 357. Also Ulrich Eibach, "Falsche Fronten: Der Streit um 'Intelligent Design,'" *Zeitzeichen* 8/9 (2007): 12-15.

106. Vatican II (*DV*, no. 10; *LG*, no. 18) speaks of "the sacred primacy of the Roman Pontiff and of his infallible magisterium."

107. *DV*, no. 10.

108. One thinks of the patronizing position on liberation theology in the statement from the Sacred Congregation for the Doctrine of the Faith (August 6, 1984): Instruction on Certain Aspects of "Theology of Liberation."

ment it wants to encourage — including new beginnings and crises — is blocked in its most characteristic vitality.

It is not the place of Scripture as such that is at issue between Catholic and Protestant churches. The controversial point was and is the question of the right interpretation, in particular the binding force of the teaching ministry's interpretation. The churches of the Reformation have no proprietary position in these questions. Here, at least in theory, the churches share responsibility for the "pure doctrine." In terms of the *critical* function of Scripture, above all in the question of infallibility, the two churches are still far removed from a consensus.[109]

3.2. *Confession*[110]

Is confession one of the flash points of unity? The Latin word *confessio* itself, not to mention a look at church history, would appear to contradict this conjecture. In the name of one's own confession — the confessional status *(Bekenntnisstand)*, as one still called it at the beginning of the last century — people have refused fellowship with others of a different confession and sometimes, as in the case of the Waldenses or Huguenots, cruelly persecuted them. Our language is aware only of "separated" confessions. The period of the Thirty Years' War — historians speak of it as wars of religion *(Konfessionskriege)* — left this historical truth indelibly imprinted on European consciousness. In reality confessional separation is much older and, as the conflict over fellowship in the Gnostic controversy showed, its roots reach back into the New Testament. The spirits part company on the confession. The confession bears witness to God's love "and at the same time clearly separates those whom God loves from the children of the world and the apostates."[111] It stakes out the boundaries of church fellowship, as the Confessing Church experienced in the Third Reich and as the conflict over apartheid or the struggle over atomic rearmament has recently brought to light. Was that simply a misunderstanding? Have the railroad switches been set wrong from the very beginning? Or does the way of unity of necessity take place in the dialectic of Yes and No, of agreement and exclusion?

109. Lehmann and Pannenberg (*Condemnations,* pp. 25-26) arrive at a thoughtful judgment.

110. This discussion follows the basic lines laid out in the confessional draft (1986) of the Swiss Evangelical Synod. On the subject, cf. Hans-Georg Link, *Bekennen und Bekenntnis,* Ökumenische Studienhefte 7 (Göttingen: Vandenhoeck & Ruprecht, 1998).

111. Cf. above, Part Two, p. 150.

3.2.1. Church Confessions

What about the confessional claims of the separated churches, their "confessional status," in which the confessional theology of the nineteenth century believed that it had to discover not only a *declarative* but the *constitutive* characteristic of the church? There are the historical confessions with their formulas of demarcation. There is the fact of sectarian churches that do not recognize one another. Today both are rightly understood to be the most aggravating obstacles on the way to ecumenical unity. Nevertheless, confessing unity has — and not only for historical reasons — uniting and obligatory power only to the degree that the "separated" churches are able to see their *own* truth in it. For how shall we hear Christ "otherwise than according to the particular leading and responsibility of . . . the church to which we owe allegiance as members, within which we were baptised and brought to belief"?[112] Can the ecumenical movement overcome the established boundaries by means of a new way of confessing, if it does not itself enter the history of the church and its divisions?

When one understands confession in terms of a firmly stated, defined text, confession is forced to assume the role of drawing boundaries and erecting walls of protection against other people. One can hardly ask these days: "What does the confession set free? What does it want to make possible?" However, the formulated confession precedes the confessing life of the church. The church confesses by bearing witness to the name of Christ. It confesses when it worships. It confesses in the way it and every one of its members behaves. A formulated confession has its meaning and its place within this many-sided *confessing* of the church. It summarizes that to which the people of the church jointly are to bear witness. The formulated confession can never become a substitute for confessing. It has only a secondary importance. It comes from the confessing life of the church and wants to serve it.

One finds such confessions already in the earliest period. The first formulations are transmitted in the New Testament itself. One thinks of the brief statement "Jesus Christ [is] Lord" (1 Cor. 12:3), but also of more detailed versions (1 Cor. 8:6; Phil. 2:6-11; 1 Tim. 3:16). These are sentences of invitation. They have no pretension other than to say to the outside world, Here is the new fellowship, the new people gathered around God's Messiah! Here is the church! Its claim never intends to mean that now the righteous and the unrighteous are to be separated. Asking about the church's boundaries, about its extent, about distinguishing between the elect and the lost makes a *law* out of

112. Karl Barth, *The Church and the Churches* (Grand Rapids: Eerdmans, 1936), pp. 77-78.

the gospel's call, its offer of the new fellowship. Where the gospel is actually testified and confessed, there is no longer the need to draw such dividing lines.[113] The confession brings the church together around the voice of its Lord. It is designed first and foremost to be an instrument of praise. It joins in Jesus' prayer: "I praise you, Father" (Luke 10:21). It can serve the church's *instruction* (catechesis) and offer an initial answer to those who are asking about the basis of Christian hope. Finally, it can also perform a prophetic task, and in a confusing or ambiguous situation it can let the gospel's plain message be heard.

From the biblical beginnings evolved the confessions of the ancient church, in particular the Nicene Creed, which summarizes what the baptismal candidates are to confess at their baptism, and the Apostles' Creed, which declares the church's belief in the triune God. Without a doubt these confessions of the ancient church have a special importance. Most Christians today regard them as guides. They are part of the tradition the churches have in common in spite of their separation. The Reformation also accepted them. Their statements continue to have an influence even in a church that distances itself from them. They have the character of a model or pattern. They are the ground in which the modern church has its roots. Even when we have to go beyond what they have said, as decisions the church once made, they remain a question our present witness cannot ignore. The creedal churches are expressly confronted with the question of the limits of their confessional claim. Where these boundaries lie, where the traditional confession about the unity of the church must become the concrete question of the *one* church — these are admittedly things only those persons will be able to say who (simply because they have no other place to stand) begin by taking themselves seriously in their divided creedal life and are prepared to investigate the intentions of their own church, including how they originated and what they mean. For the Protestant church that means remembering that in Augsburg there is not yet a "Lutheran" church over against a "Roman" church. Instead, the "Protestant" nobles and men of stature speak in the name of the "single, common order of Christianity that is one body in Christo" (Luther), and until well into the seventeenth century they value the name "catholic." An exter-

113. Bonhoeffer, "Frage," p. 658: "The true church can never determine of itself where the people are who do not belong to it. Its claim to be the church never means that the righteous are to be separated from the unrighteous. Instead, the claim 'here is the church' is itself the call of salvation that goes out to the whole world. It is the gospel itself. . . . Thus the church does not define its boundaries; rather, it comes up against the boundaries placed upon it from the outside. Now the church experiences its call of salvation as the judgment on the world, as the boundary that cannot be crossed."

nal sign of this indissoluble solidarity *in Christo* are the three early church confessions that in 1580 were included in the Book of Concord under the noteworthy title *Tria symbola catholica sive oecumenica* ("The Three Catholic or Ecumenical Symbols").[114]

3.2.2. Contextual Confessing

The confessions of the ancient church do not make additional and new confessions superfluous; they do not even exclude them. On the contrary, they call us to be involved in a continuous process of making the gospel relevant. We can, indeed we must, say it even more pointedly: only when confessions lead to new confessing are they flash points in the process of unity. When they are frozen as a confessional *status*, they actually prevent unity. There are no confessions that are valid forever; past confessions (such as the Apostles' Creed) are binding only to the degree that they are able to orient our modern confessing that the present requires. Here there are unmistakable analogies to the role of Scripture. Just as Scripture must always be newly interpreted and made relevant and in its past objectivity cannot be made the judge of truth and error, the same is true of the traditional, written confession. It preserves the decisions the church has made on its previous way, the experiences of the church in its dealings with the New Testament, yet it does so not to conserve them as the norm for all later times but to reorient the direction of the process by holding it up to the standard of its basic gift. At the same time, no confession is indissoluble or incapable of being improved. That its time has run out, that it can be formally revoked (Jer. 23:7 and 3:16!), is among the disagreeable demands even of biblical prophecy. Congregations and churches are to become confessing subjects, not the owners of confessions.

The confession is our *response* to God's Word. It is also always a question about us, about our own place as a church in the world. Thus, strictly speaking, it must always begin from our own situation and then turn around and influence that situation. "Authentic" confessions are related to their own situation. That is to say, they are contextual. They force us to confront the question whether our church's particular place and particular form are adequate to their task, whether we are a true church or a pseudo-church. Although it is true that the message given to the church is the same in all ages, in

114. Cf. the instructive study by Ernst Kinder, "Der Gebrauch des Begriffs 'ökumenisch' im älteren Luthertum," *KuD* 1 (1955): 180-207, esp. beginning p. 191; also Christian Link, "Das Bekenntnis zur Ökumene als Bekenntnis *der* Ökumene," in *Bekennendes Bekenntnis: Form und Formulierung christlichen Glaubens,* ed. Eric Hultsch and Kurt Lüthi (Gütersloh: Gütersloher Verlagshaus, 1982), pp. 82-96, esp. beginning p. 90.

new situations we must bear witness to it in new and different ways. New developments raise new questions — questions the church has never before answered in this form. They lead to decisions the church must make for the first time. To the degree that new horizons appear, new affirmations are required.

In response to the social and political challenges that have confronted the churches of Africa and Asia in the previous century, those churches have been able to take the step to contextual confessing with great clarity and a worldwide ecumenical resonance. In Hong Kong in 1966, Asian theologians developed *Criteria for Confessing,* criteria that take into account Scripture, concrete situation, and faith as it is lived. The document states: "Confessing faith [is] not simply speaking the words of an eternal and unchanging truth. It is, rather, a life-affirming act that includes the community's despair and hope and makes God's redeeming love real in the midst of suffering."[115]

The rigid South African politics of racial segregation that made it impossible for black and white Christians to worship together became the occasion for the Dutch Reformed Mission Church *(Nederduitse Gereformeerde Sendungskerk)* in the synod in Belhar (1982) to draw up a regular confession of faith that declared the *status confessionis* for its churches, rejecting the "moral and theological" justification of apartheid and leading to the separation from the "white" Dutch Reformed church.[116]

It is the church's *process,* its participation in society's basic conflicts, that leads to the confession. Conversely, it is the confession's indispensable function time and again to help keep this process focused on the risen Christ. It keeps the process from losing its direction, for the truth of the gospel is not a possession one manages; it is a way one goes (John 14:6). Therefore it can take shape only on the historical way one goes, by means of concrete decisions. Whoever wants to make the "word of reconciliation" (2 Cor. 5:19) believable in light of today's controversial questions of human rights, of the politics of peace, or of the preservation of creation, must go a certain way. The direction this way takes (also) depends on where the church is challenged and on where it is called on to offer resistance to the incursion of forces that contradict the gospel.[117] The church is a wandering people of God even in its confessional life.

The issue over which the Reformation has drawn the line against Rome,

115. Translated from Geiko Müller-Fahrenholz, ed., *Bangalore 1978: Sitzung der Kommission für Glaube und Kirchenverfassung. Berichte, Reden, Dokumente* (Frankfurt: Lembeck, 1979), p. 77.

116. See H.-G. Link, *Bekennen,* pp. 161-67. On the substantive problem, cf. the discussion in section 1.3, above, pp. 16-18.

117. Cf. here Bonhoeffer, "Frage," esp. p. 664.

the article of justification by faith alone, is today (entirely after the "Common Declaration" was passed in 1999) no longer the place where a decision must be made. Along *with* Rome, we are now challenged at a different place. Today our confession of Jesus Christ, who has reconciled the world with God, is decided by whether as a church we are a place of reconciliation and whether we champion the cause of the world's restored right as God's creation. Questions that traditionally have been regarded as ethical achieve confessional rank today, questions such as: How do we preserve the earth from thoughtless destruction? How do we protect the right of future generations to life? How do we deal with hunger in the Third World and the refugees and asylum-seekers in our own countries?

The confession belongs to the process of unity. By interpreting with binding force God's unchanging Yes to the world in view of the changing challenges of our time, it becomes the church's guide. It points in the direction the church must go if it is to follow its Lord and not the voice of a stranger. Instead of defining a standpoint on which one can stand but not go, it points ahead to the way that leads forward. The No that appears in all of the later confessions marks the way's limits. It serves as the railing to which one holds as one gropes one's way forward; but once the steep ascent is overcome or the fog has lifted, it has done its duty. It is not a permanent No. New challenges require new affirmations and new limitations. In the words of the preface to the reformation mandate of the city of Berne (the Berne synod) of 1532:

> But if something is forthcoming from our pastors or from any others which leads us closer to Christ and which, in the light of God's Word, is more conducive to general concord and Christian love than the opinion here set down, we will gladly accept it and not obstruct the movement of the Holy Spirit, who drives us not backwards but always forwards towards the likeness of Christ Jesus our Lord.[118]

3.3. *Lord's Supper*

Although in reality it is the strongest bond among the divided churches, we will not be speaking explicitly here of baptism. Baptism is recognized by Lutherans and Baptists, by Anglicans and Catholics, and basically also by the Orthodox churches. Rebaptism when one joins a different Christian church is

118. Gottfried W. Locher, ed., *Der Berner Synodus von 1532*, vol. 1 (Neukirchen: Neukirchener Verlag, 1984), p. 27.

regarded as unacceptable. It is no longer a point of controversy in the ecumenical discussion. Of course, for that very reason it is extremely difficult to say what common basis the *one* baptism actually expresses. It is given different theological foundations: Augustine and Luther regard it as an act of God, but Zwingli and, somewhat differently, Karl Barth see it as a response and act of human obedience. It also has different canonical significance: it is everywhere the basis for membership in the church, but by no means does it everywhere qualify a person for the priesthood or the office of bishop. For the time being, the mutual recognition of baptism that was formally confirmed again in Magdeburg in 2007 obviously helps us only to slide over fundamental difficulties. That, at least, is not at all the case with the eucharist.

The church's *Lord's Supper,* which goes back to Jesus himself, is one of the earliest crystallization points in which one can see the church's unity. It is a unity that has nourished and repeatedly renewed itself in the eucharist. It is much older than the flash points *Scripture, tradition,* or *ministry.* The celebration of the eucharist is the source and high point of the church's life in which the church's unity and fellowship are "both expressed and brought about."[119] It is, as the Lima document of the oecumene says, "communion with Christ who nourishes the life of the Church" and at the same time also "communion within the body of Christ which is the Church."[120] Accordingly, the eucharist is proclaimed as "the most immediate moment of the continued ministry of the historical Jesus . . . as the visualization of the promise that was fulfilled through him and that also opened the way for the future."[121] Thus understood, it is nothing less than the concrete founding act of the church.

Based on its origin, the Lord's Supper is part of the Passover tradition of the Jewish people. For this reason Paul links the eucharistic tradition with Israel's desert wandering (1 Cor. 10:1-4), and from this connection, of which we are hardly aware anymore, he derives his theological declaration. We are joined together into a new fellowship, inseparable as the limbs of a body, and thus made part of the onward movement of the life of the risen Christ whose invisible presence dwells in our midst and goes with us just as God's presence *(shekinah)* accompanied Israel in the wilderness. And as Jews even today in the common Seder meal remember their salvation from Egyptian slavery, the celebration of the eucharist is also something done "in remembrance" (1 Cor. 11:24). It is, of course, not merely a mental remembering; it is a "reality creating

119. Thus Vatican II, *LG,* no. 3.

120. "Eucharist," no. 19, in *BEM,* p. 14.

121. Leonhard Goppelt, *Theology of the New Testament,* vol. 2, trans. John E. Alsup (Grand Rapids: Eerdmans, 1982), p. 150.

action."[122] It makes the death of Jesus present as the expression of God's self-sacrificing love. It praises the creation of a new, trustworthy fellowship that (as the renewal of Israel's broken covenant) is sealed with the forgiveness of sins, and it looks forward to the coming kingdom of God, putting the church in a condition of active expectation. It is precisely this last factor, the promised life in God's kingdom, that makes Christians a church, the "body of Christ."

Thus the clear invitation in the eucharist to *become* church is not an end in itself; it has a goal. It lives in the hope of God's glory into which Christ has already been taken up and to which God has called his people. It lives from the *promise* that Christ, as the Lord who is present in the meal, will accompany the church on the way to this goal just as God led Israel through the desert. "Christ's death makes it possible for the wandering people of God to live in terms of the journey's end and to eat and drink as a sign of this reality."[123] When the eucharist is again understood in terms of this core, the inviting Lord and his coming kingdom, then once again it can become the center of the unity it was at the beginning and continue the assurance the church needs to support its gathering and its mission. It is the conviction that the Christ who is no longer historically conditioned does not retreat from history; he continues to be present in the basic spiritual and social life of the church — its prayer, its fellowship, and its social existence — and he sends it on its way.

As separated churches we are still far removed from this common way, however, in spite of our many successful efforts at achieving understanding. For more than four hundred years we have been confronting the paradoxical fact that precisely the meal of unity has provided the fermentation for ruptures and separations. Yet, we cannot tolerate our separated tables to the end of time without making the foundation of the church unworthy of belief by "dividing" Christ (1 Cor. 1:13). When one looks at the present state of our ecumenical discussions, three special areas of questioning are in need of clarification. (1) Does the Lord's Supper create the community of the people who celebrate it, or does it presuppose it? Must then a church fellowship exist (in the canonical sense of the term) so that eucharistic hospitality can be possible? (2) Does the meaning of the eucharistic celebration depend on the symbolic power, the symbolic value, of the elements? How important is it to agree on the *meaning* of the ritual in comparison with simply participating in it? (3) Is conducting the eucharist tied to the ordained ministry? Hence, is the ordained office-bearer — repre-

122. Rainer Stuhlmann, "Das Mahl des Herrn im Neuen Testament," in *Eucharistische Gastfreundschaft: Ein Plädoyer evangelischer und katholischer Theologen,* ed. Johannes Brosseder and Hans-Georg Link, 3d ed. (Neukirchen: Neukirchener Verlag, 2004), pp. 26-42, here p. 36.

123. Markus Barth, *Das Mahl des Herrn: Gemeinschaft mit Israel, mit Christus und unter den Gästen* (Neukirchen: Neukirchener Verlag, 1987), p. 97.

senting, so to speak, Jesus Christ — the visible reference point of the all-encompassing fellowship between Christ and the members of his body?

3.3.1. The Fellowship Meal

That there is an indissoluble relationship between church fellowship and eucharistic fellowship is one of the convictions that Catholic, Orthodox, and Protestant churches share. It has been given a special profile by the French Groupe des Dombes, a forerunner of today's oecumene, which already in 1972 had pleaded for a "eucharistic hospitality" beyond one's own denominational boundaries. "Partaking of the same bread and the same cup at a particular place brings about the unity of the communicants with the whole Christ, among themselves, and with all other communicants, at all times and in all places. By partaking of the same loaf they show that they belong to the church in its catholicity."[124] There are similar statements in the texts of Vatican II: "in the sacrament of the Eucharistic bread, the unity of all believers who form one body in Christ is both expressed and brought about *(repraesentatur et efficitur)* (1 Cor. 10:17)."[125] Nevertheless, the efforts to achieve understanding among the churches have not progressed beyond the circular conclusion that "without the eucharistic community there is no full ecclesial community, and without the ecclesial community there is no real eucharistic community."[126] The common declaration on justification (1999) did nothing to change the situation. According to the official statement, the agreement in the understanding of the gospel created the necessary precondition for eucharistic fellowship but not yet the fellowship itself.[127] So how are we to break into this closed circle, short of turning once again to the New Testament itself?

Paul was the first person to develop a well-thought-out concept of church unity, and in doing so he made use of the basic practices of baptism and the Lord's Supper. In 1 Corinthians 10:14-22 he emphasizes the theme of

124. Translated from "Auf dem Wege zu ein und demselben eucharistischen Glauben?" in *Um Amt und Herrenmahl: Dokumente zum evangelisch/römisch-katholischen Gespräch,* ed. Günther Gassmann et al., vol. 1 (Frankfurt: Lembeck, 1974), p. 108.

125. *LG,* no. 3; similarly in no. 11: this sacrament suitably signifies and wondrously brings about *(apte significatur et mirabiliter efficitur)* the "unity of the people of God."

126. "The Eucharist" (Final Report of the Joint Roman Catholic–Lutheran Commission), no. 26, in *Growth in Agreement: Reports and Agreed Statements of Ecumenical Conversations on a World Level,* ed. Harding Meyer and Lukas Vischer (Ramsey, NJ: Paulist; Geneva: WCC, 1984), p. 198.

127. Harding Meyer, "Die 'gemeinsame Erklärung zur Rechtfertigungslehre' . . . und die Frage katholisch-evangelischer Abendmahlsgemeinschaft," in Brosseder and Link, *Eucharistische Gastfreundschaft,* pp. 22ff.

fellowship (Greek: *koinonia*): "The cup over which we give thanks, is it not fellowship with the blood of Christ? The bread that we break, is it not fellowship with the body of Christ?" (1 Cor. 10:16). In the eucharist, the believers enter into the most intimate living fellowship with Christ. As in baptism we are "baptized into" the death of Christ (Rom. 6:4-5) that "surrounds us [like] a room," so in the Lord's Supper we are taken into Christ's existence that was "given" for our salvation and that for its part "is projected into the community's space."[128] This sphere of salvation opened to us by the death of Christ does not first come into existence *with* baptism and the Lord's Supper; it exists rather "*before* every human or ecclesiastical action." Paul emphasizes: "Because there is one bread, we, the many, are one body" (1 Cor. 10:17). Thus he makes a distinction between the *Christological* body and the *ecclesiological* "being-one-body."[129] They are related as cause and effect, whereby it is explicitly clear that the believers themselves can never constitute the body of Christ and the new fellowship. The community does not take place simply when Christians come together and constitute a corporation. Only the presence of Christ, his effective pro-existence, creates the new togetherness. Not even receiving the eucharist itself, participating in the rite, can effect this new togetherness if we do not permit to happen what he wants to bring about: community, fellowship. For this reason Calvin pointedly related the "is" *(est)* of the words of institution to this new fellowship, to the covenant that is determined and sealed in the blood of Christ.[130] The effective presence of Christ is experienced not simply in the elements of the meal but in the fact of the brother — and that means the least brother who here is accepted into or excluded from the "fellowship of the body." It is in *him* that the church professes its faith in the Lord who is absent in the body and who one day will come again. Thus the answer to our initial question is clearly this: the Lord's Supper establishes the fellowship of the participants; it does not presuppose it. Their fellowship is the consequence, not the presupposition or condition of the body of Christ. In other words, "in the New Testament [the fellowship at the table] constitutes . . . the fellowship of the church — and not vice versa."[131]

Not until the post-apostolic period, well after the unity of the church had taken on imperial-political overtones, does the emphasis shift. For Ignatius of Antioch, this unity is already no longer a basic gift; it is an ideal yet

128. Thus Johanna Rahner, "Biblische und altkirchliche Dimensionen von koinonia und ihre ekklesiologische Relevanz für die gegenwärtige ökumenische Debatte," in Brosseder and Link, *Eucharistische Gastfreundschaft*, pp. 43-60, here pp. 44, 46.

129. Rahner, "Dimensionen von Koinonia," p. 46.

130. Calvin, *Institutes*, IV.17.22 (ET: vol. 2, p. 575).

131. Stuhlmann, "Mahl des Herrn," p. 40.

to be achieved and for which one must struggle. Thus the external signs — agreement in the confession, the church's unity with the bishop — take on supreme importance, even when its standard and its source continue to be the celebration of the eucharist, for even here the change of emphasis is obvious when the eucharist can make the unity given by Christ real only under the authority of the ordained bishop (*Philadelphians* 4; *Smyrnaeans* 8.1-2). One sees a somewhat different picture in *1 Clement.* Here the unity of the church is simply presupposed, for we have "one God, and one Christ, and one Spirit of grace poured out upon us" (*1 Clement* 46.6). Therefore it cannot be a "product of human effort"; it is rather "a later realization of what was ordained by God in Christ." It becomes "a theme of the ethics" we are to prove with our faith and confession.[132] It is the tension between gift *(Gabe)* and task *(Aufgabe),* in which the question of the church's unity henceforth moves, and the celebration of the eucharist is the concrete place where it is to be carried out. One sees an example in the Orthodox church. On the one hand it "bears Christ in itself."[133] His Holy Spirit–filled body creates and renews the *ontological* unity of the church as life-giving energy in the eucharistic meal. Yet as a *visible* unity it is dependent on the authority of the bishop as well as on the faith and life of Christians.[134] Instead of being an *effective* sign and instrument of unity, the Lord's Supper is increasingly placed under conditions. No longer are all baptized persons admitted to communion; their worthiness is tested with dogma. Confessional unity becomes the price that must be paid for eucharistic fellowship.[135]

The ecumenical task of our time is to separate ourselves from this tradition and to return to the Pauline beginnings so that the Lord's Supper will no longer be only a "sign of the lost unity of Christians" (A. Bea) but will make visible for us the hope for the real unity established in Jesus Christ.

3.3.2. The Lord's Supper as Rite

At the root of the controversies over the Lord's Supper throughout the history of the church, from Radbertus (circa 832) through Berengar (1076), Luther, and Zwingli, and down to the most recent discussions, there appears to be an occurrence that has certain parallels with the role of Scripture (section 3.1). The Lord's Supper is transmitted as a rite; it begins by confronting us as part

132. Sabine Mirbach, *Ihr aber seid Leib Christi: Zur Aktualität des Leib-Christi-Gedankens für eine heutige Pastoral* (Regensburg: Pustet, 1998), p. 37.

133. Staniloae, *Orthodoxe Dogmatik,* vol. 2, p. 201.

134. See here Manole, *Ekklesiologische Perspektiven,* pp. 10-11, 300-301.

135. Rahner, "Dimensionen von Koinonia," p. 57.

of the church's firmly established liturgical tradition that is in need of interpretation. The *interpretations* begin, however, not with the act itself but with the words of the liturgy. Thus the meaning of the celebration moves farther and farther away from its original center, the community's solidarity given by Christ in the meal itself, to a meaning separate from it that one thinks one can express and "have" quasi-objectively — apart from the lived event. Already the sacrificial idea of the Catholic mass centered on transformation, but even more the controversy among Protestants over how one is to understand the "is" or "signifies" *(est, significat)* of the words of institution (1 Cor. 11:24-26) has basically taken the Lord's Supper away from the community, turning it into an event that must be intellectually explained. It has become the symbol for testing dogmatic orthodoxy that excludes, "excommunicates," people who think and believe differently, as we can see in the paradoxical wording of church law that describes the termination of a fellowship that had long since ceased to be a living, acting fellowship.

If this supper of separations is to become once again the flash point of unity, we must deal with questions and tasks similar to those that engaged us in section 3.1: How does what is hardened become fluid again? We must begin every attempt to arrive at a new answer by avoiding interpretations that separate the meal into subjective and objective poles — here the celebrating community, there the meaning and symbolic value of the "elements" — and thus miss the unifying center of the eucharist. The well-known questions about what the main thing is — the "transformation" of the elements, the individual's faith, or the authority of the duly ordained bishop — are obviously wrongly asked in this form. They make our interpretations into *conditions* of participation. What the Lord's Supper brings to us, its meaning and its effect, is not exhausted in a sacramental gift that could be appropriated by correctly performing the ritual *(opere operato),* nor does it depend on our personal faith or our "worthiness." There are essentially four areas of questioning — all of them related to the interpretation of the rite — that have led to controversies among the churches that are experienced and condemned as divisive: (1) How are we to understand the presence of Christ in the elements? (2) In what sense is the eucharist a sacrifice? (3) Does the rite require communion "in both forms" (bread *and* wine)? (4) What significance does the ministerial office have for the Lord's Supper and its celebration? With regard to the first three questions, the official ecumenical conversations have led to a wide-ranging agreement among the churches, but the fourth question continues to be controversial.[136]

136. Cf. here Lehmann and Pannenberg, *Condemnations,* pp. 84-117; also Harding Meyer, "Der Ertrag der Erörterung und Klärung kontroverser Aspekte in Verständnis und Praxis von

In this context I want to deal only with the first point, since here the dogmatic interpretations have varied widely from the very beginning. The words of institution in Paul and the Synoptics appear to suggest a simple identification of bread and wine with the body and blood of Christ, which is why the elements, as one sees in the veneration of the host in earlier days, have been regarded not only symbolically but more literally as the actual location of the presence of Christ.[137] Correspondingly, the center of the meal in the Catholic and Orthodox rite is the "transformation" in which, when the liturgist pronounces the *epiklesis,* the elements, while retaining the forms of their outward appearance (accidents), become in *substance* what in themselves they are not: "real" bearers of the presence of Christ. In order to reject the idea of a metaphysical miracle ("transubstantiation") while preserving the mysterious character of this presence, one speaks today on the Catholic side of a trans-signification (or trans-finalization), a change of meaning through which Christ himself brings the gifts of bread and wine into a completely new relationship to us so that they receive a "new being."[138]

Luther's attempt to make the "real presence" of the human nature of Christ understandable "in, with, and between" bread and wine is an alternative on the same level. Transubstantiation is replaced by the idea of the ubiquity that enables the risen Christ, like God, to be "in" the creatures, not in the sense that they enclose him but in the sense that he contains them.[139] Although in both models the symbolic value of the elements establishes and carries the sense of the celebration, on the Reformed side Zwingli and Calvin went in a new direction. Here the *community* becomes the decisive subject of the celebration in accordance with the invitation to "do this in remembrance of me." When it makes the suffering of Christ a present reality, the eucharist becomes a meal of obligation and fellowship.[140] Instead of asking about an isolated meaning of the elements, Calvin asks about the meaning of what is depicted — a meaning into which the community is drawn. With the act of

---

Abendmahl/Eucharistie durch den ökumenischen Dialog" (2003), in Brosseder and Link, *Eucharistische Gastfreundschaft,* pp. 61-84.

137. Thus canon 1 of the Trient Decree on the Eucharist, in Denzinger and Schönmetzer, *Enchiridion Symbolorum,* no. 1651 (ET: *The Church Teaches: Documents of the Church in English Translation* [Rockford, IL: Tan, 1973], p. 286).

138. See here Lehmann and Pannenberg, *Condemnations,* pp. 99-100.

139. In the formula of Concord, this sacramental union *(unio sacramentalis)* is compared to the union of the divine and human natures in the person of Christ (Tappert, *Book of Concord,* p. 575).

140. See here Gottfried W. Locher, *Streit unter Gästen: Die Lehre aus der Abendmahlsdebatte der Reformatoren für das Verständnis und die Feier des Abendmahls heute,* Theologische Studien 110 (Zurich: Theologischer Verlag, 1972), pp. 10-11.

eating and drinking, it portrays what happened on the cross *for it* and, so to speak, vouches for its truth with its bodily existence.[141] When in the acts of distributing and receiving bread and wine the *presence* of Christ's living and dying becomes an event among us, God places the fullness of life "as it were from his hand into ours" (Calvin).

This community-centered understanding of the eucharist may well come the closest to the New Testament reports. Recent exegesis emphasizes that "body" and "blood" from our liturgy's words of institution are not the referent of an *image* ("bread" and "wine") that is explained; it is "the explanation of a rite in which the disciples (or members of the community) participate."[142] What Jesus does and explains here is a "prophetic *symbolic act*," one in which the community participates in its eating and drinking. Analogous to the Jewish Passover meal, the expressive sign is the act of eating and drinking itself: "As often as you eat from this bread and drink from this cup you proclaim the Lord's death until he comes" (1 Cor. 11:26).[143] Thus the question is not whether or how much bread and wine "in reality" are more than what we actually eat and drink. Rather, the decisive thing is that when we eat and drink we participate in an event, in the death of Christ and in the blessing, the fellowship-creating power that flows from him. In the biblical texts, "the dimension of the community experience"[144] is more important than the didactic dimension. Do we say too much when we suspect that our different understandings of the Lord's Supper will not be clarified until we actually engage in a community experience? "The contradictions can be solved through a common practice, because then they *have* to be solved."[145]

3.3.3. *Lord's Supper and Ministry*

The churches have been able to agree on these dogmatic differences; they are no longer judged to be divisive. The controversies of the past are "theologically surmounted."[146] Why then has the ecumenical hospitality so hopefully

141. Calvin, *Institutes*, IV.17.1 (ET: vol. 2, p. 557); also the *Heidelberg Catechism*, question 75: "As surely as I see with my eyes that the bread of the Lord is broken for me, just as surely is his body 'offered and broken on the cross for me'" (Cochrane, *Reformed Confessions*, p. 318).

142. Ulrich Luz, "Das Herrenmahl im Neuen Testament," *BiKi* 57 (2002): 5.

143. Stuhlmann ("Mahl des Herrn," pp. 26-27) talks of a "supper that speaks." Cf. also "Eucharist," no. 1, in *BEM*, p. 10.

144. Luz, "Herrenmahl," p. 5.

145. Jürgen Moltmann, *The Church in the Power of the Spirit*, trans. Margaret Kohl (New York: Harper & Row, 1977), p. 259.

146. Lehmann and Pannenberg, *Condemnations*, pp. 84-117, esp. 114-17.

begun and practiced after the Second Vatican Council come to naught? From a Protestant perspective, it is caused by what looks like a paradox: theological declarations are able to resolve the causes that led to a church schism but not the church schism itself. As a *historical* fact it is — and this is the paradox — at the same time a *dogmatic* fact. That makes of the above-mentioned fourth question a knot that at present cannot be untied. How so? In the course of the Reformation, Protestantism left the "Catholic" communion of churches *(communio ecclesiarum).* From the perspective of the other side, it appears that with the ordination of its pastors Protestantism severed the bond of the apostolic succession that is attributed to Christ himself. Since it lacks the sacrament of ordination, it suffers from an irremovable deficiency *(defectus ordinis).* For this reason the Protestant Lord's Supper has not retained "the proper reality *(genuina et integra substantia)* of the eucharistic mystery in its fullness,"[147] even though in the meantime one may have found agreement in all individual questions: what the Lord's Supper *is* as a sacrament, what it *means,* and what it *gives.* The possibility of eucharistic fellowship is based on acknowledging the *ministries,* and that is, according to the Catholic teaching ministry, not only a dogmatic difference; it is a church-juridical difference that even today has a schismatic character.

The Catholic position goes back to the decisions of the ancient church. Following Ignatius, the Second Vatican Council says, "every legitimate celebration of the Eucharist is regulated by the bishop," and in the dialogue on "the Lord's Supper" (1978) the Catholic Church insists: "The ordination of a bishop or priest is accordingly the essential prerequisite to his presiding at the Lord's Supper: even in exceptional cases there can be no Eucharistic celebration without an ordained priest."[148] In the view of the Evangelical-Lutheran Church as well, an ordained pastor must conduct the celebration of the eucharist. Whoever has not been commissioned to do so by being called to the ecclesiastical ministry is not to lead the celebration of the Lord's Supper.[149] Since, however, the Lord's Supper is not tied constitutionally here to the ministerial office, according to the Evangelical-Lutheran understanding nothing else stands in the way of eucharistic fellowship. How does one deal with differences?

No New Testament text indicates that presiding over the eucharist required a particularly prominent ministry, in contrast to other tasks (preach-

147. Thus the Decree on Ecumenism, *UR,* no. 22.

148. *LG,* no. 26; "The Eucharist," no. 66, in Meyer and Vischer, *Growth in Agreement,* p. 209.

149. *CA* 14 (ET: Tappert, *Book of Concord,* p. 36).

ing, teaching, diakonia) for which, according to Paul, a special charisma is necessary (1 Cor. 12:28-30). Still, within the order of the three ministries that developed from these beginnings "there never was in the New Testament period a ministry for leading the celebration of the meal as indeed there was none for leading the worship in general." That was, as Stuhlmann surmises, to keep the occupant of such a ministry from acting as the host instead of reserving that place for Christ.[150] Even less is there the idea in the New Testament that an ordained officeholder could "represent" Christ in this function. (Indeed, that would be not at all in keeping with the character of the eucharist as a prophetic symbolic act.) Therefore, the Evangelical-Lutheran side will not be able to make any more of a concession to the Catholic position than is in the juridical-pragmatic regulation of the Augsburg Confession (*CA* 14).

All the more noteworthy, then, is the suggestion proposed from the Catholic side by Hans Jorissen that would make it possible for his church to recognize the ministries in the churches of the Reformation.[151] Jorissen begins with the New Testament recognition that Word and sacrament on the one hand and the ministerial office on the other hand are not on the same level. "Word and sacrament *establish* the unity of the church, the ministerial office *bears witness* to it" (86), whereby being the church is not tied to a particular constitutional and organizational model (87). Since, furthermore, the apostolic succession of the ministry has "an essential (and not-to-be-relinquished) significance for connecting the church to its apostolic origin" only in connection with preserving the faith, and according to both Catholic and Protestant views the ministry is incorporated "into the church as a fellowship of self-governing local churches," the difference lies "not in the theology of the ministry as such but in the question of the significance attributed to a particular form in which the ministry is realized" (88-89). One could well conclude that the Protestant ministries are among these legitimate forms. It was not the rejection of the historical office of bishop as such that led to the break in continuity with the previous order of bishops but the "impossibility at that time of agreeing about the teaching of the gospel and of convincing the previous bishops to ordain Protestant officeholders" (94). The right of ordination by officeholders who were not bishops was claimed as an emergency law (for which there are precedents in the ancient church!). "Thus the Reformers remain principally in the tradition of the ancient church's under-

150. Stuhlmann, "Mahl des Herrn," p. 34.

151. Hans Jorissen, "Behindert die Amtsfrage die Einheit der Kirchen? Katholisches Plädoyer für die Anerkennung der reformatorischen Ämter," in Brosseder and Link, *Eucharistische Gastfreundschaft*. In the following paragraph the numbers in parentheses refer to the pages of this study.

standing of ministries" (94). They cannot appeal to a succession of bishops, but they can appeal to a *presbyterial* succession. But since the *one* ministry "with all authority" is already given in the ordination as presbyter (93), the difference between Catholic and Protestant ministries lies "not in the (sacramental) ordination as such but in the performability of the given authority" (97).[152] Then one must come to the conclusion that in the churches of the Reformation the essence of the apostolic ministry is "preserved in the form of the ordained ministry." The effort on behalf of the unity of the churches — this is his sympathetic conclusion — "need not be wrecked on the rock of the historical ordination by a bishop" (95).

3.3.4. *The Social Location of the Lord's Supper*

If the Lord's Supper as a common celebration is to be rediscovered as a step on the way to church unity, not the least of our tasks is to bring its social and ethical dimension into the discussion, as has often and with great insistence been urged in the process of the ecumenical opening of the churches. The cited formula of New Delhi (1961)[153] speaks of a "fully committed fellowship . . . breaking the one bread, joining in common prayer, and having a corporate life reaching out in witness and service to all." In its eucharistic section, the Lima declaration (1982) has principally said what that might mean:

> The eucharist embraces all aspects of life. It is a representative act of thanksgiving and offering on behalf of the whole world. The eucharistic celebration demands reconciliation and sharing among all those regarded as brothers and sisters in the one family of God and is a constant challenge in the search for appropriate relationships in social, economic and political life. . . . All kinds of injustice, racism, separation and lack of freedom are radically challenged when we share in the body and blood of Christ.[154]

The declaration sets here a distinctly social-critical tone that reminds the church that it lives in the "as yet unredeemed world" (Barmen V). If the signs of reconciliation it owes this world are to be socially effective signs — or even signs that are merely noticed — then it must actively participate "in this

152. The remarkable addition reads: "One cannot appeal to the statement of Vatican II about the 'fullness of the sacrament of orders' in the office of bishop (*LG*, 26.1) as a counter-argument."

153. Above, Part One, p. 21.

154. "Eucharist," no. 20, in *BEM*, p. 14.

ongoing restoration of the world's situation and the human condition."[155] Since the Assembly of the World Council of Churches in Uppsala (1968), the Christian world can know that there are not only dogmatic heresies; there are also *ethical* heresies, digressions and wrong paths, of a community that can no longer claim to be the church. These heresies have their roots not in the denial of "pure doctrine" but in the refusal to live in a way that corresponds to that doctrine.[156] Today the eucharist is threatened in its very core by these heresies. It is betrayed more lastingly as a symbol of unity by the social division that cuts across all denominations than it is by confessional separations.

As we have seen, the Lord's Supper is in its biblical origins a prophetic symbolic act. Symbolic acts present what they mean in a visual image. They are understood when the symbol is decoded as an allusion to a promised or threatened reality that touches on the area of our social existence. Now the bread broken in the Lord's Supper also has a symbolic value that designates not only a sacramental but also a social — indeed, a political — reality. The bread is a symbol of Western wealth and thus at the same time an allusion to Eastern and Southern poverty. Economic justice is on trial today in the symbol of the bread. In the elements of bread and wine, in the gestures of breaking and sharing, the world is present not only in its physical materiality but also in its social neediness. Here there is no separation of spiritual and secular, of inner and outer. Thus the eucharistic celebration becomes a "true" fellowship only when those who participate in it draw conclusions not only from the dogmatic but also from the social symbolism of the Lord's Supper. From its very origin, the two belong together.

> Bread set before us brings the starving into our company. Wine set before us brings the joyless, the sick and those who are denied the fruit of the earth. Fellowship and peace bring into our company the prisoners and the mentally ill, the refugees and the stateless persons. It is a searching, committing act to be involved in. It presents its own manifesto of action for a world of need.[157]

No impulse intensified the awareness of the ethical consequences of the Lord's Supper and kept it alive until today like the "preferential option for the

155. "Eucharist," no. 20, in *BEM,* p. 14.

156. See here Norman Goodall, ed., *The Uppsala Report 1968: Official Report of the Fourth Assembly of the World Council of Churches, Uppsala July 4-20, 1968* (Geneva: WCC, 1968), pp. 319-20.

157. John Poulton, *The Feast of Life: A Theological Reflection on the Theme "Jesus Christ — The Life of the World"* (Geneva: WCC, 1982), p. 20.

poor" proclaimed by the Latin American bishops' conferences of Medillín (1968) and Puebla (1979).[158] When the "unworthy" reception of the Lord's Supper that Paul condemned with his well-known harshness refers to the behavior of the wealthy church members who were short on solidarity (1 Cor. 11:27-34), then we are here in the midst of today's challenges, especially since as a rule "poor" and "rich" are embodied today not in individuals but in the churches themselves. By no means does that make the conflict easier, for the existence of poverty in a world of wealth reflects a break in the solidarity of people (including Christians) among themselves and in their fellowship with God. Leonardo Boff has called the poor "the most intense presence of Christ in history." "Indeed, I would say — although it may sound heretical — that Christ is more present in the poor than he is in the bread and wine that represent the Lord for us in the mass."[159]

As correct and important as all of this is, ultimately one may ask whether we strike the right tone when we (especially the ecumenical texts) put ourselves under the constant pressure to perform: the church must, it should, it has the task, it is obligated — as if it were the church's responsibility finally to transport utopia into reality. The result is a sense of anxiety: we simply cannot accomplish it! In the eucharist, however, we live from abundance, not from want. Here we discover a reality that is different from the one that is constantly and unavoidably under judgment, on which the moral guillotine constantly falls — a reality that Christ creates and into which he draws us. It is not "church dreams" but "kingdom-of-God dreams" that open to us the scope of the eucharist. We are here only so that something of God's kindness be at work in the world. God needs Christians for the world "that they may see your good works and praise your Father in heaven" (Matt. 5:16). A eucharistic vision can aspire no higher than to the hope that God himself will again become powerful in his churches.

3.4. *Ministerial Office*

Given the prerequisites we have developed here, it appears that offering the church's ministry as a flash point of unity is our most difficult endeavor, for

158. See Gustavo Gutiérrez, *The Power of the Poor in History: Selected Writings,* trans. Robert R. Barr (Maryknoll, NY: Orbis, 1983), pp. 125-65; also Heinrich Bedford-Strohm, *Vorrang für die Armen: Auf dem Weg zu einer theologischen Theorie der Gerechtigkeit* (Gütersloh: Kaiser, 1993), esp. beginning p. 157.

159. Leonardo Boff in conversation with Horst Goldstein, in Peter Eicher, ed., *Theologie der Befreiung in Gespräch* (Munich: Kösel-Verlag, 1985), p. 92.

the unity of the church is realized in a living process that gives rise to conflicts and crises but also to new experiences, life-forms, and responsibilities. It shows itself in the movement that began with Jesus and that brings together the most diverse communities as a unified, acting subject. Yet from historical experience we understand a ministry as an instrument that within a legally consolidated structure serves to attend to certain competences according to precisely fixed rules. It would seem that ministries exist to shut down the process in its very vitality. The reasons for that have been discussed in the New Testament section of this volume.[160] If in the Pauline churches the exercise of every ministry was a question of personal gifts and ability, in the development that followed Clement the legitimacy of the officeholder depended decisively on his order-creating function, and that has serious consequences for the question of church unity. If in the Pastorals the church is still guaranteed by "sound doctrine" and the "entrusted gospel," with and after Ignatius it is represented in a particular structure of ministries. Nevertheless, no modern denomination can regard itself in a direct sense as an heir of Ignatius. It is understandable that, following in the footsteps of the church-law specialist Rudolf Sohm, people have repeatedly felt compelled to judge the evolution of the legally regulated idea of ministry as a critical deviation from the New Testament tradition,[161] especially since with the development of ministries secular power structures began to prevail in the area of the church.

3.4.1. The Problem

Today all churches acknowledge the need to have an ordained ministry, as widely divergent as their reasoning for such an office may be. The church's leadership requires persons who attend to special responsibilities and therefore are granted special authority. Thus, according to Catholic doctrine, the bishops preside "in place of God over the flock, whose shepherds they are, as teachers for doctrine, priests for sacred worship, and ministers for governing," for "Christ . . . has through His apostles, made their successors, the bishops, partakers of His consecration and His mission. They have legitimately handed on to different individuals in the Church various degrees of participation in this ministry."[162] On the Lutheran side, the Augsburg Confession argues: "That we may obtain this [justifying] faith, the Ministry of Teaching

160. Above, Part Two, pp. 118-26.

161. Rudolf Sohm, *Kirchenrecht*, vol. 1: *Die geschichtlichen Grundlagen* (1892; reprinted Munich-Leipzig: Duncker & Humboldt, 1923), p. 160: "At the end of the first century the epistle of Clement signaled the birth of canon law. An event of incalculable consequence!"

162. *LG*, nos. 20 and 28.

the Gospel and administering the Sacraments was instituted." It is a ministry that self-evidently carries the traditional title of bishop.[163] One sees the importance Calvin also ascribes to the (now fourfold) ministry in the statement that light and the sun's warmth along with food and drink are not nearly as necessary for maintaining temporal life "as is the apostolical and pastoral office to preserve a Church in the earth."[164] The Helvetic Confession says simply that the visible church is "constituted" by the *ministerium,* and the Gallican Confession makes use of this theme in no fewer than six of its forty articles.[165]

What is the reason for this unusual emphasis? Since principalities and powers rule the world, the church must have something visible that is symbolic of the different rule of the risen Lord, of the "polity that our Lord Jesus Christ has given." This is where "the work of God" *(Dei negotium)* is done that "though the whole world withstood and opposed them . . . was for them."[166] The declaration of Lima that, in keeping with its Catholic assessment, emphasizes the ministerial office as a "focus of unity" offers a different accent that is especially important in our context. If in the post-apostolic period it was merely one of the "unity-promoting forces," now it is elevated — even above the *regula fidei* ("rule of faith") — to nothing less than an essential condition of unity: "In order to fulfil its mission, the Church needs persons who are publicly and continually responsible for pointing to its fundamental dependence on Jesus Christ, and thereby provide, within a multiplicity of gifts, a focus of its unity."[167]

This is where the ecumenical problem, as it is reflected today in the doctrinal discussions, has its vital center. It is reduced to the question of the recognition of the ministries. That was not always the case. To restore the endangered unity of Christendom, Luther hoped for a legal general council that would be able to settle the doctrinal differences of the divided church, and especially in the Reformed Church the conciliar hope has always been kept alive by its own synodal constitution. Yet, given their dogmatic assumptions, neither Luther nor the Reformed leaders could even have accepted the invitation to such an (in Rome's sense) ecumenical council, not to mention articulate it, since it presupposes recognizing the office of the papacy. The pope convenes the council, and the reception of the council's decisions requires papal ratification, yet Protestantism lacks an office that corresponds to the Catholic (in-

163. *CA,* articles 5 and 28.

164. Calvin, *Institutes,* IV.3.2 (ET: vol. 2, p. 317).

165. *Confessio Helvetica posterior,* chapter 18 (ET: Cochrane, *Reformed Confessions,* p. 268); *Confessio Gallicana,* article 25.29-33.

166. Calvin, *Institutes,* IV.11.1 (ET: vol. 2, p. 440).

167. "Ministry," no. 8, in *BEM,* p. 21.

cluding the Roman) bishop. Regarding the ministries developed in the Protestant tradition, in Rome's eyes Protestantism is not capable of participating in a council — a Protestant synod is still not a council! — and thus ecumenically not capable of being part of a coalition. To remedy this deficiency, the Protestants would need a ministerial office with a representative structure comparable to the Catholic bishop. This, in any case, is the challenge that makes a legal-theological clarification of the question of the ministry one of the pressing ecumenical tasks.

How did the church's ministry come to this problematic position as one of the flash points of unity that still evoke conflict? There is, of course, agreement in some important points. One of them is that ministry exists "by divine right" (*iure divino; CA* 28). It does not come from a mandate of the community but represents, so to speak, the government of the risen Christ, so that the officeholders — this, too, is not controversial — do not act in their own name but "represent" the person of Christ.[168] Next to that, however, there are irreconcilable differences (with the Orthodox Church as well). First and foremost is the *sacramental* character of ordination tied to the idea of *personal* apostolic succession going back to Peter — an idea that Ignatius, by the way, did not know. There is further the superiority of the bishops in contrast to the bearers of a "lesser order of ordination" *(inferioris ordinis)* both in the area of jurisdiction and with regard to the right of confirmation and ordination denied to them.[169] The categorical distinction between clergy and laity, the question of the ordination of women, and, by no means of least importance, the exalted position and monolithic authority of the papal office separate the denominations. Rome attributes to the Protestant churches an "ecclesial defect"[170] and refuses to recognize their ministries as valid as long as they do not enter "into an existing line of episcopal succession,"[171] but the churches of the Reformation cannot accept this reservation. Their objection is: Do the questions of "succession" and of "valid episcopacy," including the connection

168. Philip Melanchthon, *Apology of the Augsburg Confession* 7.28; Calvin, *Institutes,* IV.3.1 (ET: vol. 2, p. 316); *LG,* no. 21 and often. Based on the statement "He who hears you hears me" (Luke 10:16), thus: Melanchthon, *Apology* 7:28; *CA,* article 28 (ET: Tappert, *Book of Concord,* p. 84); and *LG,* no. 20.

169. Vatican II, "Decree Concerning the Pastoral Office of Bishops in the Church: *Christus Dominus,*" no. 9; *LG,* no. 26.

170. Vatican II, *UR,* no. 22; repeated most recently in the declaration "*Dominus Iesus:* On the Unicity and Salvific Universality of Jesus Christ and the Church" (2000).

171. "Ministry," no. 38, in *BEM,* p. 30. Following this line is the much-discussed suggestion of Karl Rahner and Heinrich Fries, *Unity of the Churches: An Actual Possibility,* trans. Ruth C. L. Gritsch and Eric W. Gritsch (Philadelphia: Fortress; New York: Paulist, 1985).

between them and the "valid eucharist," really belong to the church's essence *(esse ecclesiae)?*

Is there a third position from which one can make a judgment about these differences and, where possible, make them disappear? The ministry specifies a legal structure. Now, the singularity of the church's law in contrast to all secular law comes from the reality that its source is none other than the source from which the church lives. The church cannot submit to an order that establishes human law at its own pleasure. It receives its order from God. Thus far, in the Protestant view, all church law comes from the basic functions of *divine worship,* in particular from the confession spoken there. It is, in the words of Karl Barth, *liturgical* and as such *confessing* law.[172] One cannot separate what is "spiritual," specifically Christian, from the church's legal operations. When there is no *theologically* based church law, the secular bureaucracy takes over. It is likely that all churches could agree on these fundamental statements, but how are they to be interpreted and applied? What does it mean for church order that *divine* law takes precedence over human law and is declared to be its basis? Here the separated communions have long given quite different answers, and here, in the different interpretations of the basis of church law, the differences portrayed have their roots. They are too deeply rooted to be resolved with pragmatic suggestions — a tendency of the profitable study, *The Condemnations of the Reformation Era: Do They Still Divide?*

3.4.2. *Foundations of Church Law*

Protestantism conceives of church order principally as an order of service. Its ministries are understood primarily as realizations of the gifts God distributes to the church, the management of which he puts in human hands and through which he wants to show that he is present.[173] The ministries are there to fulfill the tasks God has given the church. The Protestant pastor or presbyter is so much a supporter and servant "that the designation of office of ministry, indeed the term office itself, is not appropriate."[174] By contrast, Catholicism further developed the beginnings of the post-apostolic period portrayed here and consistently tied ministry/office to the idea of (personal) representa-

172. Barth, *CD,* IV/2, p. 695. Here the somewhat "bold" expression "liturgical law" looks at "the whole life of the community" that is centered in the special event of Christian worship. In "the law of the communio sanctorum" the law valid for the church "is really present" (p. 699). After 1945 this theological decision was accepted on the broadest basis in the Evangelical-Lutheran church law (Erik Wolf, Hans Dombois).

173. Thus Calvin, *Institutes,* IV.3.2 (ET: vol. 2, p. 317).

174. Dombois, *Recht der Gnade,* vol. 3, p. 146.

tion. It is constituted not so much by the task, the ministry entrusted, as it is by the presence of Christ to which one can call attention through a person, the ordained or consecrated officeholder. Obviously we are dealing with two fundamentally different models, and it is difficult to see where one could find a balance here, or even an agreement.

Catholic church law generally distinguishes between two complexes in divine law *(ius divinum)*. First, there is revealed law *(ius divinum positivum)*, the embodiment of legal statements that are transmitted and known from Scripture or tradition. Second, there is natural law *(ius divinum naturale)*, the moral law written by God on the human heart that constitutes the basic norm of all social behavior.[175] The hierarchical order of the Catholic Church rests on the idea of revealed law. It lives from the idea of representing (or substituting for) its unseen Lord. Valid for the church, the Christ who lives on *(Christus prolongatus)*, is the word of Jesus, "As the Father has sent me, so send I you" (John 20:21). According to Catholic doctrine, the hierarchy is a basic people-of-God-forming principle without which the church as a whole or in part cannot exist at all. The hierarchical principle — the same is logically true of the arrangement of the church into the "classes" of clergy and laity — is "of divine law and therefore is removed from the church's control."[176] As a consequence, the only persons who have constitutional power are those who have received it from *above*. Accordingly, the "holy mystery of the *unity* of the church" is realized in the leading of the people of God through "the apostles and their successors — the bishops with Peter's successor at their head,"[177] whereby the bishops represent the visible principle and the basis of unity in the local churches. A divine law of this kind and of such a character that is able to turn statements of faith into statements of law is not possible in Protestant churches, because it would violate the freedom of the gospel. Here the legitimate basic idea of canon law has long been poured into a different mold, a mold that has found its most pregnant expression in the third thesis of the Barmen Theological Declaration of 1934. "With its faith as with its obedience, with its message as with its order," the church is to bear witness that it is solely the property of Christ. The church's form and order must correspond to the gospel, but it can do this — thus Karl Barth's important correction — only on the basis of human law. "All church law, however great the seri-

175. Cf. Godehard Josef Ebers, *Grundriss des Katholischen Kirchenrechts: Rechtsgeschichte und System* (Vienna: Manz, 1950), pp. 231-32.

176. E. Thul, "Kirchenverfassung: Römisch-Katholische Kirche," in *Evangelisches Staatslexikon,* 2d ed. (Stuttgart: Kreuz, 1966), column 1282.

177. Vatican II, *UR,* no. 2.

ousness with which it is sought and found and instituted, can only be human law and not divine (*ius humanum* and not *ius divinum*)."[178] For the present, this is where the unbridgeable difference lies, for this decision rejects the canonical idea of representation as the basis of church law and thus also the hierarchical principle. Christ takes shape in the church in the love and the suffering of his members, but he is not represented by them,[179] not even by an officeholder. He remains separate from the church.

The difficulties of the Protestant understanding of ministry arise in just the opposite way, from the effort to find a human legal form analogous to the pre-given divine law — thus to keep the special ministry of the church in agreement with the priesthood of all believers. Ministry does not establish a special class ("clergy"); it is to reflect the command of love *(lex charitatis)*. It is therefore not unimportant to observe that the Lutheran Reformation — we will speak first of it — by no means eliminated the ministerial office. It merely removed it from all traditional legal associations and conceived of it as the antithesis, so to speak, of the papal office. Luther contrasted the monolithic authority of the pope with the equally monolithic authority of the Word, its sole validity and immediateness. The result is the Reformation's preaching ministry, which, in its construction, is the only ministry of the new church. In this singularity it cannot appeal to the New Testament, is moreover completely isolated historically, and there is nothing to compare with it in the development of the order of ministry portrayed in the second part of this book. It is intelligible neither in terms of the (individual) task of preaching nor as an expression of a unity given the church as a basic gift in Christ, for its bearer is not a historically conceivable preacher but in its intention the living gospel itself *(viva vox evangelii)*. Here the Word and Spirit are not adversaries of institutional orders that are thus dependent on legal forms; they are the motive force that organizes the church's process like a well-arranged body. As a result, a universal leadership authority is replaced by the figure of a subjectless consensus. According to the Augsburg Confession, the only thing needed for true church unity is agreement in questions of doctrine and the administration of the sacraments.[180] When, however, one has once achieved unity among the Reformers, there is — this is the compelling as well as problematic consequence — "no longer anyone who would be responsible and authorized by church law to bring about the re-

178. Barth, *CD*, IV/2, p. 713.

179. The idea of representing Christ (either by the church or by an individual) does not appear in the New Testament, only the idea of taking shape or form *(morphosis)* as in Romans 2:20.

180. *CA*, article 7 (ET: Tappert, *Book of Concord*, p. 32).

newal of this consensus, its improvement and correction, the deciding of new questions."[181]

On the Reformed side, however, Calvin carefully returned to a legally arranged multiplicity of ministries. The Reformed order of ministries — designed to differentiate among preachers, doctors, elders, and deacons — arises neither from the critical recasting of existing forms of ministry nor from the structure of the newly understood and ordered divine worship. It comes from biblical-theological reflection on the church's essential tasks (*Institutes,* IV.3) and unfolds in the doctrine of the church as a community of service. The ministries are the necessary, structuring element that gives shape to the church's growth. Appealing to the pure, conditionally happening Word is not sufficient here. That would destroy the connections to the historical life of the church and its existing structure in the same way as would the appeal to a Spirit who "blows where it will." Such a return to the free Word that transcends history would methodologically exclude the very thing one wanted to emphasize against the Roman understanding of ministry: the character of the church as a community and its evolving growth. One may also find here the reason why Calvin emphatically relates the *ministerium* not to faith (as in *CA* 5) but to the visible cohesion of the church on earth. Thus understood, underlying this condition is a theory of sorts of the church's actions that includes the functions of worship. Its virtue is that it clearly brings the ministries together into a definite leadership structure; indeed, on the Reformed (in contrast to the Lutheran) side, the task of church leadership has always been one of the constitutive marks of the church itself. The New Testament–collegial character of ministry is in keeping with this structure. The relationship of ministry and community in the leadership of the church is realized in a fuller way than in the (more theoretical) contrast between ministry and community in the Lutheran area.

Even here we stumble upon an obvious limitation as soon as we raise the question of the unity of the church. As much as the synodal element, the regular association of pastors and lay presbyters, is one of the characteristics of the Reformed church constitution and has kept alive the idea of a council, legally it is an element of the separated church. There are national and provincial synods in which the churches come together. The question of unity is, as in Lutheranism, principally answered by speaking of the possibility of future consensus-building. Any *binding* historical action as a community is ex-

181. Dombois, *Recht der Gnade,* vol. 3, p. 184. "It [the Lutheran Church] does not even form a church constitution from its elements, ministry and community, at best only fragments of the constitution of a separatist church" (p. 185).

hausted in the formation of a confession.[182] "Although the ancient, the Roman, and the Oriental churches progress through the decisions of conciliar assemblies and principally cling to these methods, the Reformed churches make use of non-recurring founding events. Their interpretation changes *de facto* . . . but no longer *ex consensu* and with obligatory power. They have neither the will nor the power of enforcement required for such progress."[183]

3.4.3. *Institution and Ministry*

Yet precisely this power is necessary if unity is not only to endure as a proclamation in one's mind or on paper but also to determine its everyday existence as a historical reality. It is, in fact, not yet enough to agree in doctrine and in the administration of the sacraments, for the universal church is not a league of nations that (as a natural condition) has separate nations — individual churches — as its basis. The same Spirit-produced reality that the Reformation claims for the individual churches *(congregatio)* belongs to the universal church in its total scope. The idea of unity is in principle more than a supplement or an outward form for the concept of the church; it is an attribute *(nota)* of the church itself as a fundamental reality. All Christians are directly united in the one body of Christ. Not until this reality can find visible expression in the ministerial office can it be understood as a flash point of unity. Protestantism is obviously farther removed from this goal than the episcopally constituted Latin churches, for it is composed only of individual churches. It can conceive of the universal church — here the heritage of Rudolph Sohm continues to be a force — only as a spiritual event, without historically tangible features. The consequences of the incarnation of the Word must still be drawn for church doctrine and church law. Hans Dombois has anticipated it in a drastic metaphor. "The camel of the Spirit enters history only through the eye of the needle — admittedly, to do that it must be unsaddled."[184] The unity of the church must be shifted from a spiritual postulate into a historically livable and thus institutional form.

But what is an institution? Once again Dombois: "The institution is like

182. According to the Second Helvetic Confession, the unity of the church is not to be sought in external rites *(in ritibus externis)*. It is composed, rather, of the truth and unity of the "catholic" faith. This, however, is contained not in human laws but in the Holy Scripture, "of which the Apostles' Creed is a compendium" (chapter 17).

183. Dombois, *Recht der Gnade*, vol. 3, pp. 182-83.

184. Hans Dombois, "Grundlagen und Grundzüge der Kirchenrechtslehre," in *Theologie — Was ist das?* ed. Georg Picht and Enno Rudolph (Stuttgart: Kreuz, 1977), pp. 261-75, quotation p. 273.

a house that one must occupy. It is designated for that purpose, and without anyone living in it the house will deteriorate. One must fill it with life. Within limits one can also renovate it, but its basic architectural concept, including its location — its surroundings — is unalterably fixed."[185] The heart of every institution lies in its reality as something given. Institutions are the lawful expression of typical forms of relationship and community. Although (as in a marriage) there is a certain freedom in how they are shaped, in their formation they are given. "They are like plants that one can set out, cut, and even ruin but whose final forms are given."[186] Institutions are — to return to the initial image — the playground and stage on which a universally valid relation — in our case the partnership of God and humanity realized in Jesus — enters history. It remains to be determined what we do with it — that is to say, how, given the conditions it imposes, we actually bring about reality, a new historical constellation.

What does that mean with regard to the church? The community assembled by and in the Spirit is not only a hearer of the Word, a receiver of the message. To the degree it acknowledges the liturgist and preacher as authorized servants of thc Word — indeed, by understanding itself and acting as a community, distinguishing between valid faith and false faith — it is already more than that; it is a historical institution. Even Paul's statement that through the intervention of the exalted Christ he has been "separated out" to proclaim the gospel, and that with his call he has been given special authority (Rom. 1:1, 5), clearly shows the legal structure of the personal institution. Thus those who advocate the union of individual local churches into a synod according to the New Testament pattern and who see in it the true forms of the visible church must acknowledge that in every case we are dealing with an institutional form. That in turn means that the unity we are seeking exists only as a unity that can be seen and demonstrated, or it does not exist at all. It is institutional unity, or it remains a phantom.

Thus to raise the question of the ministerial office is to raise the problem of unity in its sharpest form. An institution presents itself in its ministries. They shape the elements of its life. In them they find their legally describable expression. Thus understood, like every constitution, the church's order of ministries is only "the necessarily delimited essence of the life it contains."[187] In its essence, the church's process, which had its beginning in history, precedes the order of ministries. However, the question of the ministe-

185. Dombois, *Recht der Gnade,* vol. 1, p. 903.

186. Dombois, *Recht der Gnade,* vol. 1, p. 905.

187. Dombois, *Recht der Gnade,* vol. 3, p. 318.

rial office, unlike all theological-metaphysical arguments, cannot be separated from the actual life of the church. Stated polemically, the ministries can never express an unchanging order — whether in the likeness of a heavenly hierarchy or, as Ignatius thought he could say of the bishop, in the likeness of God.[188] They are the necessary structuring element that gives form to the church's growth. Finally, they in fact have their legal basis, as Paul describes the matter, in the service entrusted to the church. Thus, as the ecumenical document from Lima says, the multiplicity of ministries is necessarily "constitutive for the life and witness of the Church"[189] only because the process begun by Jesus cannot remain without form and structure if he is to bring together people of the most diverse cultures, nationalities, and races to a fully binding fellowship.

It is thus clear that, compared with the exemplary ways of living in which, according to Ephesians 4:13, every church must grow into the "unity of the faith," to the "maturity of the complete man," and thus to the "measure of the age in which the fullness of Christ is reached," the question of ministries is fundamentally (not only historically but also systematically) secondary. Therefore, the unity we seek today — and just may be able to achieve — must turn out to be the legitimate continuation of that earliest pre-Ignatius phase that the New Testament certifies is still *without* the office of bishop. The earliest tradition shows us "primary figures of unity" — James, Peter, and Paul[190] — whom one can easily declare to be representatives of the whole church, not, of course, qua ministerial office, but because they are authentic witnesses of what happened between Jesus' baptism and his ascension. In their person they manifest the qualitative dimension of unity that manifests itself in the living of life. It is, in the words of the Gospel of John, the life force of the branches on the vine that flows from Christ (John 15:1-8), staying on the way shown by Jesus, or the truth one recognizes and does (John 14:6). Here the institution — that, without doubt, is what we must call the early churches — is understood (corresponding to the literal sense of *instituere*) as a quantity in the process of becoming.

It should be clear, therefore, that the order of ministries we see in its beginnings in Paul and in Ephesians is not the product of a mistaken development; it is an absolutely necessary step. It is true that it has its meaning and legitimacy only in an institution that develops from inside out, as a plant develops from a single seed. A ministry that thinks it must justify itself

188. Cf. Part Two, above, pp. 124-25.
189. "Ministry," no. 8, in *BEM*, p. 21.
190. Part Two, above, pp. 106-18.

hierarchically (as the copy of a pre-existing heavenly order) denies this process of growth — that is, the carrying out of the things given the church to do, from which alone it can emerge as an earthly ministry.[191] To say it positively, ministries are to make possible the growth of the communities as a process — for example, their synodal structures and alliances. Ministries are to channel this growth and to prune all wild shoots that develop. In this way the ministries can in fact be understood as a focal point of the unity that still lies before us. We must simply ask whether the synodal structure of the church can even get started "without a ministry of leadership and unity created by the churches."[192]

So what about the possibility often considered in the modern oecumene (particularly in the Lima texts) of establishing the office of bishop as the ministry of unity — that is, as a ministry that, connected with other regional bishops, could constitute the concrete and binding unity of the church? From his ecumenical experience, Ernst Lange has enthusiastically argued for this possibility.

> From time immemorial bishops have represented and watched over Christian unity. That has been their purpose since the second Christian century. They exist for no other reason. . . . In a somewhat painful learning process I have become convinced that the ecumenical reality is that the office of bishop — although certainly no longer today in a monarchical form — is indispensable, a condition sine qua non of ecumenical success. Only when all churches renew the office of bishop will there be an ecumenical future that includes the Orthodox churches and Rome.[193]

One should not dismiss this committed vote as a pragmatic concession to Rome and the Orthodox churches. Lange was thinking of bishops who are

191. Thinking of John 10:16 ("I have other sheep who are not of this fold"), Dombois (*Recht der Gnade,* vol. 3, pp. 167-68) says even more sharply: "Thus unity is not simply a priori something to be deduced from the one shepherd or the one body; it is also historical. Jesus speaks here of a flock that obviously is not the chosen people for whom he has passionately labored. It is a flock in whose sphere (outside Judaism) he has never appeared."

192. Lukas Vischer, "Der Auftrag der reformierten Kirche in der ökumenischen Bewegung," *ÖR* 28 (1979): 410-20, here p. 418.

193. Ernst Lange, "Eingabe an einen westdeutschen Kirchenführer," *WPKG* 63 (1974): 349-54, quotation pp. 352-53. For the Lutheran churches in particular, the question is raised today of such a "ministry to the unity of the church on a universal level" whereby "even the Petrine office of the bishop of Rome . . . does not need to be excluded as long as through theological reinterpretation and practical restructuring it is subordinated to the primacy of the gospel." From the Lutheran–Roman Catholic Commission for Unity, *Das geistliche Amt in der Kirche* (Paderborn: Bonifatius; Frankfurt: Lembeck, 1981), p. 73.

"advocates of minorities, of all groups who for one reason or another do not get a hearing in the council of the godly," bishops who "are not guardians of the status quo," but who relieve "the guardians of their fear of losing the way things are, a fear that makes them fanatical." One would have to ask pragmatically, however, whether the local and at the same time whole-church network he presumes is also true even for the Catholic bishops (who, of course, are not in a local network) but is part of a top-down regional or supra-regional administration.

The Reformers, in particular Calvin, did not deny that the ancient church oriented itself on the Roman church and its bishop, and they acknowledged its special preeminence; they gave good, even spiritual, reasons for the development. They did question, however, that it could guarantee the unity of the church completely on a universal level. Appealing to Cyprian, Calvin declared that only Christ's episcopal ministry has the power, like the trunk of a tree with many branches, to unify the whole church under its authority, and only it deserves to be called universal.[194] It may be that the episcopal office, introduced by human agreement *(humano consensu)* according to the needs of the time, could make the unity of the church somewhat — even entirely *(in solidum)* — visible, but it does so not through its personal representative but through the exemplary fulfillment of the tasks entrusted to it. This is where the difference lies: the unity of the church is determined not by the *that* but by the *how* of the bishops' leadership of the church.

Even today a Protestant appeal can go no further than this. The necessity of the ecclesiastical ministry is undeniable if the church is to grow as a historical institution "to the fullness of Christ." When ministry thus described is seen to serve this growth, it undeniably points to the unity of the whole church. It is therefore undeniable that the mutual recognition of the ministries is the most important step on the way to this unity. There may be historical and pragmatic reasons, but there are no adequate theological reasons why the traditional office of bishop could be a superior instrument for bringing the divided churches together into a universal, visible community or for binding the beginnings of an oecumeme "from the bottom up" (congregational sponsorship, church-wide relief work) into a scope that encompasses the whole church. In any case, it is likely that it will be difficult for the Protestant churches to be reconciled to the personal succession demanded from the Catholic and Orthodox side, tied to the sacramental idea of ordination. Since thus far the mutual recognition of ministries has stumbled on this

194. Calvin, *Institutes,* IV.6.17 (ET: vol. 2, p. 364), referring to Cyprian, *De catholicae ecclesiae unitate,* 5 (CSEL 3 1.214).

hurdle and there is also no prospect of reaching agreement here, we will stay with the New Testament way — measuring unity by how well the church carries out its task in the modern world.

4. Conciliar Fellowship

We have understood unity as the conduct of a joint movement, as a process in which the post-Easter church continues Jesus' in-gathering and mission in the power of the Spirit and grows together into a binding community in which religious and social distinctions are overcome. For this movement to get started and to take place, there must be a number of what one might call crystallization nuclei. We have described them as flash points of unity (baptism, Lord's Supper, confession, etc.), but in order for unity not to get lost and wander aimlessly without a sense of direction, there also must be centers of exchange, of gathering. In the history of the church, the ecumenical councils have been such centers. The fifth full assembly of the World Council of Churches in Nairobi (1975) became part of this tradition, and it declared agreement about the common task of the church to be the primary goal of all unity efforts.[195] The still separated churches must come together in a fellowship that is capable of convening a worldwide council that can speak in their name. Unity — thus the programmatic claim — will be realized in a conciliar fellowship:

> The one Church is to be envisioned as a conciliar fellowship of local churches which are themselves truly united. In this conciliar fellowship, each local church possesses, in communion with the others, the fullness of catholicity, witnesses to the same apostolic faith, and therefore recognizes the others as belonging to the same Church of Christ and guided by the same Spirit. . . . They are one in their common commitment to confess the gospel of Christ by proclamation and service to the world.[196]

The model described here is a counter proposal to the widespread idea that the unity of the church can be presented and made visible only from the top down. Although the Second Vatican Council with its emphasis on the collegiality of the bishops opened the way to a process-oriented understanding

195. See here Part One, above, pp. 24-27.

196. David M. Paton, ed., *Breaking Barriers: Nairobi 1975: The Official Report of the Fifth Assembly of the World Council of Churches* (Grand Rapids: Eerdmans, 1976), p. 60; quotation above in Part One, p. 25.

of unity, today we are confronted with the renewed effort to represent the unity of the church through the person of the universal bishop *(episcopus universalis).* To be sure, a council is a much more difficult way of representing unity than is a single person, but it has the advantage of being more than a mere symbol. It lives from the exchange and the living communication among all directions and groups represented in the church. In this sense, conciliarity is the critical example of a church that seeks its unity on the path of debate, indeed, of settling conflicts among its members — that is, "from the bottom up."

How do we become part of this movement? How can this process be produced under the conditions of our own present existence? Three concepts of unity were introduced in the first part of this book.[197] With varying accents, they emphasize that the fellowship of the church must find a visible expression, and they reject the old idea that ecumenical unity is to be achieved essentially, or even solely, by overcoming doctrinal differences. Such an idea is incompatible with the model developed here. Visible unity is realized in livable and lived forms of ecumenical community. It approaches the differences in doctrine on the level of the disputed circumstances themselves: How do we *confess* our faith in the modern world? How do we *celebrate* the Lord's Supper with one another? That does not mean that one can ignore the question of truth. An oecumene that wanted to do that would come to naught. Yet one can approach this question in different ways. If one understands unity as a process, truth makes its appearance as something that happens. If it were something that could be imprisoned in unchangeable formulas, it would be unchangeable *(irreformabilis),* as Tertullian said of the confession ("rule of faith"). Then the way to unity would be impassible. Those who want to settle the dispute about truth and bring it to a decision must get involved in the "game" in which it is established. Thus, if the process in which the unity of the church takes shape is to be extended and renewed, it must have a form that does not hold the present conflicts at arm's length but permits all of the participating partners to be actively engaged.

The concepts with which we began this book offer such forms. The model of *organic unity* addresses the problem of divisions on the regional level. Its goal is the unity of denominations divided along regional lines. Of course, this is also where its self-imposed limitation lies. One no longer considers how this unity might and must be realized universally. The model of *reconciled diversity* puts the emphasis on the identities of the historical denominations in such a way that they remain recognizable. It seeks to develop

197. Part One, above, pp. 20-27.

new and better relationships among the separated churches so that they can speak and act jointly, but it does not fundamentally challenge their separate existence. The concept of *conciliar community* goes a decisive step further. It begins by practicing on the local level a new, never-before-tried community model in the hope that through the process of living debate the churches will become capable locally of conducting a council. Conciliarity is understood as a quality that can also be lived regionally and therefore actually can and must be practiced in one's own local church.

4.1. The Council

The oldest model in which the church has proven and, when necessary, renewed its unity is that of the conciliar gatherings of the first Christian centuries. From them developed the bishops' synods and, finally, the general ecumenical councils. According to Orthodox and Roman Catholic synodal theory, councils are manifestations of the church's catholicity. One of their most important tasks, therefore, is to clarify questions of doctrine and constitution in joint deliberations. Their decisions are binding on the whole church. Accordingly, the council must represent the whole church in its makeup. The whole church must receive and acknowledge its decisions. We have long known that reality does not always correspond to this ideal. Councils have left their mark on the church's memory primarily as processes of ecumenical agreement. According to the traditional ideal, their signature is the active presence of the Holy Spirit, and they have taken for granted that all participants have full eucharistic fellowship. In truth, of course, they have also always been instruments of internal power struggles, and — from Chalcedon (451) to the First Vatican Council (1869-70) — they have occasioned radical schisms. Against this background, it is an entirely new development that Christians of all denominations again place their hopes in a council. They do it in the realistic belief that people can travel the way of unity only when they are prepared to accept conflicts and to struggle openly for the truth.

In the present ecumenical movement, the newly coined concept of conciliarity combines the traditions of the ancient church with this insight gained from the experiences of the last decades. It was described in Louvain (1971) as follows. Conciliarity is

> the coming together of Christians — locally, regionally or globally — for common prayer, counsel and decision, in the belief that the Holy Spirit can use such meetings for his own purpose of reconciling, renewing and

> reforming the Church, for guiding it towards the fulness of truth and love. . . . This does not mean movement in the direction of uniformity. On the contrary, our discussions here at Louvain have emphasized the fact that, if the unity of the Church is to serve the unity of mankind, it must provide room both for wide variety of forms and for differences and even conflicts.[198]

The historic council appears in this text in a characteristic refraction. That a council could meet "locally, regionally, and globally" undercuts the classic claim of universal representation. That it is to serve the "unity of *mankind*" surpasses everything that a church assembly has ever dared to hope. Here one has passed into the realm of visions — or is it a concrete Utopia? On the other hand, measured against the traditional claims about the binding force of church law, the conciliar gatherings remain far behind their classical predecessors. In the non-Roman oecumene there is no episcopate that could guarantee such a claim. In any case, the problem of legitimacy, the issue of how a council can speak for the whole church, cannot be resolved according to the traditional rules of an episcopally constituted church.

For this reason, given the way things stand now, one must say openly that the oecumene has come up against the limits of its possibilities. In the eyes of Catholics, the Protestant churches and denominations are not capable of participating in a council; in the eyes of the Orthodox, Rome is not even capable; and de facto, Orthodoxy itself is also not able. When there is no longer any parity in ministries, any unity in faith and doctrine, or any continuity in the conduct of life, an ecumenical council cannot take place. Since 787 (Nicea II), the pan-orthodox council has remained an unfulfilled dream. Thus for the present one must realistically say that the concept of a council as presently defined by church law makes impossible a conciliar process on the universal level. From this perspective, the full ecumenical assemblies from Amsterdam (1948) to Porto Allegre (2006) were a "sub-conciliar" effort to avoid this difficulty.

That brings us to the question that can scarcely be answered today. Within what limits can the rules of church law be changed? Even the classic council never understood itself as a kind of accumulation of ministerial authorities. Invoking the Spirit, by virtue of which the participants see themselves as being "in the Lord," transcends every ministry. Still, viewed sociologically, the council generally was a uniform, homogenous group: cardinals,

198. "Conciliarity and the Future of the Ecumenical Movement," in *Faith and Order: Louvain 1971: Study Reports and Documents,* ed. Lukas Vischer, Faith and Order Paper 59 (Geneva: WCC, 1971), p. 226.

bishops, the heads of orders. It is likely that no one asked then whether and to what degree such a gathering could represent the universal church. Yet today, beyond all considerations of church law, it is a new and elementary question. To mention only one example: Can we today even conceive of a representative council without the participation of lay people, in particular of women? To be sure, traditional structures cannot be replaced overnight. Only a fanatic would want to begin by destroying the framework of church realities and solve the problem of representation immediately in a radical-democratic manner by, for example, delegating the functions of a bishop to elected representatives of the community. However, it is certain that the universality of the *present* oecumene can be expressed adequately only when the voice of the laity is represented in a way that cannot be overlooked. The ecumenical document of Louvain even goes a step further:

> The conciliarity of the Church requires the involvement of the entire lay membership, including as it should every segment of mankind. There must be opportunity within the life of the church for each community of mankind to develop and express its own authentic selfhood; for the oppressed and exploited to fight for justice; and for the marginal people in society — the handicapped in mind and body — to make their own distinct contribution.[199]

4.2. *Characteristics of Conciliarity*

An important impulse of this Louvain document is the demand to see and test conciliarity as a "constant structure" of the life of the church. The declaration of Nairobi (1975) lists as its preconditions the willingness to recognize one another as churches of Jesus Christ (and thus to revise earlier condemnations); the binding commitment to the common apostolic faith; the mutual understanding of baptism, eucharist, and ministry that makes it possible to celebrate the Lord's Supper together; an agreement about the churches' representation at a future council. That is a reorientation of the conciliar idea that has a number of consequences. If in the past the hopes for a renewal of the church looked to the universal council, now the local churches are declared to be the exemplary bearers of this hope. The growth into the "fullness of Christ" (Eph. 4:13) can begin only on the local level. The process of ecumenical unification must be nudged along here on the ground level where the sep-

199. *Louvain 1971*, p. 227.

arated churches live with, and often against, one another. Then the church's universality would no longer be a characteristic that could be expressed only in the traditional form of (episcopal) representation; it would be a symbolically expressed reality that — much like the Twelve gathered around Jesus — anticipates the unity of the people of God in a historically lived form. Thus the location of the oecumene is not initially the gathering of World Christianity; it is the local community. Conciliarity is a quality of community that must be practiced and lived at all levels of the church so that Christians become capable of carrying on the process of unity up to and including the forum of an ecumenical council. In what forms can this happen?

4.2.1. Worship

The basic form of conciliar fellowship is worship with the celebration of the Lord's Supper at its center. In worship the community is assembled. Its elements are not only liturgy, proclamation, and prayer. If it is to be rediscovered and reshaped as a "full assembly" of the Christian community, then it is also the place where the members are equipped for their common service. Thus, problems of church life and questions of public responsibility have a legitimate place in this gathering. Conciliarity comes from "trust in the possibility of reconciliation."[200] For this reason divine worship is also the forum in which conflicts can be addressed and dealt with. An especially illuminating example was the political evening prayer that was first tried in Cologne in 1968. Here Catholic and Protestant Christians focused on social and political centers of conflict — the occupation of Czechoslovakia (1968), the Vietnam War, the social dislocations in Latin America — and in prayer they prepared themselves to assume responsibility for the condition of the earth, that is, to espouse the cause of right and justice. For "the power of the gospel is manifest in the fact that around itself it crystallizes groups that oppose and annul such [political] forces — at once for themselves, potentially for all."[201] In the worship services that preceded the Leipzig Monday demonstrations (1989), passive resistance was proclaimed as an effective instrument against obvious injustice and was practiced as a sign of readiness for reconciliation.

In the Lord's Supper the community assures itself of the reality of reconciliation. It lets itself be taken back to the beginning of its journey, and

200. Wolfgang Huber, *Der Streit um die Wahrheit und die Fähigkeit zum Frieden* (Munich: Kaiser, 1980), p. 130.

201. Dorothée Sölle, *Political Theology*, trans. John Shelley (Philadelphia: Fortress, 1974), pp. 105-6.

from there it looks forward to its desired goal. Thus the broken bread takes on symbolic value for the act of wandering through the social and political realities of this world. The eucharistic community will not become an authentic fellowship with mutual obligations until it accepts the mutual consequences of the social symbolism of the meal. In the signature of conciliarity, divine worship and daily life, celebrating with one another and being there for one another, are inseparable.

4.2.2. *Conflict Orientation*

The goal of the conciliary model is a "conflict orientation of the ecumenical praxis" (Ernst Lange). It wants to publicize and help settle the conflicts that threaten to tear Christendom apart in the world's everyday life. It is guidance in how to "struggle for the truth" (Wolfgang Huber), a struggle that for some time has no longer been merely an argument about doctrinal truths. The areas of conflict change precisely when unity is regarded as a process that is continually determined by new situations and therefore never arrives at a definite goal.

That was the case even in the New Testament. The controversy over the law (Torah) was by no means the only center of tension; it may not even have been the most significant. In the various local churches, it was superimposed and replaced by conflicts that arose from the contrast between poor and rich, (non-Christian) parents and (Christian) children, charismatics and office-holders. There was no difference *regionally,* although obviously there were different issues and causes of conflict. Confessional divisions came along, but on this level they were not settled doctrinally. Instead, then and now, the process of unity increasingly takes place in settling conflicts between quite different groups. The Pietists and traditionalists are opposed by the peace groups and ecological fellowships, the church leadership by the "base," etc.

Globally there is a different picture. Here, too, the classic dissension among the churches does not have a polarizing tendency. To a previously inconceivable extent, however, the churches have been drawn into society's contrasts: poor-rich, black-white. Thus today's North-South conflict is not only the basic conflict that leaves its mark on our economic and social orders; as liberation theology and, somewhat differently, the controversy over the involvement of the World Council of Churches documents, it has also become a basic conflict within the churches themselves. It may be that the most important result of the ecumenical movement since 1945 is that it has prevented the breakup of Christendom into northern and southern churches and has made it possible for the conciliar process in fact to take place here.

Globalization, the increasingly disquieting secular counterpart of the Christian oecumene, is the process of worldwide change and — this above all — of the worldwide movement toward uniformity in the way people live their lives, all of which is driven by an international economy and technology. In many areas of modernity, our own efforts toward the "social construction of reality" (Peter Berger, Thomas Luckmann) have replaced the world we inherited. The resulting global change creates worldwide winners and losers, deepens social divisions, and leads to an epochal new evaluation of our situation that we describe today as the transition from the information society to the knowledge society.[202] The increase of practically useable knowledge is enormous, yet it is accompanied by an equally significant loss of orientation, and it generates the basic conflicts of which we spoke in an earlier context. We lack the criteria for knowing how to deal with the newfound knowledge — what we should use it for. The controversy over the peaceful use of atomic energy, the therapeutic application of gene technology, or the necessary regard for the ecological equilibrium of the earth are alarming signs of a change we can no longer control. "He who speaks of world peace, inevitably must also deal with its opposite: world wars, world hunger, world poverty, worldwide migrations."[203]

The churches are drawn into these conflict zones. This is where they must prove their unity, for at stake is not only the future of the earth, of which the Bible says that its "fullness" is "God's" (Ps. 24:1), but also the human image created by God for which the churches must give account. The curbs placed on how we live our lives, not to mention on our scientific research, are more controversial than ever, as the present debate about medical ethics illustrates. The battle lines cut diagonally across the churches. The feeling of alienation that makes people homeless in the earth is growing. The conciliar process for justice, peace, and the integrity of creation initiated by the oecumene (Vancouver, 1983) lives from the conviction that a different world is possible.

The changed situation shows up not least of all in the reality that, paradoxically enough, there is today a *guilty* expression of unity, an example of which one sees in the conflict over the apartheid practiced in South Africa even among the churches. This is where the repressed problem of the rich churches of the West lies. They know that in doctrinal matters they are one with the black churches of South Africa and the base churches of Latin America, are united with them in the World Council, and regard this unity as capa-

202. See H. Bewersdorff, "Befähigung zum globalen Wandel," in *Das Humanum im globalen Wandel: Naturwissenschaftler, Philosophen und Theologen im Gespräch,* ed. Manfred Kock (Neukirchen: Neukirchener Verlag, 2002), pp. 173-80, here p. 174.

203. Martin Honecker, "Evangelischer Glaube im Zeitalter der Globalisierung," in Kock, *Humanum im globalen Wandel,* pp. 159-72, here p. 161.

ble of maintaining their bond. They are able to do so, however, because they ignore the issues that would tear it apart — their historical complicity in the system of apartheid, their anxious neutrality in the struggle for social justice. Yet this conflict must be articulated and settled if the unity of the church really is to be the symbolic beginning of that fellowship offered us by the incarnate God who has identified with us in our situation.

The conciliar model responds to these new flash points of division. The old doctrinal differences are increasingly replaced by differences about the church's direction. They can hardly be solved doctrinally; yet they burden the church's fellowship no less than do the classic controversies about the doctrine of justification or the primacy of Rome.[204] One thinks — *intro muros* — of the demand for a greater participation of the laity, for democratizing church structures, or for the role of women in the church, all of which are increasingly significant. Controversial are the extent and the limits of Christians' political responsibility. Groups that shared in their country's movement toward political self-determination, such as the base communities of South America and South Africa, come into open conflict with their church's episcopate. People are widely aware that truth — theologically relevant truth — is at issue here, even where they react negatively against unfamiliar ways. Unfamiliar, even strangely new, is the connection between the church's talk about truth and its behavioral structure, because it involves ways of thinking for which our tradition hardly prepares us. The two cannot be separated. We have cited John 14:6 to make this connection with the recognition that the truth is the way one goes. It is not something one manages as a theoretical possession. A community is conciliar when it takes this biblical insight seriously and, instead of fixating on the other group's "position," is able to observe the way it goes. Ernst Lange speaks aptly of Gamaliel's strategy (Acts 5:38-39): "wait and see if this be of God."[205] Such waiting leads to a different way of perceiving the conflict. It makes mutual deliberation and joint decision possible, and it leaves one open to correcting one's own way. Where such self-corrections are possible, steps have been made toward unity.

4.2.3. *The Search for Truth*

Conciliarity lives from trust in the leading of the Holy Spirit who draws the local and ecumenical gatherings of Christians into the ministry of the

204. Cf. section 1.3, above, pp. 173-75.

205. Ernst Lange, *And Yet It Moves: Dream and Reality of the Ecumenical Movement*, trans. Edwin Robertson (Belfast: Christian Journals Limited, 1979), p. 118.

church's reconciliation, renewal, and reshaping. The conciliar community intentionally involves itself in the process of in-gathering and mission that, along with the New Testament, transcends the boundaries of a single nation. In its own present, it unites with the church's past, its spiritual witnesses and decisions, proving continuity with a way that has the "fullness of truth and love" not behind but before itself.

It is the truth's future-revealing power that inspires the conciliar process and keeps it moving. Here one sees again how much the changed understanding of truth can move the stalled problem of unity. The conciliar model trusts the searchers' consensus. It is a consensus that is more than the sum of all individual opinions or a compromise among controversial positions. For this reason it can allow an unusual degree of latitude to the diversity and independence of Christians, even for open confrontation among differing interests and convictions. The idea of consensus (which originally comes from the philosophical view of the unity of reason) is subject to the presence of the Holy Spirit. Already in the ancient church it is "baptized" and thus transformed in its core by the belief in the illuminating and unifying power of the Spirit. It takes into account that individual groups and churches do not encounter one another as representatives of unchangeable (and thus mutually exclusive) truths but recognize one another as historical, "incarnate" expressions of the one truth, as "concretions of the presence of Christ" (Ernst Lange), and that they therefore expect from the meeting the added value of this greater truth. In a sense, the binding truth is produced in the conflict as an "open" consensus.

More than any other, therefore, this model deserves to be tested and put into practice on the local and regional levels.[206] Ecumenical communities must be formed that, ranging from common worship events to service groups, live locally by the principle that we will do together whatever can be done together. More than has previously been the case, one must include in the process of church communication such things as initiatives for "fringe groups" (refugees, asylum seekers), peace work, and political projects. Partnerships between European and North American communities on the one hand and Third World churches on the other raise the awareness of common ecumenical responsibility. Working communities of Christian churches that in many places already exist should give theological guidance to these attempts and become places of conciliar understanding.

Only if the struggle for unity were to end and people were no longer struggling for the truth would the unity of the church be irreparably broken or inaccessibly remote.

206. Huber, *Streit*, p. 138.

5. Church Unity and Missions

When we ask about church unity on the universal level, we must also speak, at least in an epilogue, of the movement that to all appearances has demonstrated this universality: Christian missions. It has its biblical model in Israel, God's "first witness," or, more precisely, in Israel's "communities of God" that became "centers of unrest" in world history,[207] and in their hope that the nations will flow to Zion (Isa. 2:2-3). Later, the earliest church incorporated its missionary activity into this universal, salvation-history framework.[208] Yet, it is hardly possible to find a direct connection to the New Testament. Jesus certainly understood himself exclusively as God's messenger for Israel (Matt. 10:5-6) and left the winning of the nations up to God. The command to baptize in Matthew 28:19, which presumably comes from the liturgy of the Matthean community, was not regarded as a foundational text of Christian missions either in the High Middle Ages, or in the Reformation, or by the great missionaries of the sixteenth century.[209] Even today this use of the text is increasingly questioned.[210] On the other hand, as if in the same breath, missions is valued as an integral part of the doctrine of the church. As early as 1961, in New Delhi, the International Missionary Council was incorporated into the World Council of Churches.

That does not make it easier to combine the theme of unity with expansive missionary activity, and there are historical reasons for this difficulty. The modern missionary movement, in particular that of the eighteenth and nineteenth centuries, was initiated by separate denominations that passed on to the young churches of other continents the divisions of Europe and North America. In addition, it has helped expand not only Western patriarchalism and forms of government but also modern industrialism and capitalism, and thus, against its will, it has become colonialism's most important ally. This legacy has effectively hindered, if not made impossible, the creation of a universally reconciled fellowship in which the churches of Asia and Africa could have been included as equal partners.

Modern criticism speaks to a different issue. It claims that Christian

207. Friedrich-Wilhelm Marquardt, *Was dürfen wir hoffen, wenn wir hoffen dürften? Eine Eschatologie* (Gütersloh: Kaiser, 1994), vol. 2, pp. 155ff.

208. See Gerhard Lohfink, *Jesus and Community: The Social Dimension of Christian Faith* (Philadelphia: Fortress, 1984), pp. 170-76.

209. Ulrich Luz, *Matthew 21–28: A Commentary,* Hermeneia, trans. James E. Crouch (Minneapolis: Fortress, 2005), pp. 617, 626.

210. See Henning Wrogemann, "'Mission' als Thema systematischer Theologie," *VuF* 49 (2004): 3-22; also Horst Balz, "Beiträge zur Missionstheologie," *VuF* 49 (2004): 23-37.

missions violate today's highly discussed ideal of the religious and cultural identity of other nations that one is obligated to respect. It disturbs the inter-religious oecumene. In addition, there is a theological argument that is worth considering. Do not its addressees, the so-called foreign religions, also belong to God's providential action in the world? Do they not also result from "God's creative power"?[211] The missionary church began in the conviction that salvation — that is, ultimate truth — is promised and "given" to people only in the name of Jesus Christ (Acts 4:12). However, can it advocate today the reverse side of this conviction with the same certainty, namely, that the "others" — be they Muslims or Buddhists — live in "falsehood"? Here we need new and better answers than the nineteenth century has given.

Thus new questions are being raised today about the theological justification of missions. Compared with earlier authors, Theo Sundermeier has described the missionary movement more cautiously as "the church's encounter with a stranger." With this definition, however, the legitimate motive of missions can be neither the expansion of Christianity in a cultural-civilizing sense, nor the "saving of souls," nor even a frank claim of universality for the message that is proclaimed. Those are all misunderstandings based on one-sided interpretations of Matthew 28:19. On the other hand, in my judgment Gerhard Sauter has cited correctly the Pauline charge of reconciliation (2 Cor. 5:18-21) as the biblical foundation of missions: "Christian mission takes place when, without restriction or limitation, we beseech people to be reconciled with God . . . to expose themselves to this reconciliation." The point is not to bring Christ into the world but rather "not to get in the way of Christ. In what [people] say and do they must leave room for Christ."[212]

Thus Paul places the church in a much more comprehensive horizon than we can see from looking back at its history, for the ministry of reconciliation includes the entire cosmos. God is faithful to his creatures. Reconciliation makes right even the non-human creation.[213] The risen Christ not only fills the church with his presence; he also, as the Ephesian epistle later says, fills the universe with his might (Eph. 4:10) and is Lord even of the cosmic powers. In a new creation, God has made room for a reconciled humanity. In

211. Thus the study of the Arnoldshain Conference and the United Lutheran Church of Germany, *Religion, Religiosität und christlicher Glaube*, 3d ed. (Gütersloh: Mohn, 1993), p. 127. Also: "With his deity God is the goal of every religion, even as he ordains its origin" (p. 128).

212. Gerhard Sauter, *Gateways to Dogmatics: Reasoning Theologically for the Life of the Church* (Grand Rapids: Eerdmans, 2003), p. 173.

213. See here Peter Stuhlmacher, *Gerechtigkeit Gottes bei Paulus*, FRLANT 87 (Göttingen: Vandenhoeck & Ruprecht, 1965), pp. 203-7.

some measure the church is the intersection in which this becoming new is made real; it is the crystallization core of the unity of a new world.

The understanding of missions in the Pauline school is radically different from its modern concept. Even for Ephesians, the missionary preaching of the gospel — what the nineteenth century called "foreign" missions — belongs to the past. It is a past to which one looks back as the apostolic age. With Paul, the church has reached the ends of the earth. In its present existence, it is the result of, but no longer a possible bearer of, the mission. That is not to say that its growth had ended; growth must continue to happen. But now it does so in a different direction — no longer outwardly, but inwardly. Now it is important "to portray Christ in his complete measure" and no longer to be "immature children" (Eph. 4:13-14). The church's universality, its extensive breadth, is contrasted with the church's catholicity, its intensive density,[214] which is pointedly expressed in the maxim, "If one member suffers, all suffer together" (1 Cor. 12:26). Thus, it can continue to move and to grow only when this second pole is also involved. Therefore, its mission is never an activity done in addition, as if externally, to its other activities. It cannot be measured quantitatively by the greater or lesser extent of its reach. Its legitimate goal is rather to enable the churches to realize the new quality imparted to them with Christ. The nineteenth-century concept of missions disregarded this internal dimension. In order to engage in missions effectively in their own existence, our churches would have to conform to their New Testament design (Matthew 10 and 1 Corinthians 12) — in Paul's words, to make the nations "jealous" and to provoke them to imitation (Rom. 11:11).

Thus, the problem of today's oecumene is not its universality but its lived catholicity. Long ago it reached the (geographically greatly extended) ends of the earth and erected there not only isolated beachheads but entire colonies. It has changed the world to an extent inconceivable for Paul. Now the question of Ephesians comes back to the church today with unexpected sharpness: Has its inner growth kept up with this enormous expansion? What form must its descendent assume in the Christian world that has become universal? How does a community *live* the witness of reconciliation in view of the polarity between poor and rich, black and white, oppressed and oppressors, which today is a polarity *within* the world of Christianity? The world can be reached by the movement of reconciliation proclaimed in 2 Corinthians 5:18-19 only when the church lives this reconciliation with conviction in its own innermost life. In other words, the church will reach its outer frontiers

214. Cf. Hendrikus Berkhof, *De Katholiciteit der Kerk* (Nijkerk: Callenbach, 1962); German: *Die Katholizität der Kirche* (Zurich: EVZ-Verlag, 1964).

only when inwardly, as well, it goes to its utmost limits as a fraternal church of solidarity and compassion. When this inner unity fails, its outer unity also remains a phantom. Its mission here is definitely not over.

Index of Names and Subjects

Apartheid, 208, 242

Apostles, 43, 93-94, 101-2, 106-18, 193. *See also* Itinerant

Apostolic Council, 58-60, 166, 179

Baptism and unity, 48, 77, 95, 128, 209-10, 212-13

Basic gift of unity, 32-34, 42-43, 47, 53-54, 76-79, 89, 95, 96, 101, 104, 117, 128, 151, 161, 165-67

Bible, scripture, 8-15, 17-18, 195-204; authority of, 199-202; interpretation of, 202-4; principle of, 197-99; scripture and tradition, 8-11, 195-203

Bishop, overseer, office of, 118-21, 124-26, 155

Body of Christ, 57, 77, 79, 88, 127, 170, 210, 213

Canon, canonization of the New Testament, 14-15, 106, 117, 195, 201. *See also* Bible

Cerinth, 144, 149

Church: catholicity of the church, 191, 212, 237, 247; characteristics, attributes of the church, 41, 65-66, 230; church fellowship, 211, 213; church as an institution, 230-35; church law, 218, 226-30; church schism, 168, 173-76, 218, 237, 241; invisible church, 20, 35. *See also* Body of Christ, Church, the whole, Disciples, Ecclesiology, *ekklesia,* Local church, People of God, Temple, Unity

Church, the whole, 54-57, 79-84, 111-13, 127-32, 134-36, 138-40, 163, 193, 230, 237

Collection for Jerusalem, 71-73

communio. See koinonia

Communions. *See* Denominations

Conciliarity, 24-27, 235-38, 239-44

Confession, Credo, Creed, 10, 14, 49-50, 78-79, 95, 106, 150-53, 177, 186, 204-9, 226; conflict between confession and fellowship, 160-61, 174, 198; contextual confession, 207-8

Confessions. *See* Denominations

Consensus, 229, 234, 244

Council, 58-60, 198, 224, 235, 237-39; Second Vatican Council, xiii, 22, 23, 172, 177, 189, 196, 203, 212, 218, 235

Deacon, office of, 118-22, 124

Denominations (confessions, communions), 14, 24, 195, 204, 206, 226, 249

Disciples of Jesus, 36-39, 41, 54, 111-12, 140-41; Beloved Disciple, 137-39

Discipleship (following Jesus), 37-40, 45

Doctrine (dogmatics), 24, 34, 40, 105, 167-68, 195; teaching ministry, 200, 203

Ecclesiology, 54-57, 74-77, 79-81, 126-42, 126-42, 190-91, 212-13 *ekklesia* (Greek: church, assembly), 54-56, 80, 127, 156

Faith and Order, 21
Fellowship, community (= *Gemeinschaft*), 41-42, 66, 68-69, 83, 87-88, 89-91, 134, 140-42, 152, 160-61, 170-73, 210, 212-14. *See also koinonia*
Forces of unity, 47-54, 76-79, 95-96, 224

Gnosis (Gnosticism), 142-47, 158-59
Gospel and fellowship, 66-69, 89-91, 159-61

Heresy, false doctrine, 89-91, 94; ethical heresy, 90-91, 175, 221

Irenaeus, 143-44, 153
Israel, state of, 181-82
Itinerant charismatics, teachers, prophets, 43-45, 50, 95, 136, 147, 158

James (brother of the Lord), 61-64, 75, 107-8, 190
Jerusalem, 52-53, 61-62, 81, 131-32, 134-35
Jesus Christ: Jesus and church, 34-43, 48, 205-6; Jesus Christ the basis of the church, 36-37, 174, 210-12; the Jesus tradition, 100-101, 111. *See also* Basic gift of unity
Judaism, 179-92

Kingdom of God and church, 35, 38-39, 41
koinonia, communio (= fellowship, community, share), 13, 26-27, 72, 170-73, 213

Letters, ecumenical, 101-3; pseudonymous, 102-3
Leuenberg agreement, 176
Lima documents, 194, 210, 220, 224, 232
Local church, 55-56, 80-83, 84-88, 119-21, 126, 130-32, 158-59, 219, 240
Lord's Supper, Eucharist, 40, 49, 77, 87-88, 95, 209-222; as prophetic symbolic act, 219, 221-22

Mission and unity, 16-17, 19, 37, 50, 57-60, 81-84, 104, 109-10, 115, 134, 245-48; Gentile mission, 57-58, 109, 192; Jewish mission, 66-67

Oecumene: ecumenical movement, 2-4, 13-14, 19-21, 22, 25, 167, 205; ecumenicity, 180; Nairobi full assembly, 24-25, 235, 239; New Delhi full assembly, 21-22, 220, 245; World Council of Churches, 2, 19, 189, 242
Office and offices, ministerial, 118-26, 160, 217-20, 222-35
Order of ministries, 226-27, 229, 231-33; hierarchy, 227, 232-33; recognition, 224, 234; representation, 226-27; service, 226, 229, 232. *See also* Bishop, Deacon, Peter, Presbyter
Ordination, 122, 218, 219-20, 225, 234
Orthodoxy (Orthodox churches), 126, 214, 233, 238

Paul, image of Paul, 64-91, 113-18, 129, 167, 189-90, 246-47
People of God, 30, 37-38, 48, 52-53, 56, 57, 59, 61-62, 64, 67, 76, 98-99, 133, 180, 189, 211
Peter, papal office, 67, 108-13, 138-39, 225, 228
Presbyter/elder, office of, 94, 121-22, 124
Primitive/Jerusalem church, 43-44, 62, 65, 72, 111, 134

Reconciliation, 178, 188, 209, 220, 240-41, 247
Resurrection of Jesus and church unity, 42, 95, 151, 210-11

Substitution theology, 98, 130-31, 133, 189
Succession, apostolic, 93-94, 117-18, 126, 218, 225, 234

Temple, building, building up, 56, 79-80, 88, 125, 127
Tensions and conflicts, 44-47, 57-76, 88, 91-94, 142-61, 173-77, 179, 241-43; cultural tensions, 46, 92, 194; generational

tensions, 46, 93, 123; social and ethical tensions, 46, 93, 175, 221-22, 242-43; theological tensions, 47, 67, 94, 147-61, 174-75, 193, 225-26
Tertullian, 154, 156
Tradition, 8-11, 14, 16, 22-23, 27, 51-52, 95-96, 100-106, 111-13, 114, 117, 122, 147-49, 160, 196-99. *See also* Bible, scripture and tradition
Travel, contacts, 50, 69-74, 82, 95, 136
Truth, 68, 90, 104, 142, 152, 158, 161, 163, 202-3, 208, 243; struggle (debate, dispute) for the truth, 173-74, 200, 236, 241, 244
Twelve, the, 38, 240

Unity (the term), 12-13, 29-30, 124-26, 128-29, 141-42, 166-67; boundaries of, 69-70, 89, 150, 175-76, 204, 229, 238; criteria of, 167, 195; flash points of, 168-69, 193-94, 200, 207, 215; forces of, 47-53, 76-79, 95-96; preconditions of, 33, 126, 159-60, 175, 215. *See also* Basic gift of unity
Unity of the church with Israel, 37-40, 41, 57-76, 98-99, 107-8, 114-15, 129-31, 179-92
Unity, concepts of: confederated unity, 18-20; organic unity, 20-22, 236; unity as conciliar fellowship, 24-26, 235-44; unity as process, 5, 31-32, 125, 129, 169-70, 195-96, 197-98, 201-2, 203, 223; unity in reconciled diversity, 22-24, 236; unity as a way, 163-79, 208

Valentinus, 144, 145, 146, 152, 159

Women in the church, 39, 93, 225, 239, 243
Worship and church unity, 88, 127-29, 131-32, 240-41

Index of Selected New Testament and Other Ancient Texts

NEW TESTAMENT

Matthew
1:24 101
4:16-18 110
4:23 101
7:22-23 100
10:2 110, 111
10:5-6 245
10:5-52 50
11:3 185
14:28-33 110
16:13-23 110
16:18 109, 110, 111
16:19 111
18:15-18 120
21:43 76, 99
23:8-10 120
23:34-39 97
26:69-75 110
28:19 245-46
28:20 101, 120

Mark
1:1 100
1:16-18 110
6:7-11 50
8:27-33 110
16:7 110

Luke
1:3-4 101
1:32 187
2:34-35 133
10:2-16 50
10:7 50
10:21 206
11:30 190
24:21 185
24:34 109

John 136-42
2–12 97
3:22 48
3:26 48
5:18 97
6:68 110
9:22 97
10:16 139
10:33 97
11:47-53 97
11:51-52 139
12:38-41 97
12:42 97
13:6-9 110
13:21-30 137
13:34 140
13:34-35 97
14:6 142, 208, 232, 243
15:1-8 232
15:5 140
15:9 140
16:2 97
17 141
17:11-12 139
17:20-21 15
17:20-24 139
17:21 141
19:15 98
20:2-12 138
21:15-17 110, 140
21:15-19 111
21:24 138

Acts 133-36
1:6 185
2:42-47 43, 134
4:12 246
4:32-37 43, 134
5:38-39 243
9:10-22 162
11:26 99
14:4 115
14:14 115
14:23 93, 119
15:1-11 59
15:7-11 162
15:8-11 112, 114
15:13-21 107, 162
15:16-17 63
20:22-24 162
20:28 119, 147

20:29-30 135, 147
21:10-14 162
21:17-30 73
24:17 74
28:26-28 133
28:28 133, 141
28:31 133

Romans
1:3-4 49, 79
6:4-5 213
8:32 187
9:6 133
10:4 189
11:1 189
11:5 192
11:11 247
11:11-32 75
11:17 181
13 11
14–15 68-69, 90
14:9 78
15:7 15
16:1 118

1 Corinthians
1–4 85-86
1:2 101
1:9 32, 70
1:13 211
1:18-25 78
7:19 69
8–10 86
8:6 128
10:1-4 210
10:14-22 212
10:16-17 32, 77
11:17-34 87-88
11:24 210
11:27 90
12–14 88
12:3 78
12:4-6 78
12:12-31 88, 141
12:13 77, 78
12:26 247
12:28 118
14:34 203
15:3 49
15:3-5 51

2 Corinthians
1:1 101
3:17 78
5:18-19 247
5:18-21 246
5:19 208
8–9 71
11:4 70, 89
11:5 70
11:13 89

Galatians
1:1 101
1:6 70, 89
2:11-21 66-68
2:12-14 62
5:2-3 63
6:16 190

Ephesians 114-15, 127-29
2:11-12 98
2:12 181
2:14-18 98
2:20-22 127
4:1-6 15, 127
4:5 95
4:10 246
4:11 119-20
4:13 232, 239, 247

Philippians
1:1 118
2:6-11 205

Colossians
4:16 101

Pastoral Epistles 94, 95, 103-5, 113, 119, 121-22, 147-48

1 Timothy
2:1-6 95
6:20 147

2 Timothy
2:18 148

Hebrews 99, 103

James
1:1 63, 98, 107
2:8 186

1 Peter 103
2:6-8 98
2:9-10 98

2 Peter
1:10 192
3:15 112

Johannine Letters 149-51

1 John
2:18-27 150
4:2 150

3 John
9 140
9-10 153

Revelation (Apocalypse of John) 92-93, 100, 120, 129-32
2–3 130
7:1-17 131
12 130
14:1-5 131
15:2-4 131
21 131
21:14 43

EARLY CHRISTIAN SOURCES

Authentikos Logos (NHC VI, 3) 155-56

Didache
9:4 95
10:5 49
10:6 49

1 Clement 93
42:4 94

Gnosis, Inter
(NHC XI, 1)

Ignatius of
Antioch

120, 151-52, 167, 213, 223, 232

Romans
9.1 119

Philadelphians
2.1 119

Peter, Apocalypse of (NHC VII, 3) 155

Philip, Gospel of (NHC II, 3) 155, 161

Pseudo-Clementines 107

gos of the
2) 156-57

ospel of
61, 107